Praise for THE JUGGLER'S CHILDREN

"*The Juggler's Children* is many things, each one spellbinding: a thrill-erish quest for origins, a continent-spanning travelogue and an eye-opening foray into the annals and ethics of genetic science. . . . Abraham's family is unusual, but so is her virtuosity as a writer; she's probing, intelligent, dryly funny but enough of a writer's writer that she can make the awkward process of DNA swabbing seem magisterial. . . . Abraham's book is riveting not just because of its superb writing and suspenseful storyline, but because, in the end, it's not just about her, it's about *us*." *The Globe and Mail*

"Abraham is the ideal guide to the brave and crowded new world of internet genealogy. . . . *The Juggler's Children* is a perfect match of memoir and journalism. . . . An artfully crafted *pas de deux* between DNA testing and family identity . . . Abraham writes with ease and humour, undaunted by complexity, and the narrative unfolds like a detective story." *Literary Review of Canada*

"With an irreverent sense of humour and the smarts of an experienced medical-science journalist, Abraham describes how questions about her ancestry had gnawed at her since childhood. . . . What her genes wind up revealing—about not only her own background but everyone else's—is richer than any tall family tale." *The Georgia Straight*

"I love this book. Period. If you are a fan of history, auto-biographies and genealogy—this book is for you. Carolyn's family history turns out to be quite romantic and mysterious. You will learn about DNA testing (but not in a dry way), and some history of India, China,

Jamaica and England. Even though it's non-fiction, this book is written like a fluent, page-turning, exotic novel. Carolyn's writing style is so personal and exciting, she made me care about the outcome of her search. I wanted to find out why the juggler disappeared and whether the captain comes from a family of slaves or slave owners. This book certainly makes me feel guilty that I don't know more about my own family's past!"

Justine Lewkowicz, NEWSTALK 1010 (5 out of 5)

"In describing her interaction with internationally renowned geneticists, Abraham creates a scrupulous blend of science and personal anecdote. . . . *The Juggler's Children* is as entertaining as a beautifully constructed novel and as informative as a rich work of history or biography."

The Record (Kitchener-Waterloo)

"Abraham's story of personal connection—the stories, the letters and the memories—end up being more compelling than the scientific revelations. . . . *The Juggler's Children* is a fascinating tale of truth, lies, perception and, ultimately, family."

Winnipeg Free Press

"It is, by turns, a detective story, a primer on the science of the human genome, and a revealing family portrait . . . This highly personal story not only entertains and informs, it forces us to ask ourselves some very basic and universal questions about the nature of identity."

Quill & Quire

"If you are a Genealogist, interested in DNA, love a good detective story, mystery or memoir, then *The Juggler's Children* should definitely be on your reading list."

Ontario Genealogical Society

"With this daring act of tracing her genetic genealogy all the way back to its widely scattered origins, Carolyn Abraham redefines the meaning of the expression 'know thyself.' *The Juggler's Children* is as exciting as any explorer's account of the discovery of a new land, as carefully written as a fine novel, as rigorous as it is entertaining. But its greatest achievement is its astonishing, profoundly moving findings, its proof that the human race is, in fact, one family after all."

Ian Brown, award-winning author of *The Boy in the Moon*

THE JUGGLER'S CHILDREN

A Journey into Family,
Legend and the Genes that Bind Us

CAROLYN ABRAHAM

VINTAGE CANADA

VINTAGE CANADA EDITION, 2014

Copyright © 2013 Carolyn Abraham

Published in Canada by Vintage Canada, a division of Random House of Canada Limited, Toronto, in 2014. Originally published in hardcover in Canada by Random House Canada, a division of Random House of Canada Limited, in 2013. Distributed by Random House of Canada Limited.

Vintage Canada with colophon is a registered trademark.

www.randomhouse.ca

Library and Archives Canada Cataloguing in Publication

Abraham, Carolyn
The juggler's children: a journey into family, legend and the genes that bind us / Carolyn Abraham.

Includes bibliographical references.

ISBN 978-0-679-31460-8

1. Abraham, Carolyn—Family. 2. Abraham family. 3. Genetic genealogy. 4. Genes—Popular works. 5. Genetic disorders—Popular works. I. Title.

QH447.A26 2014   929'.20971   C2011-904088-3

Text and cover design by Jennifer Lum

Cover images: (braid) © Karina Bakalyan | Dreamstime.com; (red canvas) © Luceluceluce | Dreamstime.com; (vintage background) © Chan Yee Kee | Dreamstime.com; (double helix) Comstock / Getty images; (family photos) courtesy of the author

Maps: Paul Dotey

Interior images: All photos are property of the author.

Printed and bound in the United States of America

2 4 6 8 9 7 5 3 1

For Jade and for Jackson,
my x and y, my moon and sun

CONTENTS

"If you cannot get rid of the family skeleton,
you may as well make it dance."

George Bernard Shaw, *Immaturity*

Map of JAMAICA

CARIBBEAN SEA

COUSINS COVE

LUCEA

MONTEGO BAY

FALMOUTH

HANOVER PARISH

SPANISH TOWN

KINGSTON

CARIBBEAN SEA

20 MI.
40 KM.

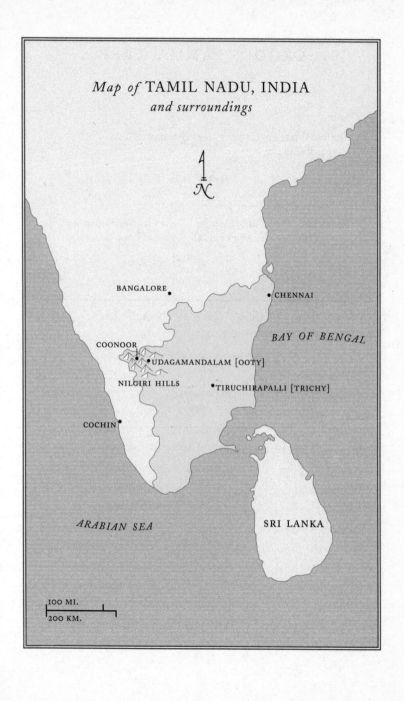

Map of TAMIL NADU, INDIA
and surroundings

N

BANGALORE

CHENNAI

BAY OF BENGAL

COONOOR
UDAGAMANDALAM [OOTY]
NILGIRI HILLS
TIRUCHIRAPALLI [TRICHY]

COCHIN

ARABIAN SEA

SRI LANKA

100 MI.
200 KM.

CROOKS FAMILY TREE

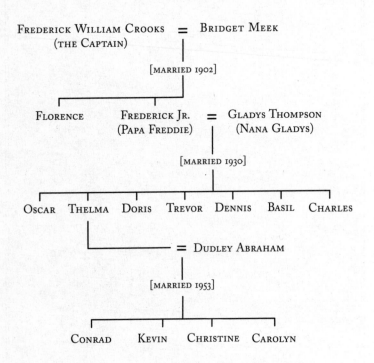

ABRAHAM FAMILY TREE

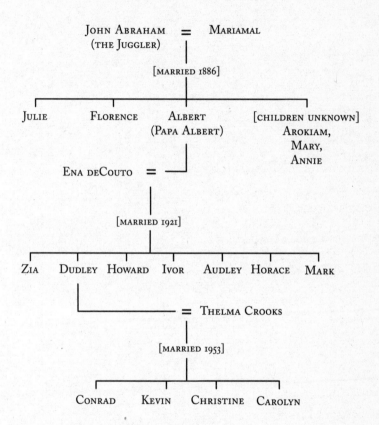

PROLOGUE

There is a picture of my daughter taken about forty-eight hours after she was born. She's propped up against pillows in our hospital room, pinched and scrawny, as newborns can be when they come early. Her eyes are half open, taking in the outlines of her new world, oblivious to the questions she pushed to the forefront of my mind in those first days of her life.

On her head is something that looks like a bonnet. It's white, shaped like a dome, and even has an elastic strap that stretches under her chin. If you look closely you can see it's not a bonnet, but a mask, a regulation issue N-95, touted to keep out 95 percent of airborne particles—dust, pollution, viruses. In the spring of 2003 masks were as common as streetcars in our city. The hospital provided them to keep people from catching or spreading infection to others. But aside from a few doctors with masks of their own, and nurses in biohazard suits, there were no others. My husband and I never put the mask over her face while we were in that room.

Ten years later, if I try to pinpoint when the desire to know became the determination to find out, or why my daughter would know about DNA before she knew how to read, or how I became preoccupied with collecting it, from both the living and the dead, I keep returning to that picture. The birth of any child pushes the past into the present. It just so happened that Jade was born into a time and place where the clocks seemed to have stopped. An unexpected gift of time had come with her arrival—six long days we spent under quarantine when the city had gone half-mad with fear and confusion.

A strange pneumonia had broken out that winter, a new viral disease called severe acute respiratory syndrome (SARS). Worldwide it infected more than eight thousand people and killed more than nine hundred. Forty-four died in Toronto. As a science reporter, I was writing about it for the *Globe and Mail*, and there was a lot to write. Ten thousand people were confined to their homes. Schools were closed. Conventions were cancelled. People stopped riding the subway and shaking hands, even in church.

For three months I chased the story, until the hot afternoon of June 5, when I became part of it. Eight months pregnant, I was at a meeting in a downtown coffee shop when my nose started to bleed heavily. I hailed a cab to the hospital, where nurses hooked up a fetal monitor, took a blood pressure reading and told me to call my husband.

"My pressure is through the roof," I told Stephen. "They're going to induce. Can you stop at the house and pack an overnight case?"

He arrived with a hockey bag stuffed full of nearly everything we'd bought or been given for our unborn child: washcloths, rattles, baby-safe detergent, a snowsuit sized for a three-year-old. It was just as well; we had to stay much longer than we expected.

A medical student working on the maternity ward developed the symptoms of SARS the day I was admitted. Anyone who had had contact with him was placed under strict ten-day quarantine. Women about to deliver would have to do so in a skeleton-staffed ward closed off from the rest of the world. That included me.

By nightfall of the following day, as the induction drugs took effect, I paced out my labour in a long, eerie corridor, quiet and dark except for the red glow of the exit signs. When the time came, Stephen had to run around the ward just to find a nurse.

Our daughter arrived before dawn, healthy and screaming, and just like that, the rapid pulse of our lives slowed. Alone in a double room with nowhere to go and no one to see, we snatched sleep at odd hours, fired N-95s across the room like slingshots, and took photos—lots of photos.

She was the first baby in our family in more than a dozen years. Since no one could visit, everyone called. They asked the questions people do when a new life appears: What does she look like? *Who* does she look like?

She might have been fair and blue-eyed, like Stephen's side, with hair of gold or red, or darker, like me. On my side the possibilities were wide and endless: a complexion of white or deep brown or anything in between. Her hair could have been smooth as black silk or coiled into springs too tight for a comb. She might have been a living testament to the ancestors whose stories had captivated me since I was a child, stories that inspired her name. We called her Jade, after China's imperial gem, beautiful and strong as an axe-head.

I wished my mum's mother had lived to see her. I used to tell my grandmother about my work, the stories I was writing, the trips I took. She would lean in and whisper, "But what about babies, my girl? When are you going to have babies?" Oh, eventually, I'd say and shrug. But there was always another story and new jobs and newspapers, and then one July morning in 1999 my mother called to tell me my grandmother had died.

I saw her before her body was taken away. Nana Gladys was still in her bed, the silver hair she curled meticulously lying in strings on her pillow, her mouth turned down in a grimace that reminded me of the expression she'd wear if we were late picking her up.

My mother asked me to give her eulogy. Two days later I made my way through the crowded funeral home with a pen and notepad, expecting to fill it with memories and anecdotes. I had a hard time filling more than a page. No one seemed to be sure where Gladys Crooks had grown up or gone to school, or where her family was from—not my uncles or my mother or me, for that matter. But everyone spoke earnestly about her devotion to the Catholic Church, how often she said the rosary and how, even in hard times, she dressed her seven children smartly in homemade clothes and whisked them to Mass every Sunday. All of this was true. Even at the end my grandmother kept an illuminated statue of the Virgin Mary on her nightstand to guide her in spiritual matters, and on night trips to the bathroom. She was a practical woman, my Nana.

Gladys Crooks had been a seventeen-year-old bride in India, and a young widow too. She'd made a life on three continents and travelled the world, riding alone on its trains and buses and rickshaws, her money stashed away in secret pockets she sewed into her petticoats. But death had shrunk her to a cliché: devoted wife and mother. Maybe grief blocks recollections. Maybe memories are trumped by the hope that emphasizing piety will pave the way to heaven. Either way, she was the last of a generation in my family, and when she died, I felt a window to the past had closed for good.

Then came Jade. Six pounds of new life that made me see the past through a different lens. We spent long stretches of time just gazing at her, stoned on the wonder of her sudden existence. Holed up with us in that abandoned ward for a week, she lay in her Plexiglas bassinette like a prized specimen, and we studied her. She had Stephen's deep dimple on her chin, his long limbs and mouth, my colour and fingers, my grandmother's expressions, and, on her lower back, the faint blue patch of a Mongolian birthmark. What I saw in my daughter, in that quarantined room, was the past and the future all at once.

The past is never lost, not completely; we carry it with us, in us, and we look for it in our parents and in our children, to give us our bearings and ground us in the continuity of life. And the past accommodates. It shows off in dazzling, unpredictable ways—a familiar gait, a gesture, the timbre of a voice, a blot of colour along the tailbone. The body has a long memory indeed. Written in the quirky tongue of DNA and wound into the nucleus of nearly every human cell are biological mementos of the family who came before us. And science is finding ways to dig them out, rummaging through our DNA as if it were a trunk in the attic.

Advances in genetics had consumed my professional life before SARS came to town. Scientists were homing in on evermore genes linked to diseases, personality traits and behaviours. I wrote about the discoveries and the sticky questions they were dropping into humanity's lap. But I had never been tempted to know what secrets my own DNA harboured until it became possible to use genetic testing to learn about ancestry.

It was the prospect of solving the mysteries surrounding two of my great-grandfathers that lured me most. One was a sea captain and the other a circus juggler. Both were nomadic types who turned up in India in the nineteenth century, and neither man stuck around long enough to dispel or confirm the legends that grew up around him. One died young and the other disappeared, but their genetic legacies remain. Was it really possible, in this shiny new millennium, that the genes they had passed down through the generations could somehow reveal the secrets they took to their graves? Why—when questions of our heritage and identity had been with me for so long; when my daughter might grow up with the same questions; when my parents, with everything they know and all the secrets hiding in their living cells, could vanish in a breath—would I wait to find out?

In the months that followed Jade's birth, after SARS finally disappeared from the headlines, I decided to begin. I pictured myself armed with swabbing sticks, tracking distant relatives around the globe and asking them for their DNA. *Hello, I'm Dudley and Thelma's daughter from Toronto. May I have a bit of your spit?* I imagined the cool blade of science cutting to the truth of us, after more than a century of speculation, denial and myth. I didn't expect that my quest would push me to the moral brink, make me wonder about the existence of ghosts and the propriety of grave-robbing. I didn't foresee that unearthing the roots of my family could bury the story of someone else's. But a genetic journey has a way of bending the road in ways you might never imagine.

I

———

"WHAT ARE YOU?"

Every family has its myths and legends. Families can be as twisted as the genetic strands that bind them, old as time, born of chance and random couplings. From the linen petals of a matrimonial bed to the vinyl ardour of back seats, carpet burns, hayrides, gin-fuelled fumblings—blessed are the fornicators! All families owe them a debt, one way or another. The Mormons believe that by knowing your family history you can get all your ancestors into heaven. My own family has always been very clear about heaven; ancestry has been the murky subject, as it must be for many families. The Mormon family-search website receives more than ten million visits a day. On the Internet, genealogy ranks as one of the most popular subjects after pornography, which seems logical, since all that sex does lead to families. I didn't know much about sex when I first wondered about our own origins. My parents used to tell us they were counting money when they disappeared into the bedroom on Saturday mornings, and my siblings and I grew up thinking we were very rich.

I started asking questions about our heritage in the late seventies, after people started asking them of me. We had recently moved from the Toronto area to the small southern Ontario town of St. Catharines. Each time we moved, one of my siblings had stayed behind. When we left England for Canada three years before, it was Conrad, the eldest of us four. My mother was emptying his pockets for the laundry when she found a note from his girlfriend announcing that my brother was about to have a family of his own. Con returned to London and got married. When we left Toronto, my brother Kevin stayed to become a chartered accountant. So it was just my sister, Christine, and me who arrived in the Garden City with my parents. She was almost fifteen and I had just turned seven.

They call St. Catharines the Garden City because the soil is so rich that everything grows like a weed, fruit in particular: strawberries, grapes, cherries, Red Haven peaches the size of softballs. Half the trees in our yard bore fruit, and Mason jars boiled on the stove all summer. But the real money in town had more to do with industry than agriculture. There was the General Motors plant, where boys straight out of high school could make twenty bucks an hour on the assembly line. There were jobs with the shipyards and the historic Welland Canal, which ran along the east side of our neighbourhood. It was built in 1829 to give ships a safe detour around Niagara Falls. It also gave the teenagers who parked on its banks a place to make out. Watching the submarine races, they called it.

Other than the high school boys, nothing moves quickly on the canal, least of all the freighters, which could be two football fields long and ten storeys high at the bridge. They cast a long shadow over us. From the neighbour's backyard we could count the rivets on the huge steel plates of their hulls, and the drain holes, which looked like they cried tears of rust. A long time ago my father had been a marine engineer on oil tankers like these, in the British Merchant Navy. He never said if those ships reminded him of that life. Only years later did I learn that the drone of their engines kept him up nights, suspending him in the half-sleep of expectation as he waited to be summoned to his watch in the engine room. My father rarely spoke of the past then, even when it sailed by his own front door.

We lived in a tidy subdivision that must have sprung up in the Space Age of the sixties. There was a Star Circle and Venus and Saturn courts, and in our roundabout of mostly German families, we were the aliens at 43 Neptune Drive. Before we moved in, the Pontellos had been the most exotic clan. There were loads of kids my age and we hung out during the summers, riding our bikes or playing basketball in the driveways. Sometimes we'd pretend to be detectives investigating versions of crimes we'd seen on *Charlie's Angels*. All the girls wanted to play the blonde and bodacious Farrah Fawcett character, and when arguments broke out over whose turn it was or whether my dark looks should exclude me from eligibility, an interrogation usually followed.

"So where you from, anyway?" one of the kids would ask.

"Mississauga," I'd say.

"No, really, where are you from?"

"Well, I was born in England —"

"No, I mean, like, *what* are you?"

It's true that kids can be mean, but my friends weren't. Most of them were just curious about a brown girl with a Jewish last name who went to the Catholic school. I was curious too. I wanted to say Italian, like the Pontellos. I wanted freckles and hair that swung like Dorothy Hamill's. But more than that I wanted an answer.

"Just tell them you're English," Mum would say. "You were born in England."

"But I don't look English. . . ."

"Tell them you're Eurasian," my father would offer.

"Where's Eurasia?"

Those conversations always left me with the uncomfortable feeling that we had something to hide. My parents never said simply, "We're this" or "We're that." They said, "*Tell* them this . . ." But "tell them" sounded like they were suggesting an excuse to offer a teacher for not doing your homework—*Tell her you lost it . . . Tell her your dog ate it. . . . Tell her you're English. . . .*

Of course, I knew India had something to do with us, or we with it. My parents were born there. Their parents were born there. My father, my brothers, and I sported year-round tans. We called okra "ladyfingers" and eggplants "brinjals," and my mother cooked a mean curry. When I was four, my parents took my sister and me on a world tour that stopped in Mumbai. It was still called Bombay then and I had strange kid memories of the place we visited: women on their haunches plucking chickens, a lizard creeping up the wall, red dirt, hole-in-the-floor toilets that seemed designed to make me pee on my feet. My parents also paid close attention if anything related to India appeared on television. When Michael Caine walked up the red carpet on Oscar night with his gorgeous Indian wife, Shakira, my father would whistle with patriotic pride—"Indian women are real beauties," he liked to say. But if I asked, the answer was no, we weren't Indian, really. We were English, sort of, and Portuguese, probably a little Irish and Scottish, a bit Dutch, and maybe Russian. Luckily, no one mentioned China or Jamaica at the time. What I already knew was enough to inspire panic attacks at grade school on Heritage Day.

My family landed in Toronto on a November night in 1972, six of us in matching sheepskin coats, bought in fear of arctic winters and the threat of hypothermia. Canada was a year into its grand multicultural experiment at the time, and federal policies not only welcomed immigrants of colour, they set targets to encourage it. Federal politicians—Prime Minister Pierre Trudeau in particular, whom my mother referred to as "that lovely man"—pushed programmes to support cultural diversity, and the philosophy trickled down to the towns and schools.

Bring a traditional dish from your homeland to share with the class, the teacher would say. Bring a flag. Wear your native costume.

I felt sick. "We don't have a native costume. Do we have a native costume? What am I supposed to take, a curry?"

"No, don't take curry. It will be too spicy for the children," Mum said. "What about Yorkshire pudding?"

"We hardly ever eat that."

"Okay, I'll just make stew."

How I envied my Ukrainian classmate, who turned up with her golden hair braided into pendulous loops, a folk-embroidered dress and a plate of perogies. I wore a velour tracksuit and stood in front of the class, in front of a map, wildly waving a pointer over the eastern hemisphere. "So we are kind of a mix of a lot of countries . . . maybe forty." I much preferred hot dog days, when a buck fifty bought everyone a wiener and a can of pop.

In the summer of 1978 I flew back to England with my parents for a visit. One afternoon we gathered at the home of my Aunty Zia and Uncle Douglas in Wembley. Zia is the eldest of nine in my father's family, a pint-sized and energetic woman who had invited the whole Abraham clan to lunch. Everyone clogged the front hall when we arrived—my parents, my father's brothers, their wives and children—greeting one another in a chaotic huddle of long hugs and kisses. At some point, jostled between hips and legs, I caught a glimpse of my grandfather sitting in the living room. It is the earliest memory I have of him.

Papa Albert was too frail to join the welcoming mob at the door. He was seated in a plump chair by the front window, tiny and delicate as a bird. He had a head of white stubble and a golden complexion. He wore a tie, a woollen vest and a herringbone jacket that gave him a distinguished air. Suddenly he looked up at me and grinned, as though he knew I'd been staring, and I saw something instantly familiar and yet utterly foreign in his face, in the gentle slant of his eyes. He looked Chinese. I was dumbstruck. My grandfather was Chinese? We were Chinese? On top of all the quasi-Indian, English, Portuguese, Dutch business, we were Chinese?

"Dad," I said, "are we Chinks?"

I don't believe anyone answered.

Most of that day I spent with my grandfather. He'd had a stroke a few years before and he didn't speak much, although my father says he never had. I probably spoke enough for both of us. While I prattled on Papa Albert pulled funny faces, pretending his ears controlled his tongue, tugging them left and right, making me laugh. He went upstairs early that evening. I followed, waiting in the hall while my grandmother helped him with his pyjamas. I sat on the edge of his bed after she tucked him in. At some point my parents came in, and we all kissed him goodnight and said goodbye.

My parents were quiet as we drove away that evening. I cried in the back seat. We would never see my grandfather again and we all knew it.

I had a million questions after that trip. Why did Papa Albert look Chinese? Was his mother Chinese, or his father? How did we end up with a name like Abraham?

My father didn't have many answers. His father didn't either, or if he did he had never shared them. All I could gather from my parents was that many years ago in India, Papa Albert's father was somehow given the name John Abraham. Other than that, only three things were known about him, and none with certainty: he was Chinese, he was a juggler and he had disappeared.

If we had something to hide about our heritage, John Abraham stood out as the thing that was hidden. A secret Chinese patriarch, a juggler, a lost culture, a lost name—all discovered just when the Abraham name was causing me a schoolyard-full of grief (to prepubescent boys, my prepubescent chest was the Plains of Abraham).

The mystery of my great-grandfather marinated in my imagination. Somewhere in my parents' basement crawl space is a school essay I concocted about the great-grandfather who abandoned the circus for love. I was eleven or twelve when I wrote it, and at that age it's hard to envision anyone leaving the circus for anything, so I made him out to be a terribly romantic figure. Although

Great-Grandfather had predated Mao Zedong by several decades, I featured a cold Communist Party official surveying local birth records in a small Chinese village and assigning each new baby a future occupation: farmer, cook, tailor, juggler . . . .

Weng Lin (the name I invented for him) was soon snatched from his peasant parents and forced into the austere life of the circus. He ate nothing but rice, slept in sheds on burlap sacks and tossed things in the air constantly—fruit, balls, knives, rings, flaming sticks, anything he could lay his hands upon. He was brilliant, single-minded in his art, until he spotted *her*, my great-grandmother (about whom we knew exactly nothing). She was a beautiful face in the circus crowd, a demure young woman from Burma, which according to my atlas was wedged south of China near India, and seemed a plausible choice. She smiled at Weng Lin and he was a goner. But the circus ringleaders frowned on desertion, so Weng Lin fled in the middle of the night. He changed his Chinese name to one he had read in the Bible and became Catholic to marry his Burmese sweetheart (whether the Burmese were staunch Catholics, I had no idea). It was an epic, entirely fabricated, yet as I would one day learn, not entirely off base.

On a bright April morning in 2002, a year before Jade was born, I was sharing a loveseat with the American scientist J. Craig Venter in the lobby of a Toronto hotel. Venter's company had mapped a private version of the human genome the year before, and the biologist-cum-businessman was in town to pick up one of Canada's Gairdner Awards. People often call the Gairdners "baby Nobels," because a third of scientists who receive one go on to win the big Swedish prize.

Venter was fifty-five at the time and he looked like he'd stepped off the cover of *Forbes*—fit, bald and well-tanned, with electric-blue eyes that seemed to burn with the wattage of a brain working overtime. He wore a dark suit and the irrepressible grin of a man who knew he'd made history.

Mapping the genome was hailed as the moon landing of the twenty-first century. When the first draft was in hand in June 2000, U.S. president Bill Clinton stood on the White House steps and compared it to "learning the language in which God created life." Researchers were barely at the "See Dick run" stage of understanding the language then, but the mere prospect of being able to read it made even the most conservative types fantasize. We'd cure diseases with genetic tweaks, prevent illnesses before they started, improve our species and possibly outwit death itself. Clinton mused that genetic manipulation might allow us all to live to 150.

Yet for all the razzle-dazzle, there was nothing glamorous about decoding DNA. It's drier than a phonebook and at least two hundred times longer. Deoxyribonucleic acid may be the world's most boring script. It has only four chemical letters in it—A, C, G and T—and they are repeated over and over, in different orders, six billion times.

The letters stand for adenine, cytosine, guanine and thymine, chemical units called nucleotides. All of them are connected to one another along a structure that looks like a spiralling ladder of three billion rungs. Each rung forms what's known as a base pair, with an A at the end of one rung connecting to a T at the other end, and a C to a G. The ladder is wound so tightly that two metres of it fits inside a human cell, and the average cell is so small that ten thousand can fit on the head of a pin.

But, unlike most things in life, the way DNA looks is nearly as important as what it does, which, in the case of the genome, is pretty much everything. DNA is like the chief executive officer. It sits all coiled up in its cellular head office, dictating operations in every division of *you*—the texture of your ear wax, how your heart beats and your brain is wired. It looks a bit scattered under a microscope, with its code broken up into forty-six chromosomes, twenty-three passed down from each parent. Yet add it all up and it's been said it would take a person typing sixty words a minute for eight hours a day fifty years to transcribe.

Computers hummed in eighteen countries on behalf of the public effort to spell out the alphabet of the human genome, with initial predictions that it would take fifteen years to finish. But Venter, who used to hop on his bike and race planes on airport runways when he was a kid, bet he could do it faster. In the end, Celera Genomics, the company he founded in Rockville, Maryland, completed its draft map in two and a half years, pushing the public project to keep pace. The public genome was a compilation of DNA from more than seven hundred people, and everyone had assumed that Celera's private map was a similar amalgam. But as Venter gazed out over the suits and high heels marching through the hotel lobby where we sat, he let something slip.

He was musing about babies having their genomes decoded at birth, and everybody carrying their DNA encoded on something like a credit card, when he said he knew better than anyone the potential of knowing your own code. The Celera genome, after all, was his own. The news would turn out to rile Venter's many critics. They would call it audacious and vain, an unethical stunt to hijack biology's big moment for personal publicity and commercial gain. But that morning, sitting with his legs stretched out on a sea of polished marble, Venter cast his decision to become the first human to have his genome decoded as a reasonable one, noble even. For the science to progress, to understand what is normal in a genome and what is not, researchers will have to recruit all sorts of people to have their DNA sequenced, he said. The more genomes that could be read, the more easily researchers could one day understand what those nucleotides spell out.

Already he'd discovered he carries genes linked to a higher risk of heart disease and, possibly, Alzheimer's. But then, he said, the genome holds the same sort of information that doctors can collect by learning the medical history of a patient's family. As I scribbled away in my notepad, he added that people could learn a lot about their ancestry from their DNA. He described the genome as a compilation of a person's ancestral parts, since the chromosomes a person inherits from each parent are recombined versions of the chromosomes the parents inherited from their parents, and that they inherited from theirs, and back it goes. His own code had provided evidence of his British ancestry. He likened it to an archive that would reveal the past in a way no paper record ever could.

I stopped listening. Venter had mapped himself. From his genome he had learned things about his own ancestry, not human ancestry in general. Not further proof of our evolution from ape-like forebears or primitive creatures, but his personal history, where his ancestors were from, as in a *place*. I suddenly imagined the human genome map as an actual map, capable of leading a person back through her foggy history, pointing the way to foreign lands and forgotten stories.

When my attention snapped back, Venter was describing his next project: sailing his yacht around the world in search of new energy sources in the genomes of ocean creatures. It hit me then that reading one's own genomic map for clues to ancestry was probably the exclusive purview of people with ninety-five-foot-sloops and sea-deep pockets. The Celera map of Venter's genome had cost more than $100 million. The public effort devoured close to three billion dollars. I filed the idea away under "Things to Do If I Win the Lottery."

When we left St. Catharines in 1979, it was my sister's turn to stay behind, to attend the nearby university. My father's job had changed to include more travel, so we returned to Mississauga to be close to the airport. For the next seven years I was the only child in a quiet house, except for Sundays. On Sundays Nana Gladys came to visit.

Before she came to Canada, I had always thought of her as my very English Nana. She lived in a Victorian row house outside London and shopped on the high street, where the clerks called her "Glad" and she called them "love"—"Just some bread today, love." I spent a few summers in England with Nana Gladys and she always let me sleep in her bedroom. It had been the dining room until my grandfather died in 1972. It had French doors that opened to a wild English garden, and a floor layered with Persian rugs. There were two single beds pushed together and three coat stands that had disappeared under the tarp of cardigans and nightdresses that weighed down their hooks. On the far wall was a fireplace, where perfumes were lined up on the mantel like chorus girls in their pretty glass bottles. I don't know that Nana ever wore them. She always smelled the same—like Yardley's lavender scent—most of all when she padded down the stairs after a bath, wearing only her petticoat.

The skin on her arms seemed as thin as cellophane, and so pale it was nearly translucent. Nana liked being white. She would go to her dressing table with its tall mirror and make herself whiter, patting her face with powder until it fell like snow on the carpet and her eyebrows disappeared. Then she'd pin the penny-sized medals of Saint Christopher and Our Lady of Vailankani to her bra strap, pencil in her eyebrows to match her Marmite-coloured hair, paint her lips bright fuchsia, puckering them together with a loud smack, and step into the puddle of one of her "going-out frocks," a pleated chiffon or the red A-line with polka dots. "Zip it for me, my girl," she'd say, her holy medals tinkling like a wind chime. Then she'd be off to the pub to play cards.

Nana might never have left that life, but she had a nasty fall from a bus in 1978, and that was it. She packed it all up—even my grandfather's study, which she hadn't touched since his death—sold the house and moved to Canada. Every Sunday we picked her up from her apartment for the twelve-o'clock Mass, and after lunch she and my mother would spend the rest of the day in our kitchen making dinner.

The smells and sounds of those afternoons would become a yardstick for every Sunday since: my mother at the back counter, chopping onions and garlic, grinding spices into a paste; sharp scents of cumin and coriander frying in a pan, the crackle of cardamom pods bursting in hot oil; my grandmother at the kitchen table, pouring cups of rice onto an orange melamine plate, sorting through the raw grains, picking out stones. All the while they talked, about places in India with names full of vowels—Poona and Dhoand and Jubalpore—and communities they called railway colonies, where it seemed they had always lived, in houses by this train station or that station—as had most of the people they talked about.

"What happened to the Bretagnes?" my mother would ask.

"They went to Australia."

"What about the Correys?"

"Australia also. The Changers landed up in England, and the Orchards."

Practically everyone they knew had gone somewhere, after India won its independence from Britain in 1947. None of the people they talked about had Indian names. The only Indians they mentioned were the ones who worked for them, their servants. There was the kind one who boiled rice in broth for their dogs Rover and Toby, the wretched one who spiked the vindaloo with sleeping tablets and ransacked the house while they slept, and the sweet boy who ran from Nana's kitchen to the railway station every day to deliver a lunch of hot chili fries and chapattis to my grandfather.

"How many silver tiffin carriers he could stack on his head—and so small he was!" Nana would say.

They spoke of railway-colony dances, convents where they had gone to school, and picnics at Juhu Beach while I, pretending to read or finish homework, listened. It was my introduction to the in-between world of my ancestors, a small swatch of mixed-blood people known by various labels when Britain ruled the subcontinent, many of them pejorative—*half-castes, chi-chis, bastards of the Raj.*

The community's official description, still entrenched in India's constitution, is "Anglo-Indian." It refers to citizens descended from a paternal line that originated in Britain or Europe. They were not to be confused with English-born people who lived in India, who were called "domiciled Europeans." There were also people of "Continental extraction," which implied that something European ran somewhere in their veins. Then there is "Eurasian," the all-encompassing term to which we usually subscribed. All that taxonomy works hard to stress the non-Indian fraction of a hybrid heritage, but never hard enough. Every syllable sags under the baggage of an uncomfortable maternal history, not that I knew it at the time.

As a child, my knowledge of Anglo-Indians came from watching my parents, our relatives, and their friends, usually at one house party or another, with the Johnnie Walker flowing and laughter erupting from the basement like machine-gun fire late into the night. There were rice-and-curry buffets and British pub-song singalongs, and if it was a good night, at least one booming verse of "I've Got a Lovely Bunch of Coconuts."

Everyone spoke perfect English, but their words rose and fell with the musicality of a unique subcontinental lilt. They came in all shades and wore Western clothes, except for their bangles of yellow gold that jangled like tambourines when they danced—and Anglo-Indians love to dance, the jive in particular. Even now, with my mother's sciatica and my father's titanium knees, turn up Glenn Miller and away they go. It made the front page of the *Times of India* in 1998 when a reporter discovered an attendee at an Anglo-Indian gathering in Bangalore who didn't know how to jive.

Everything about us was Indo-Euro fusion, right down to religion. We were raised to be staunch Roman Catholics—church every Sunday, fish on Fridays, a little shrine in the living room dedicated to the Sacred Heart, where electric candles burned day and night and good report cards were placed when (and if) they arrived. Still, the flavour of Eastern superstition seeped into our spiritualism, bringing with it notions of the evil eye, the bad omen of an overturned slipper or anticipation of an unexpected visitor if a knife fell to the floor.

Yet for all the obvious signs of our Eastern roots, there was often a kind of deliberate amnesia among the Anglo-Indians, as though the Indian bit had crept in by osmosis. My grandmother would never acknowledge that Indians, however many generations removed, had figured somewhere in our bloodline. If anyone challenged her on it—and as a goading teenager, I did—she would look up sternly from the orange rice plate and shake her head. "There are no Indians in our family."

"Come on, Nana. Look at us, look at our *tans!*"

"No, never. My father was English."

"But who were his parents? And what about your mother?"

"There's some Portuguese, but no Indian."

Who taught them to how to grind spices and make curries, I wondered. Who passed down the recipes?

Nana said everyone had learned from the servants.

One Sunday afternoon, a few years after I'd moved out to my own apartment, I found myself craving Indian food. I called home for a recipe, and my grandmother was so genuinely happy to pass on her tricks for a quick chicken curry that she stayed on the line and walked me all the way through it.

"This is how my mother taught it to me," she said.

"Your mother? I thought she was Portuguese."

"Yes, Portuguese," Nana said, and then she laughed.

I had always assumed that one day I would investigate our heritage. But I'd also assumed that I would be older—retired, shuffling around archives in caftans and orthopedic shoes. But the idea that modern genealogy could have as much to do with labs as with libraries kept luring me, and never more than in the months that followed the birth of my daughter.

Jade's arrival in 2003 not only coincided with an international epidemic, but also the fiftieth anniversary of the discovery of DNA's double-helix structure. Talk of things genomic was everywhere—how genetics had revolutionized forensic science, fingering the guilty and freeing the innocent; how it had helped to identify human remains and put names to old bones—and every week researchers were pinpointing the genes linked to a long list of ailments. At the same time, the technological ability to sequence DNA was improving in giant leaps. Stretches of the genome that had once taken researchers a month to decode could be pumped out in a week. Between 2000 and 2003, the cost of reading a single letter of DNA fell from $1.50 to less than a penny. Suddenly DNA was mass-market.

Academics started holding public workshops on "personal genomics," convinced that DNA would soon be decoded for the same price as a pair of designer shoes. Sequencing all six billion letters of an entire genome would still run to millions of dollars, and in 2003 no one had a complete code in hand, not even Venter. But sequencing bits and pieces of DNA became affordable to the average pocketbook. Dozens of companies sprang up to cash in, making qualified promises to predict disease risk, design diet and fitness plans to suit your genome, or even find you the perfect date—a molecular love match. Experts described it as the rise of "recreational genomics," implying that these direct-to-consumer tests were more sport than science and most likely to be treated as a kind of biological bingo game by fit baby boomers in tennis whites.

Most scientists agree that a straight line can rarely be drawn between a gene and a particular trait, not even height or eye colour. In most cases the science of genetic prediction was nowhere close to being able to accurately forecast a person's health risks based on DNA. There are too many variables, too many unknown genes that might protect against that risk, or environmental factors that might increase it. As more than one expert put it, people might learn just as much from reading their horoscopes. But there was a crucial difference between relying on DNA to predict the future and using it to learn about the past. Tracing ancestry with DNA is arguably a simpler science, one of comparing one genome with another. The more the genetic codes of two people look alike, the more likely they are to be related. If two different populations share common stretches of code, they are likely to share a common ancestry.

Even as I sat in the hotel lobby with Craig Venter on that sunny morning in Toronto, the first companies to offer genetic tests for ancestry had already popped up, spinning off from research at major universities. I started reading about them shortly after Jade was born, and the more I read, the more curious I became as to whether DNA could provide the answers to the questions I'd asked ever since our alien invasion of Neptune Drive. Would DNA confirm the Eurasian mix of our heritage? Would it reveal any trace of the juggler? I had read enough to suspect that I needed more than my DNA alone to find the answers. I needed my parents— their support, their stories and—if I could convince them to give me some—their cells.

I drove the half-hour to their house in Mississauga one day during my maternity leave, one of those grey, wintry afternoons when Lake Ontario was the colour of dishwater and the traffic was light. Jade was dozing in the back and I had nothing but my thoughts to distract me.

I thought about my father, seventy-eight that year, and how the past he'd rarely discussed when I was a child had come back to him vividly since he'd retired. I was sure he would be on side. A letter from England that he received in 1996 had focused his attention squarely on the history of his father's family. His sister Zia had sent him a card for his seventy-first birthday that said she had recently visited India, where she had discovered that Papa Albert's older sister, Florence Abraham, long thought to have left this world, was alive and well in the Nilgiri Hills of south India. A daughter of the juggler, lucid and living at 103—my father was astounded. He'd never known his Aunty Florence well, but the news that she was alive tantalized him with the possibility of finding answers to questions he'd assumed were long past answering.

Maybe, he thought, he'd even discover the family's true surname, and that it would prove to be a Chinese name after all.

My father has always felt an affinity for Chinese people. He made fast friends of Chinese work colleagues and forged an unusual bond with his Chinese doctor. A few times he told me—only half joking, I suspect—that he hoped I would marry a Chinese man, to return us to our roots. Over time I realized that China was like one of those tankers on the Welland Canal, casting a long shadow over his life.

For him, as it was for me, the mystery was rooted in his childhood. He told me it reached all the way back to 1932, when he was a boy sharing a two-bedroom apartment with his parents and seven of his siblings. They lived where most Eurasians lived, behind a walled compound in central Bombay. My grandfather had a job with the telegraph service; he spent long days, and sometimes nights, in a cavernous hall that echoed with the steady *tick-tick-tick* of everyone tapping through their shifts. Desperate for quiet, he'd come home to the newspaper and lose himself in the silent language of a crossword puzzle. My father would find him there when he came home from school—a fixture in the corner, half hidden by *The Times*, in his shorts and undershirt—and he would stare at his father's yellowish skin and hairless limbs.

"Completely hairless he was. Not a hair, not a hair on his legs or his chest." To my father, the pale and hairless skin was proof of Chinese blood. But Papa Albert "would never be drawn out about his background." It was only from his mother, Ena, and her family that he learned his father was half Chinese, and why Papa Albert never spoke about it.

Two of my dad's maternal aunts stayed with them in Bombay for a while, teenagers who liked to dance and play their music loud. When Albert asked them to turn it down, they told him a few things in return. "Shut up, you bloody Chinaman," they'd shout. "What do you know about anything, Mr. Wong?" It happened so often that the insult took on a deep meaning for my father. He was seven at the time and came to believe that Wong was his father's real name, and that being Chinese was a shameful thing that ought to be kept secret. "It was like a silent world hidden away from me," he said.

Eventually my father heard from his mother that Papa Albert did not have much to share about his heritage. His mother had died when he was a baby, and his father, John Abraham, had vanished when he was very young. My grandfather was raised by his older sisters, Julie and Florence, and they had done the practical thing, sending Albert to a boarding school, then to train as a telegrapher, at that time the cutting edge of long-distance communications.

Albert's first job took him from Nilgiri's tea hills to the bustling seaport town of Cochin. He met my grandmother walking on the beach, and Ena deCouto married Albert Abraham in 1923, despite the protests of her family. It was unfortunate enough to be an Indian in British India at the time, and uncomfortable to be an Anglo-Indian, but to be Chinese was beyond reckoning. To their minds, "Chinamen" were poor, non-English-speaking wallahs who fried noodles at roadside stalls or roamed the countryside with bolts of silk strapped to their backs, stopping at homes, unfurling sheets of pink and saffron in your garden, until you ran them off or threw them your rupees. In their world of mixed-blood people, Papa Albert looked like one mix too many. Yet for reasons I did not understand as a child, my father had quietly held on to that inscrutable fraction of his heritage like a lucky penny.

Yes, my father would certainly embrace the prospect of trying science to finally set the record straight. It was my mother I was worried about, intensely private as she is, and still haunted by Old World prejudices that being something other than "Anglo" was a liability. Yet my mother knows well that her heritage is an enigmatic mix; even in the mélange of British India's railway colonies it was unusual. But unlike my father, she had always seemed resigned to the mysteries of her bloodline.

Albert and Ena Abraham, my paternal grandparents, after arriving in England from India in 1970.

Jade was still asleep as I pulled up to the house. I carried her in from the car and my mother and I shared a pot of tea at the kitchen table.

"So, Mum," I began, "I've decided I'm going to research our family history."

"Oh, that's good," my mother said. "You've always been keen."

"Yes, but I'm going to research it with the *genetics* of our family. You can do that now, you know, with DNA tests. They can reveal things, like whether your ancestors really were European or Chinese or African—"

"DNA?"

"Yes, with DNA. I want to explore how far it can take us in figuring out who our ancestors were, where they came from."

For a long moment my mother didn't say a word. She bit her upper lip and pinched her eyebrows together as though the very idea contorted her sense of well-being.

I imagined the images that might be dancing through her mind. The disapproving gaze of her mother, Nana Gladys, shaking her head—*"We're English."* The hopeful look in her father's eyes when he spoke of Jamaica and a tattered portrait of the sea captain he'd never met. I could see all of it weighing on her, even as she tried to make a joke.

"Why can't you just make up a family?" my mother asked.

2

NIGHT OF THE SWAB

Eons before my family memorized the provinces and swore
an oath to Canada and the Crown, before there was a
captain or a juggler, complexions or countries, we were
cells—primitive specks clumping together under a young sky, mutating into higher beings—anchored polyps, flatworms, fish with
teeth and backbones. We were a busy lot, sprouting lungs, legs and
little brains, slithering out of the water to lay eggs on land. We
outlived dinosaurs and morphed into mammals, small, hairy and
warm of blood, like shrews and lemurs. We suckled our young and
swung high in the trees. But with the passage of glaciers, volcanic
eruptions and time, most of all, we lost our tails. We grew into
bipeds, too big for the branches, longer of torso and neck. Up we
stood, brains blossoming by the generation. We stoked fires,
cooked food and became tinier of teeth. We made spears of sticks
and hammers of stone. We were hominids, and grunts grew into
words. We wandered over land and seas, painted and prayed,
farmed and beat famine, survived plagues, wrote books and fought
wars. We made pottery, medicine, music, money and love—lots of
it, until the first fancy Q-tips arrived to swab the nucleotides swirling in our cells and in a blink of evolution, we were there, eating
cake in the suburbs.

"Happy birthday, Mum," I said, putting my arms around her.
"You look fantastic."

And she did, and not just for a woman in a filmy leopard print blouse turning seventy-three. My mother has those features that never seem to fall out of fashion: high cheekbones, good skin and thick, full lips. My mother has never liked her lips. I tell her that women pay top dollar for lips like hers, sucking fat from their own behinds to get that bee-stung pout. Given all the efforts to find genes behind this and that, I wondered if one day it might be possible to use DNA to trace my mother's lips all the way back to the Gold Coast of West Africa. But DNA testing was not an easy sell to my mother.

The conversation that we had started over a cup of tea had continued for two years. I always thought that the chance to try something new would overcome whatever qualms she might have about using genetic tests to uncover our family's past. She was the force that had propelled us to new countries, from India to England and then to Canada, even when my father was content to stay put. She never hesitated to hunt for new jobs, charging into executive offices with her Pitman shorthand and seventy words a minute. After she left secretarial work, she taught herself to play the stock market, and to play it well. In many areas of her life she's a risk-taker. And hitting her seventies hadn't slowed those appetites. Laptopped, iPodded and wireless, my mother was an early convert to the digital revolution. Yet the novelty of using genetic technology to reveal ancestry—a science in its infancy—held no such sway.

My mother once told me that she feared I might dig up frightening things from our genome, genetic proof that cancer or a heart attack would come her way no matter how much flax she ate or red meat she avoided. I insisted that I had no interest in our future health risks, susceptibilities or vulnerabilities. This was about uncovering the past. Didn't she want to know, I asked, about the Captain, her grandfather? Wouldn't it be wonderful to know his story at last?

Maybe it would, she said. But she remembered vividly how

much her father had wanted to know too, and look how it had turned out for him: "He was heartbroken."

Both my grandfathers grew up fatherless. Papa Albert was a child when John Abraham disappeared, and Papa Freddie, my mum's father, was just eighteen months old when the Captain died. Where the juggler's legacy was shrouded in secrecy, the Captain's was clouded by wild speculation. Over the years, Frederick William Crooks Sr. seemed to be many things: a high-ranking Freemason with mysterious clout; a hero who saved a boatload of drowning people from the Indian Ocean; a man of distinction who came from Jamaica and money—plantation money. None of our Crookses had forged a lasting connection with the Crookses of the Caribbean, or even seemed to know if we were related. There was something spooky about that disconnect, as if something dark had kept us from our island kin all these years, and from the legendary Crooks fortune that apparently came with them.

My seafaring great-grandfather left such tall tales in his wake that it was hard to distinguish truth from details invented for the sake of drama or a good joke. After all, most of what I knew, or thought I knew, of the Captain I had learned at Crooks family parties, where drama and good jokes flowed like the whisky. It never occurred to me as a child that tall tales might be preferable to the truth—that anyone who owned a plantation in Jamaica more than a hundred years ago might well have owned slaves. The prospect of genetic testing raised an obvious question to ask about the Captain: was he—were we—descended from slaves or slave owners? Did the answer lie in our DNA?

Wouldn't it be something, I said to my mother, to finally know whether we have family in Jamaica, to learn if there was a plantation, and the history of the Crookses on the island?

"Yes," she agreed, "that would be something."

But I knew from her tone there was no guarantee that something would be better than nothing.

In June 2005 I stumbled across a place to begin the testing. I was researching a story on the prickly topic of race and genetics when I learned about an unusual DNA test that police had used to track a serial killer in Louisiana. Several women had been raped and murdered in the Baton Rouge area in 2002, and based on witness reports, police had been looking for a white man driving a suspicious white van. But a biotech company in Florida that tested a crime-scene sample of DNA concluded that the killer was not a white man.

The idea that you could know something about the "race" or physical appearance of anyone from a DNA sample alone was revolutionary. Crime-scene DNA is usually valuable for its potential to be compared with the DNA of possible suspects: find a match and you might find the perpetrator. But DNAPrint Genomics Inc. of Sarasota said its test could tell police something about the ancestry of a perpetrator from one sample alone, and use those results to infer physical characteristics—skin colour in particular—without the benefit of any other information. The sample from Louisiana, for instance, indicated that the killer was 85 percent sub-Saharan African and 15 percent Native American. According to the company, this meant police should be looking for a black man, or at least someone who was brown. The company likened the test to a kind of "molecular eyewitness." Two months after the test result, police arrested Derrick Todd Lee, a black man who now sits on death row, convicted of murdering two women.

Scotland Yard, the FBI and the RCMP all came calling to try the test themselves. But the work was controversial; ethicists cautioned against a new age of racial profiling. They pictured police hunting suspects of certain colours based on DNA tests that might be wrong. People with African ancestors might look white, they charged, and those who look black might have more European ancestry than African. But other ethicists argued that DNA might be a more reliable way to generate physical descriptions than relying on live witnesses, whose reports are notoriously biased.

For me the debate was academic; I knew what my family looked like. What caught my attention was that the same test police were using to catch criminals was available to the public for tracing "bio-geographical ancestry." The Florida company claimed its test could provide an overview of the continental populations that had contributed to a person's genome—East Asian, sub-Saharan African, European and Native American. It was the only test on the market at the time to scan points in all twenty-three pairs of chromosomes. With the apparent mix within my family, I wondered if those points would span the globe.

My mother's curiosity eventually got the better of her. I had started taking a notepad when I visited, interviewing my father about his family history. My mother couldn't help but join in. Along with names and dates, she often knew details that my father had never heard, like why his 103-year-old Aunty Flo had never married, or how she had learned, even before my father, that John Abraham was a juggler.

These sessions usually unfolded over pots of tea and often ended with my mother and me taking off for a walk in the park near their house. One day she started asking questions about DNA and how it worked.

"Isn't it strange," she said, "that people in the same family can look so different? Look at Aunty Sarah. She had that red hair—no one else had the red hair. But see how it comes out so many years later. How does that happen?"

We were pushing Jade in her stroller, following the path that runs along the creek. I started to pick my way through an explanation of how DNA is inherited. "Well, you know how a baby is made, how sperm carries the father's DNA into the egg and it mixes with the mother's?" I said, or something like that. And then we laughed, because I was giving my mother the *sex talk*. I wheeled through an ugly thicket of false starts before settling on analogy, comparing a woman's DNA to a deck of playing cards that's copied and shuffled and cut in half before it ends up in her mature egg. The sperm that invades the egg carries the father's half-deck of DNA, which has also been copied and shuffled. When sperm and egg get together, they make a new life with a full deck, unlike any that has been dealt before or will be again. So there's always a chance, I said, that a red-hair card belonging to some long-ago ancestor will get played.

Coming from a family of regular poker players, this seemed to go over well. "Amazing," my mother said.

We walked on but hadn't gone far before she asked the question that mattered most. "But how can anyone tell from your DNA where your ancestors came from?"

By the mutations you carry, I told her. Each time that deck is copied and shuffled, changes can spring up in the DNA. Certain changes became common only in specific parts of the world—in China or Europe or Africa—mutations rarely seen anywhere else. So people who carry these certain mutations likely inherited them from ancestors who lived in those places.

"All right," my mother said, as we neared the playground. "Let's see."

The great message that scientists delivered with the first draft maps of the human genome was one of harmony: we are all 99.9 percent genetically identical. At the level of DNA, Dolly Parton and the Dalai Lama look like twins. Race, they concluded, is nothing more than a social invention, with no basis in biology. There might be more genetic variation between two Greeks than between a Greek and a Swede, or between two men who look white when one carries the genes of an African forefather. Under the skin, we're kin.

Even so, many experts doubted that a mere 0.1 percent could account for the vibrant diversity of our species. A few years after the maps were in hand, scientist Alan Bernstein predicted, "That figure is going to come back to bite them in the ass." Bernstein was president of the Canadian Institutes of Health Research at the time, and he turned out to be right. The premise that so-called racial groupings were not absolute wasn't wrong, but the estimate of our homogeneity was off by a full percent, or more, some researchers say. In the context of DNA, a script of three billion pairs of letters, 1 percent is a Grand Canyon of diversity—thirty million changes to a code in which even one can spell the difference between health and disease, life and death.

Figuring out how these changes differed between populations became a priority for many researchers. Most were looking for differences between genes that would reveal why certain diseases affect some populations more than others, the way genetic glitches trigger high rates of sickle cell anemia in Africans or cystic fibrosis in Europeans. Others were asking more provocative, if not incendiary, questions around the role genes play in abilities. Why are so many Jews so smart; why are West Africans such brilliant sprinters and East Africans leaders in long-distance running?

Others were using genetic mutations to map human history: how and when people migrated out of Africa to populate the planet, where they went and how they evolved into such a dazzling panoply of shapes, colours and sizes. Mark Shriver was one of those researchers, a young molecular anthropologist at Pennsylvania State University whose research had spun into the genetic ancestry test that DNAPrint was selling. Shriver had been compiling a catalogue of the unique genetic mutations that exist in populations, studying something called single-nucleotide polymorphisms, or SNPs (usually pronounced "snips"). They're the typographical errors that can pop up in a genome during the copying and shuffling of the chromosomal deck of cards that goes on before conception.

Nature is not perfect. With every new generation, typos creep into the code, resulting in a T where there used to be a C, for instance, or an extra A in place of a G. Sometimes these typos lead to maladies so disastrous they cause a miscarriage or early death.

Others spread widely through a population, for all sorts of reasons. Some of these mutations gave their carriers a survival advantage, such as the one that allows Europeans to tolerate lactose from cow's milk all through their adult lives, and the SNP that helps shield sub-Saharan Africans from malaria. Those who didn't carry the mutation were more likely to die off. Or it may simply be that the initial carrier of the SNP had many children, who in turn passed on the mutation to future generations. Or, as Mark Shriver suggested the first time we spoke, it may be that the initial carrier's mutation resulted in a trait many found attractive, upping the chances of winning at the mating game and passing that mutation on within the region.

However a SNP finds its way across a population, certain SNPs have become what researchers call "ancestrally informative markers"—signposts in the genome associated with the regions where they are prevalent, and possibly originated. Testing these SNPs often turns up surprising results, Shriver said, and usually reinforces the idea that most of us are "racially mixed" even if we don't look it. Shriver, a white guy, had learned that first-hand when DNA testing uncovered his African ancestry. It turns out his genome bears a certain mutation known as the Duffy Null allele, a gene variant that offers protection against malaria and is found almost exclusively in sub-Saharan populations. When we spoke, Shriver was developing a test to scan ten thousand of these ancestrally informative markers across the genome. But in the meantime, needing a place to start, I bought the 176-marker test that DNAPrint was offering for $250.

I was keen to test my whole family—my parents, my siblings and me. I wondered what different combinations of their genes my parents had passed down to each of us and whether our DNA would be as different as we each look. Would some of us bear biological evidence of a Chinese or Jamaican heritage? Three generations later, would our ancestral markers bear any trace of the juggler or the Captain?

My siblings and me on holiday in the English countryside before leaving for Canada in 1972. From the left, Conrad, me (on his lap), Kevin and Christine, with Dad.

There are things you can count on when my family gathers for an evening at my parents' house. Shoes will pile up at the front door like discards at a bowling alley. Someone will ask for the good Scotch and one of my parents will disappear trying to find it. My father will turn on the stereo and someone will turn it up loud.

That night it was "Volare" blasting through the house as I set up a makeshift clinic in the kitchen. Eventually everyone ends up in the kitchen. I set out the DNA kits on the table while my father lined up the booze on the counter—wine, Johnnie Walker, vodka, soda and, that night, the ice bucket. When the ice bucket is out, it's an occasion.

I liked the idea of holding the inaugural swabs on my mother's birthday. Birthdays were often subject to my grandmother's wishful thinking—Nana Gladys felt they ought to coincide with major holidays. She always celebrated her own birthday on Christmas Eve, even after my father found documents proving she was actually born three days earlier. Nana also used to insist that my mother was born on Remembrance Day, even though her birth certificate said November 12. Collecting the first round of DNA on the actual anniversary of my mother's birth felt somehow like a small jab at the truth.

My sister volunteered to go first. Growing up, we used to play an absurd game to fill in the gaps of our ancestry, each of us spinning a yarn more far-fetched than the other. In the days before the swab we'd bet five dollars on who would be most surprised by the results. I thought it might be Dad, she thought Mum. We both assumed that nothing would surprise either of us.

Christine sat down at the table as I opened the packages that had arrived from Sarasota in a big white envelope. Its return address was Coconut Avenue, which made me picture lab techs in Hawaiian shirts spinning a little reggae along with DNA in their centrifuges. Each kit contained two "cytobrushes," one for each cheek. They were white, nearly as long as a toothbrush, and had stiff, jagged cotton ends for scraping buccal cells off the inner cheek. Buccal swabs became popular in the DNA-collecting field because their storage requires no refrigeration or preservative. They don't always provide as much reliable DNA as a blood sample, but they're more appealing to study subjects than a prick in the flesh.

I peeled off the plastic and handed the first stick to my sister as Jade buzzed into the kitchen with her arms extended like an airplane. "What's that?" she asked, stopping to watch my sister jiggling the stick in her mouth. "Is it a Popsicle?"

"Okay, I've gone up and down fifteen times," my sister said. "Should I keep going?"

"Can I have a Popsicle?" Jade asked.

"Yes," I told my sister, "keep going."

My mother came into the kitchen. "Oh, you really are doing it?" she said. "I don't know, Carolyn—we're drinking."

I was beginning to see this as a blessing. All DNA clinics should serve whisky with their screening tests, to wash away the apprehension.

"She's serious. She's really doing it," Mum said again. "I should brush my teeth."

I read my mother the instructions when she returned. They outlined the potential for unlikely injuries associated with swabbing, such as slashing your inner cheek and subsequent infection. My sister pointed out that there was also a chance that someone would miss her mouth completely and jab herself in the eye.

My mother didn't laugh. She looked very serious. Maybe it was the video camera that Stephen had set up to record the event. She took long, hard, deliberate strokes, as though with enough pressure she could erase the past and any anxieties that came with it.

Conrad was happy to open wide, which was something. Genes had not been kind to my eldest brother. He was diagnosed with schizophrenia in the mid-eighties and it had cost him dearly: his children, his marriage, his home and career. Life since had been an odyssey, an endless run-on sentence of hospital stays, impulsive globetrotting, medication and too few merciful stretches of stability. The most recent years had been better. He has his own apartment, friends, hobbies and the tonic of routines to keep him grounded. And as much as his brain chemistry can let him down, his encyclopedic memory can be a marvel.

As the eldest of us four, he had spent more time with my mother's father, Papa Freddie, than any of us. He remembered hearing our grandfather talk about how much he had longed to sail to Jamaica, to meet the Captain's family—his family—and toil on the Crooks plantation. "He wanted to sweat in his father's fields," Conrad told me once. That night, as he passed back the swabbing stick, he asked me if I thought DNA might lead us to that plantation.

"Maybe, Con," I said. "I hope so."

By the time my father took the chair he was in a fine mood, as he tends to be when the family gets together. The alcohol has little to do with it; my father sets up a hospitable bar but he has never been much of a drinker. I did a story once about a gene mutation that people of Asian descent tend to carry, one that blocks the metabolism of alcohol, making them particularly vulnerable to the effects of even a small amount. Any more than two glasses of anything and Dad sings "Pennies from Heaven."

As I suspected, my father had championed the family project from the get-go. He even did his bit to persuade my mother to give DNA a try. "What are you worried about, Tweet?" he'd said to her one afternoon, when we were in their car, stuck in traffic. (My father rarely calls my mother by her first name, which is Thelma, unless he is talking about her to someone else.) "DNA will be a much more reliable way to find out about family history than depending on hearsay or folklore," he added. My father wrinkled his nose when he said *folklore*, as if the word itself smelled of something rotten. "This is science, Tweet."

Before the first swab session, he had begun lending me his favourite books on Indian history, pointing out passages with special relevance, such as Nehru's address to the nation on the eve of independence, when my father had huddled with his family around the radio, fearful of what the change would bring. He seemed to feel about DNA the way he felt about books: at least one reliable version of our story was written there. I also think using science to explore history appealed to the engineer in him, although my father usually balks at the stereotype. He spent most of his career as an executive in the energy field for large engineering firms, and spent more time at boardroom tables and power lunches than with blueprints. But on the home front where my mother managed the people, my father was the chief engineer, constructing desks, and wall units, a conservatory, and cubicle shelving to hold the shirts he irons into factory-perfect rectangles. My father is no expert in genetics, but he could appreciate its methods, its attempt at precision. That it might now, in his ninth decade of life, reveal his mysterious grandfather to him was, he told me once, a gift.

He swabbed slowly, one cheek, then the other, and handed me the sticks.

From behind the video camera, Stephen told my father he could now be cloned.

Dad laughed loudly and started out of the kitchen. But then he froze, turned back and stared straight into the camera. His eyes were moist behind his glasses as he raised his snifter of cognac high above his head. "Well, here's to you, grandfather."

I was tucking his swabs into their sealed packages and stopped to watch him for a moment, suddenly realizing—and fearing—the expectations my father had riding on his DNA. But then I heard him return to the living room to tease my mother.

"Now that they have my DNA, they can clone me," he said, "which means there will be a few Dudleys running around. You better make sure you know the true one."

"How will I know that?" my mother said wearily.

"How will you know? Oh, I'll have to tell you in private."

"Oh, Dud," she said.

A few weeks before my mother's birthday, my brother Kevin and I had been at a soccer fundraising dinner for my niece. We were waiting in the buffet line with our plates when he asked me why I was so interested in DNA testing—if I thought it truly represented who we were as people, if a mere string of molecules encoded our souls. Success had given my brother the luxury of time to mull over some of life's big questions from varied and exotic perspectives. He travels widely and devours books on world history, mysticism and philosophy.

His was a valid question. But even if the answers DNA provided were imperfect, I told him, it was already clear that it revealed the story of human evolution. By those same measures it was possible that DNA could tell us something about where we had come from in the more recent past.

But would that change anything, he asked, about me, or us as a family, to know those things about our heritage?

I didn't think so, I said. But the truth was, I didn't know.

I understood why Kevin decided to take a pass on the DNA test that night. Our talk had left me wondering if I'd leapt to the far side of biological reductionism, searching for our identity in the filaments of ourselves. By the time the results came back, I would have many of the same misgivings.

3

BLACK ARTS AND RED HERRINGS

My great-grandmother Bridget Meek Crooks believed she could communicate with the dead. I presume she must have felt someone from the other side pick up, or she wouldn't have kept calling. Even when she travelled, she took a homemade Ouija board with her. If no one staunchly religious or easily spooked was in sight, she would pull out her hand-cut letters of the alphabet, arrange them on a flat surface and set to work channelling. My mother was twelve the first time she saw it—her father's mother sitting bolt upright, eyes shut and chanting, trying to summon the dearly departed to the kitchen table. It was 1945 and Nana Bridget had come to look after my mother and her six siblings at their home in Poona, south of Bombay. Nana Gladys was in hospital, recovering from the miscarriage of what would have been her eighth child.

Bridget knew about loss. I suspect that's what drew her to the spirit world. She had been married to the Captain for only four years when he died. We don't know exactly how they met; only that ships had something to do with it. After the Suez Canal opened in 1869, the port of Bombay was as busy as a Dutch brothel. The whole world sailed in, ships full of women, traders and fortune hunters, wool, tin and textiles, often spun from the same bales of raw cotton that India shipped out. American independence had cost the British their cheap cotton supply, and soon after it was Indian cotton that covered the backsides of the Empire. It also helped to weave a metropolis. Bombay's population swelled from a mere thirteen thousand to roughly a million over the eighteenth and nineteenth centuries.

My great-grandfather was among the newcomers. Frederick William Crooks arrived as chief officer aboard a vessel that may have come by way of the United States or perhaps Jamaica, his homeland. Ships between Jamaica and India had always been frequent, with the exchange of sugar, salt, coffee, tea and spices; but, in the Captain's day, between 1845 and 1915, Britain also shipped 36,000 Indians to Jamaica as indentured servants to replace slaves after abolition. No one knows if the Captain had intended to stay in India, but after he met Bridget Meek he did. She was from a well-to-do Anglo-Indian family, her father an overseer in the public works department and eventually a supervisor of the railway. Bridget had four brothers, and they were the ones who first met the Captain. Apparently they picked him out instantly as a fine catch for their sister. He was dashing, worldly, distinguished. As my mother says, "All I ever heard about the Captain was that he was outstanding."

Only one image of the Captain survives. It's a large charcoal sketch that has been folded in three for so many decades it's practically in pieces now. In it, wearing a tailored suit jacket and tie, he looks regal, confident. There's certainly something alluring and serene about his gaze. He has slim, chiselled features, a handlebar moustache that must have lashed his cheeks like a bullwhip in the ocean winds, and light eyes like my grandfather's and Conrad's. It's difficult to tell if he was black or white. More likely he was like the rest of us—some shade in between.

It's impossible to guess his height from the portrait, but family lore has it that Bridget Meek looked like a child at his side, at least a foot shorter. When she lost her temper, he used to pick her up under the armpits and sit her on top of a tall cabinet until she cooled down. They married in Bombay in 1902, when he was twenty-nine and she was eighteen. A year later they had a daughter, Florence, and in 1905, a son—my grandfather—named after his father, whom most people knew as Freddie.

The only known image of the Captain, Frederick William Crooks Sr., produced at some point before he died in 1906.

It was in Bombay that my great-grandfather became a captain; he earned his master mariner's certificate and joined the Mogul Line, a fleet of British ships that often ferried pilgrims to Mecca. Every able-bodied Muslim who can afford it is obliged to travel to Saudi Arabia's holiest city at least once in a lifetime, so the hajj gave the Captain steady work sailing up and down India's coast, picking up the faithful. On one trip, the story goes, he happened upon a boat that had capsized in the Red Sea. He pulled so many drowning souls to safety that he earned a commendation from the king of England. That royal recognition from Edward VII is said to have promised the Captain and his family free passage to England at any time.

But my great-grandfather never lived long enough to take advantage of the offer. His steady shipboard diet caught up with him quickly, and like so many nineteenth-century men of the sea, he developed beriberi. There was no cure for it then, and the dire lack of vitamin B_1 came on like a wasting disease. Masked as fatigue or congestive heart failure, it can cause the limbs to swell and the mind to collapse, often leaving its victims delirious until they die, which the Captain did, at the age of thirty-two.

My mother heard that his Jamaican relatives had made contact with Bridget after his death, by letter or by telegraph, asking if they could adopt my grandfather, who was just eighteen months old. Bridget turned them down flat. It's said that the Freemasons helped to support her. The Captain had apparently been a high-ranking member of the brotherhood, and they financed the education of my grandfather and his sister. The Captain's membership in a secretive ancient society only added to his mystique—that and the idea that my great-grandmother managed to continue her relationship with him for at least thirty-nine years after he passed.

It could have been otherwise. Bridget Meek was a handsome woman, my mother says: "A backside like a peacock she had." There were plenty of suitors; even the maharaja of Hyderabad had hungry eyes for her and actually proposed. But Bridget never remarried. Instead, even at the age of sixty, she was still holding tight to the Captain's memory and her homemade Ouija board.

I thought of Nana Bridget when the first DNA results arrived. My great-grandmother had her chants and portable alphabet and I had the wizardry of lab tests and fancy Q-tips as I waited for the whispers of long-lost souls from a smudge of buccal cells. Was this budding branch of genetic science any more reliable than her dark arts?

The first results arrived from DNAPrint in January 2006. Stephen brought them in with the mail on a snowy evening after work. I'd sent in his DNA sample as well, to see how his would compare to the alleged mix of mine. Based on Stephen's looks alone, his heritage seems to be a straightforward story: he's tall, blondish, fair and blue-eyed, German-Swedish on his mother's side, British and German on his father's. Both sides sailed to North America in the nineteenth century and homesteaded in the west; the last three generations were all born and bred under the big sky of the Canadian prairies. Still, his family had its tales too: that mingled in with the lily white of his father's side was a bit of Native ancestry.

Before making their way to central Alberta, the Rouses had farmed in Kentucky, where, folklore had it, a Cherokee great-grandmother had dipped into their gene pool, leaving certain descendants with a touch of swarthiness in the skin and an epicanthic fold to the eyes. Stephen has always relished the idea, believing it deepens his ties to the land where tribes and buffalo once roamed free. Plus, he tans well. After a day in the sun he'll hold up his arm next to mine and say, "Look at that, Abraham. I'm darker than you. See? One-sixteenth Cherokee."

In many ways my husband harbours the same affinity for First Nations people that my father does for the Chinese. But I didn't really see it until that night, as he stood there in his wet boots, poring over DNAPrint's "certificate of ancestry." It looked like a diploma—an extravagant border of emerald green, embossed with a gold seal, clearly suitable for framing. But the look on Stephen's face suggested it was heading straight to the recycling bin.

"One hundred percent European," he said, tossing the paper on the table. "One hundred percent! I'm boring."

"Oh, come on, let me see, Paleface. Nothing about Cherokees in there?"

Stephen didn't laugh. He looked genuinely disappointed, bewildered even, as though he'd just lost something, his keys, or his wallet.

"Look, I don't think anyone could really be 100 percent anything," I offered. But his mind was far away, back in his boyhood, those nights on the farm when the neighbours would sit with his folks around the big kitchen table, drinking coffee from a giant stainless steel percolator. His father told stories of the Rouse ancestors who had ended up in Missouri, three kilometres from the homestead of Frank and Jesse James, and the ones in Kentucky, near the Cherokee reservation. The aboriginal link resonated with Stephen, adding a certain mystery to the Native farm workers who arrived with the spring as hired hands. But now here he was with a fancy piece of paper that cast doubt on all of it.

"You have to wonder if there was any truth to the stories at all," Stephen said.

I reminded him that this test was a scan of only 176 markers in a code of three billion. "Look, it may be that you do have markers that would suggest a Native connection, but those markers weren't identified in this test," I said. Maybe a broader test would pick them up, I added. Who knows what stories other markers might tell?

I waited until later that night to open my own results. I doubted that anything would surprise me the way it had Stephen, but I was wrong. European: 49 percent; East Asian: 21 percent; sub-Saharan African: 8 percent. Those numbers should have been intriguing enough: the first real evidence of a Chinese heritage, and a hint that the Captain may well have passed down genes from Africa. But all of this was overshadowed by a fourth figure that scattered my mind in a thousand directions, making me read and reread it: Native American, 22 per cent—as in Indians, not of India but of the Americas.

"Okay," Stephen asked, "what does yours say?"

"Well, according to this, I'm the Native American around here."

"Come on," he said, grabbing the paper from my hands. He read it and then feigned a scowl. "Did you switch our samples? Or is all this just crap?"

I shrugged. Was it?

Stephen had believed he was part Native and the test told him he wasn't. I had no inkling that Native American ancestry played a role in my heritage, and the test says it did—and not just a trifling drop or two but a whopping 22 percent. Did 22 percent of the 176 "ancestral informative" markers the company had tested make me nearly a quarter Native? In which Native populations had these markers been found? North America has more than three hundred different tribes. Was I part Cree, Ojibwa, Mohawk?

It seemed more plausible that those markers had been passed down through the ages from the same Asian population that Native Americans were descended from. But if that was the case, why had they not been diluted by the genes of more recent ancestors? Didn't such a high reading suggest that I had a Native ancestor from not so long ago? Maybe this was another family secret buried under the blankets of time and denial. The company's research suggests that a person begins to exhibit the physical characteristics of a group with a reading of 30 percent. Do I look a little Native? I thought of my father's nose. I thought of the Indian warrior featured on the logo of the National Hockey League's Chicago Blackhawks and tried to do a mental overlay of the profiles—the noses in particular, that distinctive slope. Had I noticed the similarities before?

My father is not one for cursing, even if he nails something into his thumb. At home, just about the only time we could count on Dad to use bad language was after Bob Barker asked a Miss America contestant about her lifelong ambitions. If her answer involved anything that included the phrase "world peace"—as in working towards it, praying for it, or promoting it—my father blurted out a resounding "Bullshit." As I handed him his first DNA results, I wondered if he would break out a four-letter word when he got to the Native part.

A news channel was droning in the background and my mother was at the kitchen counter making lunch. My father adjusted his glasses and read out loud: "European, okay, 35 percent . . . East Asian, 36 percent—look at that, Tweet, there it is— 36 percent! That must be from my grandfather. . . ."

And then, like me, instead of delighting further in the very detail my father had hoped to find, his attention was consumed by the line he read next. ". . . Native American, 25 per cent. . . . What's this? *Native American*?" My father leaned closer to the paper to confirm what he'd read. "Twenty-five percent?!"

"Wow!" he said, "Golly! Goodness me, I didn't expect this. Native American? Red Indians, not brown Indians?"

"Wow!" my mother said, "Where does that come from?"

I didn't think any member of our family had set foot in North America before the 1970s, I suggested, so it could be that the markers were not really Native American but Asian. But the company had been clear from the outset that it could not distinguish European ancestry from South Asian ancestry, because there had been so much mixing between Europe and India. So I wondered why the reading was so high if it was from ancestors so long ago.

"Yes, of course, from Asia . . . the Natives came across the Bering Strait," my father said, referring to the stretch of water between Siberia and Alaska. His mother's people, the mysterious Snalleckz branch, had sprouted somewhere in Russia before making their way to India, he added. "Given Russia's proximity to that north-eastern passage, that might explain it. Or," he said, rolling with it as my mother set down sandwiches, "you must remember the early explorers who came to the Americas, then went back to Europe and to Asia. They took some Native Americans with them."

Launching into the history, my father recalled reading that Columbus had dragged dozens of Native Americans back to

Europe with him, trying to convince his royal benefactors of the potential labour pool in the New World. The handful that survived sickness and the sea made a lasting impression in the courts of Europe, and my father said he remembered something about a few Natives even ending up in India. Over lunch we continued on like this, wondering if a kidnapped Native had sired one of our ancestors in the subcontinent, whether Indians of India had a common heritage with the Indians of North America, and how I had read somewhere that Sanskrit words of ancient India actually form root words in the language of Native American cultures. And on it went.

That afternoon we all accepted this science as truth, and instantly felt a need to explain it, to find a narrative that would put flesh on the bones of this discovery. Stephen had lost a story and we had gained one; we just had no idea what the story was. Not that it mattered. Word of our newly discovered Native ancestry spread through the family like a smoke signal. To my sister-in-law, Sheri, the result explained why my niece Candice had looked "like the real thing" when she dressed up as Pocahontas one Halloween. My Uncle Horace said it wasn't the least bit surprising. "Do you know how many people ask if I'm Native?"

For my sister, the Native finding was proof of our prescience. Hadn't we joked as kids that we belonged to a long-lost tribe of wanderers who ate samosas and slept under the stars? Remarkably, Christine's DNA didn't have nearly as much of the Native quotient as mine and my father's. She came in at 11 percent Native, 51 percent European, 2 percent sub-Saharan African and 36 percent East Asian (was this why her son had silky jet-black hair?). Our results were dissimilar enough to suggest that our genomes had clearly been dealt from different decks, which was not a big surprise, since my sister has freckles and enjoys playing Sudoku. My mother's results had not arrived yet, but it appeared that my sister was more like her and somehow I had inherited nearly all of my ancestral markers from my father.

I told Christine that Conrad's results also looked more like Dad's and mine. Con's had said: European, 49 percent; East Asian, 23 percent; sub-Saharan African, 9 percent; and his Native American markers were high as well, at 19 percent.

"So does this mean we really are Native?" Christine asked.

"What do you mean *really* Native? Genetically, culturally, politically—what?"

"You know, as in does it have implications?"

Her list was succinct: could we join a tribe? move to an Indian reserve? apply for tax-free status? open a casino? We agreed these were probably politically incorrect questions. But then we started cracking jokes about whether it was legitimate to ask those kinds of things now, since, it would seem, we are Native, and so therefore it would be acceptable, wouldn't it?

A few days later, when I called DNAPrint in Sarasota to clarify my family's results, I learned just how seriously some people take these kinds of questions.

Emanuela Charlton, or Lou, as she prefers to be called, has a PhD in pharmacology and the perfect telephone voice for someone in customer service. A plush drawl that wraps words in velvet is nothing short of a gift when Lou has to tell Mrs. Jones, "This particulaah test cannot possibly reveal whetha you descend from a Russian czaah," or confirm to the white supremacist that, yes, his DNA does suggest he is 22 percent sub-Saharan African.

Lou said she had to be as quick and calm as an air traffic controller or run the risk of a caller crashing headlong into an identity crisis. Often she referred customers to the bar graphs that plot DNA results onto a range of estimates, helping them understand there is a margin of error that suggests a few markers may be linked to one geographic region or another that the test did not pick up. "I can generally get them calmed down enough that they believe the test," said Lou, who pegged its accuracy at 98 to 99 percent. "There are some people who take the test for the wrong reasons, to prove they are something—100 percent wonderful, or whatever they think they are. You do get some kooks."

But most callers, she said, were simply puzzled by unexpected results. In those cases she laid out the randomness of the way DNA recombines with every generation (cue the half deck shuffle) and how a person can inherit genetic bits and pieces from every ancestor they've ever had, even a nucleotide or two of a forebear from thousands of years ago. "You know, you go back five hundred years—which isn't a lot—that's fifteen generations, and you have thirty-two thousand ancestors to deal with. You go back twenty generations, you've got a million ancestors to deal with," Lou said. "So when people wonder why they're getting these strange results that they didn't expect, I tell them, well, that's why."

Most of the gratitude, she added, for this type of testing comes from people who know nothing of their heritage because they were adopted. Then she told me where most of the frustration comes from: "There's been an explosion of people who want to be Native American. They just want to be—it's like the in thing these days. Most people that I talk to are annoyed with the test because it didn't show that they have Native American ancestry. Apparently they want to tie in to casino funds. The government also offers a lot of grants for people with Native American ancestry, for college for their sons and daughters. They scream at me on the phone, asking why they don't have Native American ancestry."

But did these people have reason to believe they were somehow Native? I asked.

"A lot of it is lore. They've had all this history over their lifetime that says their great-grandmother was a Cherokee Indian princess, yet we show no Native American in their DNA sample. But it may have gone somewhere else; their brother may have it, or their cousin. But ultimately, if it's not there they get furious."

A Cherokee princess. Stephen's story sounded more like a rural legend the more Lou talked. She told me about a fellow who had called the day before to complain that he was banking on Native scholarship funds to put his kids through college. She told me about tribes that have people storming their doors claiming to be 16 percent Native American, and that many tribes simply won't accept DNA as evidence.

And really, I thought, why would they? To be Native American, or to be anything for that matter, is a question of culture and tradition, not biology. Even if we had a pile of genetic markers in common with First Nations people, it did no more to cement our identity as *being* Native than hanging dream catchers on our bedposts or seeing my father's nose in a hockey team's logo.

I assured Lou that I had no interest in exploiting our newfound Native ancestry, and that I had quite the opposite problem— it was totally unexpected. The test had turned up a percentage of Native markers in my father, my brother and me that was so high it had left us bewildered. We believed we hailed from parts of Europe and India, and possibly China, and this was the very last thing we had imagined.

"What was your percentage?" Lou asked.

"For my father, it was 25 percent; for me, 22."

"Wow," she said, "that's pretty high."

If Lou "I've Heard It All" Charlton thought that sounded like a whole lot of Native, then I figured our result warranted further explanation. I asked if there was a way to find out in which tribes those markers had first been identified, and whether they were also common in people from other parts of the world.

Lou said she couldn't be sure but that it was not uncommon to find Native ancestry in southern Europeans, herself included. "It was my biggest surprise too," she confessed, "and I wasn't even that high, maybe about 10 percent." Her Italian ancestors had come through Ellis Island in 1900; they didn't speak a word of English and "probably didn't even know what an Indian was." Even Tony Frudakis, who is of Greek descent, she said, discovered he had "a bunch of Native American in him too."

For weeks the words "call Frudakis" appeared on my to-do list. But DNAPrint's chief scientific officer was hard to reach. In the meantime I tracked down Ripan Mahli, the young geneticist who had helped to design the Native ancestry component of the company's test. In fact he'd recently left DNAPrint to start his own firm, specializing in Native ancestry testing, and he agreed it was a tricky business. Basically any reading below 12 percent could be inaccurate, or not strictly reflective of Native American ancestry, depending on what other geographic areas were mixed into a person's origins. People from southern Europe all the way to Japan can carry many of the same mutations that can be found in Native Americans. That doesn't make the mutations "Native," but rather more Central Asian, reflecting the genes of the ancient Asian population that migrated from that part of the globe and populated other regions: the Americas, East Asia, South Asia and Oceania, in the South Pacific (one theory has it that Natives arrived in the Americas in successive waves from Oceania).

Ripan forwarded me an academic paper he had co-authored. It noted that for someone with Native ancestry below 3 percent, it might not be detected by the test (a statistic I promptly offered to Stephen, like a pillow). Neither could any specific tribe be identified by genes alone; through the millennia, tribes had intermarried, adopted, split and merged, and in the process traded genes like they had horses.

Ripan said the markers used in the test had first been identified in samples taken from Native and Mayan populations in the south-western United States, but other studies show they are generally representative of the various Native groups in North America. The most compelling detail he shared was that these markers are particularly difficult to distinguish in people who also have East Asian ancestry. Someone of East Asian descent has to have a Native American ancestry reading of at least 13 percent to conclude that she actually has Native ancestry, he said, explaining that East and Central Asians have many mutations in common.

When I told him I had South Asian roots, as well as a high reading of East Asian and Native ancestry, Ripan suggested the combination might not reflect any input from the Americas at all. In all likelihood, in our case it was all Asia, all the time.

Over time my father became less captivated by the prospect of Native ancestry than with the idea that he had somehow passed down to me all his Native ancestral markers. In fact it led to the development of his "super-sperm theory," which he shared over dinner one night.

"I wonder if the mood, the emotional state of the parents, has some bearing on what happens at conception," he offered gingerly.

"What do you mean?" I asked.

"At the time you were conceived in England, I was at the peak of my career. I was managing a team of 250 men! We were putting in a large proposal to build a power plant in the Midlands, and there was a deadline to meet. I was a bit of a tyrant. I kept the men there all night. Remember, Tweet?" he asked my mother. "You had to bring me breakfast and my toothbrush. When they called and said we had won the bid, well, I was elated!"

"So then what?" I asked. "You thrust your chromosomes upon me?"

"I'm just saying, you wonder if that has an effect on the way a child is conceived," Dad said. "I was in a domineering state and somehow that affected your DNA."

My mother rolled her eyes and I laughed, dismissing my father's theory as a testosterone-clouded perspective. But just a few months later, Stephen Scherer, a leading geneticist at the University of Toronto, found the first evidence that the way parents' genes divide when making a new child was not necessarily in a fifty-fifty split. Working with researchers from Harvard, the Sanger Institute in London and the University of Tokyo, his team discovered that a child can inherit more genes from one parent than the other. Ever since Gregor Mendel set down the laws of genetic inheritance

150 years ago, people have assumed that each person inherits two copies of every gene, one from each parent, making each child equal parts mother and father. But Scherer and his group found that people do not necessarily have the same number of genes, that one person can inherit as many as ten copies of a gene, several from one parent and none from the other, or even receive no copies at all of a gene and still appear to be perfectly healthy.

Scherer told me that scientists were not certain how one parent's genes might come to dominate the other's, which of course made me wonder if my father was on to something with his super-sperm theory. After all, men make sperm every few days, and perhaps the same hormones sloshing around the male body that affect mood might also affect their sperm. Next thing you know, you're a quarter Native. Scherer laughed when I asked him about it. "Who knows?" he said.

It is hard to overstate the impact of Scherer's discovery, since it turned the basic idea of genetics on its head. But it was also a powerful reminder that genetics was still a very young science—one that could be skewed by naïve definitions of *normal* or even warped by the words used to describe it.

When I finally reached Frudakis, that's how he explained the confusion over our Native ancestry result—semantics. The Florida company had pegged its markers as being Native American to appeal to the American market, he told me. But it was accurate to consider them Central Asian markers, he said, that had been carried to different regions by those who migrated from that part of the globe long ago—into the Americas, into East Asia, South Asia and even southern Europe—finding their way into today's Greeks, Italians and Turks. "We may do ourselves a favour and change the name of this ancestry [component] in the test," he said, since apparently I wasn't the only one baffled by it.

But no matter what he called it, I had to question whether the markers involved could even be considered "ancestrally informative." Connecting a relatively small group of mutations found in many different populations to a single ancestral group was bound to breed confusion. Calling our mutations Native seemed to be like calling us Arabs because we have swarthy skin. The only information it seemed to provide was that all these far-flung, diverse groups—Turks and Mayans, Italians and Cherokees, Indians of India and of the Americas—share a few strands of common heritage.

But just as Nana Bridget had done with her channelling, people could take from this DNA result whatever they wanted to believe. Stephen contented himself with the idea that the test was inadequate to find his Native connection, and I ignored it for suggesting that somehow we had one. If it had personal value, it was the proof that our DNA is indeed as mixed as I had always heard it would be.

Our heritage spans at least three continents. But scanning the whole genome to try to learn our history was like tossing a loose net into a sea of nameless ancestors when it was the juggler and the Captain I wanted most to catch. For that I had to cast my line narrowly, down to the tiny slivers of a chromosome that each patriarch had left behind.

4

A MOLECULE OF MEMORY

The first time I talked to my parents about the Y chromosome, it unfolded like the old "Who's on First?" Abbott and Costello skit. It was late in 2005, before the first DNA results from Florida had arrived, and I was at their house laying out plans for the next round of testing, telling them it was a terrific coincidence that the deepest mysteries on both sides of our family involved grandfathers. Being men, they both carried Y chromosomes and passed them down to their male children. From what I'd read, the most powerful genetic tool in genealogy research is the Y chromosome.

"The what?" my mother said.

Jade, who was about two then, was sitting on the kitchen floor bashing Tupperware with a wooden spoon.

"The Y," I said.

"Why what?"

I had a vague sense that I had become the family eccentric. But I continued, while Jade drummed, explaining why the Y chromosome seemed the most promising way to learn where John Abraham and Frederick Crooks had actually come from, and how it may even lead us to details of their histories.

The Y was the one gift they had unwittingly bequeathed each of their male descendants. Papa Freddie had inherited the captain's Y chromosome and passed it on to my mother's brothers. Papa

Albert had inherited the juggler's Y and passed it to my father.

"It is only the men who pass down the Y, isn't it?" my mother said.

Yes, it's one of the two sex chromosomes, I told her. Women have a pair of Xs and men have an X from their mother and a Y from their father, and their father's father, and their father's father's father, and on it goes. If sperm carrying an X chromosome fertilizes an egg, the baby will be a girl. But if the sperm carries a Y, the chromosome flicks a molecular switch and testicles sprout.

"Look at that," my mother said. "Henry VIII beheaded all those poor wives and it was his fault."

Not to defend the sixteenth-century uxoricidal monarch, but it wasn't until the seventeenth century that a Dutch scientist put his own semen under the microscope and discovered sperm. And it was another two hundred years after that, at the dawn of the twentieth century, that the male's Y chromosome was first identified—in a sublime twist, by a woman, the American scientist Nettie Stevens. Even then the Y was largely overlooked for much of the twentieth century, especially as a guide to trace paternal ancestry. Studies that had unravelled stretches of its code from a few dozen men found very few differences between them, leaving the impression that if you'd seen one Y, you'd seen 'em all. Instead, scientists were reconstructing the history of human populations with research on mitochondrial DNA, a special form of genetic information that only women pass down to their children, male or female. The package passed down by men to their sons was largely dismissed as a genetic wasteland.

Under powerful microscopes, most chromosomes look like plump, fuzzy caterpillars. The Y, the smallest chromosome in the human genome, looks more like a slug. In her landmark paper in 1905, Nettie Stevens referred to it as an "accessory," as if the molecule of manhood were a clutch purse. But next to the elephantine proportions of, say, human chromosome 1—which boasts some 2,500 genes and the imposing swagger of 246 million base pairs—or its opposite chromosome, the full-bodied X, with more than a thousand genes doing thousands of jobs, the Y is a 58-million-base-pair pipsqueak with fewer than two hundred genes and, for the most part, a one-track mind. Making sperm and testicles is its chief job.

The only story the Y seemed to tell was the sad and lonely tale of the chromosome nature forgot. Once upon a time it was as large and robust as the grande dame that is the X, delivering malehood to stags, rams, jacks, bulls, boars, tomcats, mane-frilled lions and men. But in the 300 million years since it first appeared in the genome, the Y has suffered mightily. Every other chromosome has a chance to refresh itself before it builds the next generation, by swapping genes and correcting mutations as it bends and unwinds with its matching partner. But the Y has no matching partner; it trades only bits and bobs with the X, at its tips. With little chance for self-improvement, mistakes have piled up. Most of the Y chromosome's original genes have been shed or rendered completely useless by mutations. Even the genomic carcasses of long-dead viruses hide in its code.

The human Y, however, has come up with ingenious ways to preserve itself, madly copying its own code like a hall of mirrors, evolving so quickly that it now looks nothing like its counterpart in, say, the chimp. Still, the fate of the male chromosome has prompted a flurry of studies, essays and entire books on the genetic future of men.

Yet it was the not the future but the past that drew a new crop of geneticists to this embattled chromosome late in the twentieth century, pursuing the idea that a secret history might be written in the mutations of its jumbled code. Generally mutations that pop up in genes tend to cause malfunctions or disease, and they don't stick around long in a population. But mutations in regions that have no genes—stretches of code nicknamed "junk DNA" before anyone realized their crucial value in regulating genes—can have a much longer shelf life. And the Y is a treasure trove of junk. It has more junk than genes: 98 percent of it is nothing but junk. It's the attic of the genome, the garage, the flea market. (The Human Genome Project did not even try to decode the entire Y chromosome, because of all the junk it carts around.) Yet these are some of the very characteristics that happen to make the Y an invaluable tool for tracing family roots.

Precisely because most of the chromosome does not recombine before a new sperm cell is made, the only changes or mutations it accumulates are the ones that spring up randomly in the man who carries it, and subsequently in the males who inherit it from him. As the technology to sequence DNA improved, so did the ability of scientists to spot those mutations and read them as the genetic signature of a male lineage. By the nineties, studies had emerged to indicate that every man's Y chromosome does indeed carry a unique set of mutations corresponding to certain parts of the world. Men from Africa have distinct mutations on their Ys that are different from the markers on the Y chromosomes of men from China or northern Europe or southern Europe.

The more unique mutations researchers uncovered in different populations, the more they came to see the Y as a living archive. It might encode not only an ancestral record of the world's men but the paternal heritage of any one man, passed down to him through the ages in a chain linking fathers to sons, much like a surname. In 1994 someone decided to put that hypothesis to the test.

That year, on a Saturday morning at a synagogue in north Toronto, just half an hour from my parents' house, Karl Skorecki had an epiphany. Skorecki was a researcher and kidney specialist at Toronto General Hospital at the time, and he was saying prayers and waiting to be called to read from the Torah. He was accustomed to being one of the first called to read, since he belongs to the caste of high priests in Judaism known as *kohanim*. The term is plural for *kohen*, the family name of those said to be direct descendants of Aaron HaKohen, the brother of Moses, a birthright that carries certain responsibilities to lead ceremonies of worship. But that day it was a *kohen* visiting from North Africa who was called first, and the fair-skinned, light-eyed Skorecki found himself staring at the man, taking in his swarthy complexion and distinctive features and thinking, *He is from North Africa, I am from eastern Europe, and we look nothing alike . . . yet we are both of us* kohanim.

Skorecki looked around at the other *kohen* men in the synagogue and noticed that, physically, they all looked different—in stature, in skin colour, in facial features. Nothing about their appearance suggested a common ancestry, yet apparently they had one. They all shared the same family traditions of spiritual leadership, the same rites and the same knowledge required to perform sacred duties at temple, as the teachings hold, by way of their mutual connection to a forefather who lived 3,300 years ago. Was there any genetic evidence of this bloodline legacy, Skorecki wondered. Did *kohanim* share a common biological marker as well as a sacred culture?

He realized instantly that any such marker would likely have been lost in "all the mixing and matching that goes into DNA through the generations." But then it struck him that the Y chromosome remains more or less unchanged generation after generation, passed down through centuries—*like a family secret*, he thought—so that the Y chromosome of a man alive today should be essentially the same Y as that of his ancient male ancestors.

Until then Skorecki's genetic research had been focused on kidney disease. But after that day at the synagogue, he began looking into research on the Y to see if anyone had used it to trace male ancestry. As Skorecki told me on the phone one afternoon from the Ramban Medical Hospital in Haifa, Israel, where he had moved in 1995, "Most of the early papers were fairly ho-hum." But eventually he came across the work of Michael Hammer at the University of Arizona.

Hammer was among a small cabal of pioneers who were charting new territory for the Y in the nineties, collecting samples of the chromosome from men all over the world and comparing their codes. His studies revealed that the Y harbours all sorts of unusual mutations, not just the single-letter typos known as SNPs but also unique blips where stretches of code are mysteriously duplicated or completely missing. Like SNPs, however, these mutations emerged once in one man in history and were then passed down through the ages to his male descendants for eons to come.

In one striking example, Hammer found that some men have three hundred extra nucleotides, or letters, on their Y chromosomes, a mutation he called a YAP. His research suggested that the YAP had originally sprung up in a man in sub-Saharan Africa, where it is most common. But that man's male descendants had since spread to various corners of the world, taking the YAP with them to northern Africa, Europe, Oceania and Asia. Using the Y, Hammer reconstructed the peopling of Japan and also took an early stab at pinpointing the existence of a genetic Adam—the forefather of every man alive today. Thought to have lived about 59,000 years ago, this Adam (unlike the biblical Adam) is not cast as the first man on Earth but rather as the one man whose male descendants survived to populate the rest of the planet.

In 1995 Skorecki called Hammer out of the blue and asked if he'd be willing to investigate whether there was a common marker on the Y chromosomes of *kohen* men. Hammer agreed it was worth a try. They worked together with researchers at London's University College, gathering DNA from 188 unrelated Jewish men in three countries. And just as Skorecki suspected, they found that Jews who identified themselves as *kohanim* did indeed carry a specific set of mutations on their Y chromosomes. The markers, a combination of the YAP along with one other unique hiccup of code where nucleotides were repeated, were found in *kohen* men regardless of geographic origin. The finding jibed with religious beliefs that the family roots of the *kohanim* predated the split of the world's Jews a thousand years ago into its two major ethnic groups, the

Ashkenazi Jews from central and eastern Europe and the Sephardic Jews from southern Europe.

After the British medical journal *Nature* published the paper in 1997, a flood of people called the researchers to ask if they could have their Y chromosomes tested for *kohanim* markers. It was one of the first reports to raise the possibility that a genetic test could answer personal questions of ancestry.

As it happens, the paper appeared the same year that my father's interest in his paternal ancestry became a mission. After receiving news that his 103-year-old Aunty Flo, the juggler's daughter, was still alive in south India's Nilgiri Hills, my father set out to find her. He and my mother flew there in January that year with high hopes of learning more about his mysterious grandfather and our possible bloodline connection to China. He had no inkling then that his own biology might provide the answer. If the little we knew about the juggler was true, my father would have an identifiable link to China wound through nearly every cell in his body. But as it was, in 1997 the Y was just a letter to my father (and to me), and he planned to investigate John Abraham the old-fashioned way, by scouring records and asking questions of his Aunty Flo, questions he had never thought to ask the first time he met her.

In the red tartan bag of old family photographs there is a handful of black-and-white pictures from the only trip my father made to the Nilgiri Hills when he lived in India. It was 1958, a few months before my parents left the country for good. I say "for good" because they left India twice. The first time was in 1953, just a few weeks after the wedding they had narrowly pulled off.

Work on the oil tankers kept my father away at sea for months at a time. Wedding invitations had already been sent when he discovered that he would still be in the Far East on the day they planned to marry. Finding an engineering officer to relieve him in time was impossible, but a shipmate told my father he knew a

Calcutta doctor who could give him an injection to make him ill enough to qualify for sick leave. On a tanker where a hundred men lived in close quarters, a sudden, violent malady seemed like a sure ticket to shore.

I've always thought that it says as much about my father's fierce pragmatism as it does about his romantic inclinations that he took his shipmate's advice. He left his ship anchored at the Calcutta port town of Budge Budge, and took two rickshaws and a train deep into the city, where he gave a back-alley doctor 100 rupees for a dose of "amoebic dysentery." My father got what he paid for—a wretched, shivering fever that swelled his hands and turned his stomach. But the more unfortunate thing was that he woke up on his ship the next morning feeling fine. The wedding was cancelled. When he finally made it back to Bombay in February 1953, my parents had just enough time to plan a reception on a tennis court before they sailed for England in March.

They lived in Liverpool. My father completed his degree at the College of Marine Engineering while my mother, who was twenty at the time, tried to become a good housewife. Having grown up with servants who did the cooking and cleaning, she found housework to be as foreign as England. She had to buy eggs and butter with postwar ration cards and feed a coin-operated coal heater to stay warm. She still hears the *clink-clink* of shillings dropping when she thinks of those days.

They rented a second-floor flat in the home of a kind Irish lady by the name of Mrs. O'Donnell, who had two bad knees and a husband on the third floor. Mrs. O'Donnell gave her newlywed tenants a set of blackout curtains she had used to hide from the Germans—"Take these," she said with a wink. My mother was pregnant within a month. Nausea came in waves, and in between, all she craved was home cooking. But home was very far away and my mother had no idea how to cook. She made tea with the same water she boiled eggs in. My father came home to dinners of store-bought biscuits arranged in fancy patterns on a plate, sometimes augmented with cubes of cheese. At the supermarket, looking for lentils, she used the Indian word and asked for *dal*. "Oh, love, you're in the wrong shop," the store clerk told her. "You'll want the toy shop to buy a doll."

Mum and Dad as newlyweds in Sefton Park, Liverpool, 1953.

In July my father put my skinny, pregnant mother on a boat back to India. "Legs like hairpins she had." My father followed after graduating in December, arriving a week before my brother Conrad was born. Then came their good days. Returning to India with an English education launched my father into the executive tier of the Malabar Group, where he became the engineering superintendant of a fifteen-ship fleet. My brother Kevin was born in 1956 and they all lived in a swank Bombay apartment, with a cook and a nanny, a swivelling bar in the living room, a chauffeur for their Italian car, and rupees to burn.

But the dust of anxiety covered it all. India was nearing the end of its first decade of independence. Prime Minister Nehru's socialist government was chasing a bold plan to nationalize India's economic base and turn the country into an industrial powerhouse. Anglo-Indians had once dominated the civil service, with preferential treatment from the British, but that advantage was disappearing. No longer would English be the only language taught in schools. Urdu and Hindi were coming to the classroom, and Indians were coming to the cities by the millions—refugees of partition, migrants from the villages—all of them eager to join what historians called India's "revolution of rising expectations." Anglos, Anglo-Indians, anyone with a European heritage, and many Indians too began leaving the country by the thousands.

My mother's parents left for England in May of 1958, and my mother longed to go too. She always regretted that pregnancy had forced her to leave the country prematurely. She was certain the family's future would be brighter in England—even a weary postwar England—than in a poor country finding its way. My mother found ways to make this point to my father every day (this was the usual course of things, my mother convincing my father to take a leap into the unknown). She banged around the kitchen to convince him. She read out loud the letters her parents sent: "Look at this. They've already bought their own house! See how quickly anyone in England can buy a house." Acquiring property in Bombay was out of reach for all but the very rich or the very lucky.

But my father was not convinced life would be better in England, particularly when life in India was still so very good. Unlike my mother, who had grown up in the insulated world of Anglo-Indian railway colonies, my father had had more contact with Indians. From the age of seventeen when he'd started his maritime training, he had worked alongside them on the tankers. His own parents had no plans to leave, and wouldn't for a dozen years. So when I ask why my parents decided to immigrate to England in the fall of 1958, there are two answers: "More opportunities," my mother says. My father says, "Marital peace."

In the midst of preparing to move the family from one part of the world to another, my father made the remarkable decision to pack everyone up and drive to the Nilgiri Hills, a four-day road trip from Bombay. He saw it as his last chance to meet his father's sisters, to see where his father had been born—and the Abraham name as well. My grandfather Albert never had much contact with his sisters after he left the Nilgiris, not with Florence or Julie, the eldest, who had raised him after his mother died and his father left. It was my grandmother Ena who kept in regular touch, with Christmas cards and letters. Albert's family had never visited the hills, and the aunts never left them.

My father cursed on that trip, back when he apparently did curse. His prized Fiat Millicento buckled on the ascent, sputtering under the weight of passengers and luggage. Everyone had to get out, unload the suitcases and push it up and around every switchback. Coonoor seemed like heaven when they finally reached the hilltop tea town and the aunts threw their arms around my father as if they'd waited an eternity for his arrival.

There's a small photograph of all of them, smartly dressed, standing in front of the temperamental Fiat: my parents, my brothers in matching wool V-necks, and my father's younger brother Mark, who had joined the road trip. Aunty Julie stands in the middle of the group, a striking woman with her hair pulled back in a bun, accentuating high cheekbones and eyes that look Asian even without close study. Florence didn't join them in the photo. She was like her brother Albert in that way, my father says—quiet, content to keep to herself. She did needlework for the local churches and never married.

I used to wonder why my father didn't ask his aunts about John Abraham in 1958, when he had the chance. He told me it was the future that preoccupied him then. "My mind," he said, "was in a different place." They were about to leave India, a life of comfort, of luxury—and for what? At thirty-three he felt as if he had everything, yet he was about to move his young family to a country where they might have nothing at all. Fearing that the emigrating masses would empty the banks, the Indian government imposed strict regulations, limiting the amount of money émigrés could take out of the country to the equivalent of just three pounds per person. Even in the 1950s three pounds couldn't buy a family a week's worth of groceries. How would life in England be with a wife, two small boys, no money and no job?

Instead, it was my mother who asked the questions about John Abraham on that trip. She and Aunty Julie were in the backyard of her hillside bungalow, a little yellow house they called Sunnyside. It had white shutters and French doors that opened to a garden of flowers and fruit trees. They were sitting on the patio when Julie told my mother that her father had come to town in a travelling circus. She said that he had settled in Coonoor after he married; then, she said, he did many different things to make a living, such as drying and selling his own condiments and candied peel made from local fruit, and blowing and selling his own glassware. But after her mother died at a young age, her father went away—back to China, she suspected. Florence and Albert were just children at the time, so Julie and her husband took them in. She seemed to hold no grudge against her father for leaving them all. Julie felt there was little else he could do under the circumstances, but she stopped short of telling my mother what those circumstances were.

My mother must have shown a keen interest in John Abraham that day. At the end of the visit, Aunty Julie gave her some of his possessions: a yard of silk and a set of glasses he had hand-blown.

"I don't know where that cloth has gone," my mother told me when she recounted the conversation. "The glasses I still have."

"What sort of glasses?" I asked her.

"Drinking glasses," she said. "Tumblers, a set of four. . . . Now, where did I put them?"

Tumblers. Of course—what other sort would a circus juggler make?

5

TRICKS OF JOHN CHINESE

Whenever my mother speaks of her grandfather, she often calls him "the Captain." But my father rarely, if ever, refers to his grandfather as "the juggler." He told me once that he felt it reduced the man to a caricature. It is not the lowliness of the profession that bothers my father. Having pulled himself up and out of a tiny Bombay flat crowded with eight siblings, parents and assorted aunts, my father tends to view humble roots as incentive. I suspect that puts him—us—in a league that includes most souls in North America. If your ancestors weren't of modest means—fleeing poverty, natural disaster, disease or persecution—they would never have come. The New World celebrates the lowly start, the goat-herding forefather, the potato farmer, the labourer who stepped off the boat without a word of English and the sum total of his savings jangling in a pocket. The more disadvantaged the ancestor, the greater the glory of eventually making good. No, it was something else that irked my father about a grandpa who had juggled for a living.

For me, the juggling made my great-grandfather irresistible. He was my trope while I was growing up, my party trick, the ancestor I invoked when I tossed things in the air—tennis balls, books, oranges, anything really—betting that the ghost of dexterity would rise from the gene pool before I incurred a concussion. But he was also more. He was my shield, the forefather I whipped out to deflect the "What are you?" question whenever it cropped up, as if to say, *Look, if the Chinese juggler is the short answer, do you really want the long one?*

Juggling was the iconic image that seared him into my childhood memory. And what could be more iconic than a Chinese juggler? The Chinese have been juggling since the Stone Age. All prehistoric hunters had their pastimes, most of them practical—boomerangs, slingshots, some variation of a javelin—but according to the twentieth-century scholar Fu Qifeng, Chinese hunters juggled. In his 1985 text *Chinese Acrobatics Through the Ages*, Fu writes that throwing sticks and spears (and presumably catching them) evolved into a pleasurable activity in and of itself—one that birthed a rich legacy, adds cultural historian Arthur Chandler.

In 480 BCE, during the Warring States period, when seven regions clustered around the Yellow Sea were battling for supremacy, jugglers were held in great esteem, and even at times revered. Fu tells the story of Yiliao, who, "in a battle between the states of Chu and Song . . . appeared in front of the Chu troops and calmly, in the face of the enemy's axes and spears, juggled nine balls at the same time. His superb performance stupefied the officers and warriors. The Song troops fled helter-skelter without fighting and the Chu troops won a complete victory." But it was during the Han Dynasty, around 200 BCE, in the golden age of acrobatics, that China's jugglers blossomed. In a regular extravaganza known as the Hundred Entertainments, held in the courts of the ruling class, juggling had top billing, says Chandler. It was an art, a vocation, passed down through generations of a family.

Gifted children were sent to dedicated schools to master the hallmark feats of Chinese juggling—rolling heavy vases along their limbs, tossing swords, spinning plates on the tips of several poles simultaneously, twirling devil sticks, manipulating heavy props on the soles of their feet—tricks of balance and contortion that would enthrall the world. Centuries later, the Chinese juggler made his way into novels, films and, in the 1980s, one of the first video games, designed for the monochrome computer screens of the Commodore 64, was called *The Chinese Juggler* (the player had to control a figure spinning plates on pedestals without allowing any plates to fall).

In the West, jugglers never enjoyed much respect. Seventh-century clergy tried to ban them; writing in the edicts of the Sixth Council of Paris, they lumped them with whores and criminals: "The duties of the King are to prevent theft, to punish adultery and to refuse to maintain jongleurs." Medieval observers saw them as crass buffoons tossing their balls and reciting bawdy verses. Shakespeare slammed them in at least eight different plays— "O me! you juggler! you canker-blossom!"

By the time my great-grandfather arrived in India in the nineteenth century, the Western view had spread. Even the Chinese juggler fell out of favour with aristocrats in his home country, he was the bewitching alien who dazzled and disturbed, a crook, villain and opium fiend in the dime novels of the day. Ancient words for *juggling* in Greek and Latin carry dual connotations, and even modern dictionaries still define the verb *juggle* in at least two ways: "to keep several objects . . . in motion in the air simultaneously" and also "to manipulate in order to deceive, as by trickery."

It was this notion of chicanery that nagged at my father, that there was something to mistrust about a juggling man. He didn't see it as a lowly station so much as an unsavoury one, and never more than after his second trip to the Nilgiri Hills, where he discovered that his grandfather had known something about deception. His life, it seemed, had imitated his art: becoming John Abraham was a cunning sleight of hand.

There's a saying in the Nilgiri Hills about the longevity of the people who live there: that on one hill they live into their eighties, on another into their nineties, and on the tallest hill they never die. My parents could believe there was truth to that when they met Aunty Flo again. She was living in the small tea town of Coonoor with Julie's granddaughter Hazel, and at 103 she had the stamina of someone in her prime. Up and down she'd go, climbing the steep footpaths to the market in town, a tawny slip of a woman with a thin halo of white hair. She shopped, cooked and insisted on making my parents lunch. For dessert she served pears and plums she had preserved herself. My mother asked if she had learned how to can from her sister, Julie, or if her father had taught her, since Julie had told her he had made his own candied peel from the local fruits. But Aunty Flo said she could tell them nothing at all about her father, that she didn't remember him. She had been a child when he left.

Any distant memories Aunty Flo did have seemed to seize her in odd jags. Sometimes she would suddenly take my father's hands in her own, clutch them tightly and gaze into his eyes. "Albert's son!" she would say, beaming. "Albert's son!" At other times, she would remember an old flame. My mother had heard Flo had always been in love with a local man by the name of Leo Enos, but that Julie had never permitted them to marry. In the end, neither she nor Leo ever did.

Sometimes, Aunty Flo seemed confused. "Where is my sister Mary?" she asked them.

"You mean your sister Julie," my father replied.

"My sister, Mary," she would insist. "Where is Mary?"

My father assumed that his old Aunty's mind was not quite as clear as he had hoped it would be. Still, it was something to see her, his dad's sister, older than the century. He thought she looked even more Chinese in her old age.

As so often happens, my father stumbled on the first bits of information when he wasn't expecting it. He and my mother visited an apothecary in Coonoor one afternoon, and my mother, who has a keen interest in natural remedies, was chatting with the proprietor about the medicinal powers of the local plants. Their conversation eventually drew in my father, who explained their family connection to the Nilgiris and the unanswered questions he had about his grandfather.

The store owner perked up instantly. "I know someone you have to speak with," he said. "My grandfather!"

A few minutes later, Dad was speeding into the hills on the back of the proprietor's motorbike. They pulled up to a large house outside of town. It belonged to a Mr. C. Balchand, a wealthy local developer and philanthropist. My father assumed that Balchand must be failing, because his grandson ushered him straight to the bedroom. But the old man proved to be surprisingly spry. He bounded out from under his blankets, asked his daughter-in-law to bring tea and biscuits, and invited my father to stroll in his garden.

As they walked, Balchand told my father that he'd known his father, Albert Abraham, and they had gone to the same school. Then he said he remembered Albert's Chinese father as well. My father stopped short and took a good look at Balchand, trying to calculate the old man's age and the odds of meeting someone in 1997, other than his aunt, who had known his grandfather.

Yes, Balchand insisted, he had been a child and it was a vague memory, but "the Chinaman," he said, was hard to miss in Coonoor. He said that old Mr. Abraham used to travel around the hills on a bicycle, selling his wares. He often wore a loose-fitting black jacket and a small black cap, and a long single braid hung down the centre of his back. Then, one day, no one saw him anymore.

It was Balchand's recollection that would become the enduring image for my father. Far more than the juggling man, it was the man in black, visible only from behind, flying along on a bicycle with his pigtail trailing behind him.

My father's investigations puzzled his relatives in the Nilgiris. "Why do you want to go into all that?" they asked him. "Best to leave the past alone, no?"

But on a walk with Julie's grandson Ron one night after dinner, my father recounted his forays in search of information, telling him that any lead would help. Ron, who was visiting from Chennai, on the coast, suggested there might be something about

John Abraham in the records at St. Anthony's Church, where Julie had been a long-time parishioner. Then, casually, he added, "You know John Abraham came to India as a fugitive."

"No, I never heard that," my father said. "I thought he came as a juggler."

"A juggler and a fugitive," Ron said. He explained that his grandmother had told him so once, years ago. She said that John Abraham had murdered someone in China, and that he had joined a travelling circus as a juggler in order to conceal his identity. In red pen and capital letters, my father wrote that revelation in his journal that night: "John Abraham commited a crime in China: MURDER!"

The next morning my father went to St. Anthony's Church. The parish priest was a strapping young Tamil man who called himself Father Francis Xavier, after the sixteenth-century Spanish missionary and saint who propagated Christianity in India. Any other day, my father might have been keen to chat, but after Ron's revelation he felt a certain urgency to see the records.

Father Francis took him to the small back room where they kept the old church documents, explaining that many had been handwritten by French missionaries dispatched to India two hundred years ago. Each volume spanned about five decades and contained all the baptismal, marriage and death rites conducted at the church during those years. Most were legible, he said, but they were also quite fragile. Then he left my father to his search.

The room was a windowless rectangle. A dim forty-watt bulb dangled over a single wooden table and chair. Cupboards lined one wall, and inside them were the records, large maroon leather–bound volumes, frayed at the edges. My father gently tugged out a few of them, set them on the table and began looking for his Aunty Julie's marriage record, thinking it might have a few details about the parents of the bride.

Yellowed pages slipped away from gummy spines, and some crumbled between his fingers. Soon he forgot where he was, absorbed by the past lives of strangers—the baptism of ten children in one family . . . the sudden death of three . . . the funeral of their father . . . daughters married off at thirteen. The day disappeared. He had found no mention of John Abraham, or indeed any Abraham. But the cupboards were still packed with volumes he hadn't touched.

Father Francis greeted him like an old friend when he returned the next morning. Over a pot of the local tea, the priest told Dad he was a native of Ootacamund, the Nilgiris' most popular hill station, and that he loved the hills, and ran through them at dawn every morning. The rest of the day, he said, he spent saying Masses and being driven around the hills in an SUV to see parishioners. As they finished their tea, he invited my father to join him on a tour of the area and then Father Francis walked him back to the file room.

This time, Dad started with records from 1901, the year his father was born, hoping to find a record of his baptism. But in which month, which day? As he scanned the pages, a word jumped out at him—not *Abraham*, but *Chinaman*. Listed as the father at Albert Abraham's christening was John Abraham, occupation "Chinaman carpenter." It was the first reference to his grandfather that he'd seen, and all the incentive he needed to keep working backwards, assuming that his grandfather would be mentioned again at the baptisms of Julie and Florence. But as my father read through the records of 1886, he discovered the baptism of John Abraham himself.

On September 11 of that year a male recorded as "John Chinese," age thirty-five, was christened and reborn as John Abraham. The father of John Chinese, as best my father could read it, was A.T. Chu, or possibly A.T. Choi—the priest had been French, judging by his surname, Peyramale, and his cursive was difficult to read. In the column denoting John Abraham's occupation was a word that started with C that my father didn't recognize.

Then, weirdly, in an entry nine days after John Abraham's christening, he turned up again, but five years older. It was a marriage record from September 20, 1886. It read:

Groom: John Abraham
Age: 40
Condition: Bachelor
Caste or Profession: Chinaman Carpenter
Parent's Name: Assay [or Assoy]
Bride: Mariamal [no last name given]
Age: 17
Condition: Spinster
Parent's Name: Joseph [no other name given]

My dad kept flipping forward through the years. He found his Aunty Julie's birth in July 1887, when John Abraham's occupation was listed as "merchant." He went looking next for his Aunty Flo's christening, but before he found it, the records revealed something startling. John and Mariamal Abraham had three other children between the births of Julie and Florence: a son, Arokiam, in September 1889, when John Abraham was listed as an artisan carpenter; a daughter Mary in November 1890; and another, Annie, in June of 1893. Florence arrived a year later, and finally, in December 1901, they had my grandfather, Albert.

My father had no idea there had been six children, that his father, Albert, had three more siblings. What had happened to them? Had they died? It was common to lose young children to sickness in those days, and even more common in a country battered by outbreaks of cholera, malaria and a long list of parasites. My father himself had a brother and sister who died of typhoid in childhood. Still, he wondered, why had no one ever mentioned them? Then suddenly it struck him that he had heard one name at least—that very week, from his Aunty Flo. *Where is my sister Mary?* she had asked him. *Where is Mary?*

My father had assumed Florence was confused, but she hadn't been. She did have another sister—two others, in fact. And where *was* Mary, where was Annie, and Arokiam? Had they, like his grandfather, disappeared?

St. Anthony's had no photocopier, but my father had his camera with him, and he intended to shoot every page where John Abraham was mentioned. Those old, frayed ledgers contained at least one version of his story, confirming his existence and setting out an approximation—but still, the first indication—of his true Chinese surname, Chu.

The Church may have imposed the name change on "John Chinese" as part of his Catholic conversion, and it appeared that the Abraham surname was a favourite of missionaries to south India at the time. But if the juggler was a fugitive, my father suspected the name change might have been no imposition at all. John Chinese may have been perfectly happy to disappear into the hills with a Christian bride, a biblical name, and a brand-new identity.

My father leaned the volume upright against a stack of other ledgers and stepped back to shoot them, but the camera shutter jammed. He pressed it again with more force but the mechanism refused to budge. Then he turned away from the ledger and aimed the lens at the cupboards; it snapped with ease, flash and all. So he turned back to the book, but the camera failed again and again, though each time he shifted it away from the records, it worked.

My father has never been a superstitious man. He usually bites his lip when my mother alludes to anything woo-woo. But that afternoon, as he stood alone in the dim file room with his fickle camera, suddenly hyper-aware of the faint drone of the priest praying with a distressed parishioner and the slight breeze rustling the curtain that separated the room from the corridor, my father was spooked. John Abraham had worked hard to keep his true identity hidden, and there he was, exhuming his secrets.

We should have dismissed John Abraham as an ancestor with nothing to recommend him, a murdering fugitive who left his six children fatherless after their mother died. But quite the opposite happened after my father's discoveries in 1997. We talked about him often, my father and I. We talked about the Chu name, whether it was real (as in faithfully recorded) and if it could really be said to be ours. (Would you give your real name if you were on the run?) We talked about the adventure that had been his life. If he had once been a caricature, he was now our very own cliché—the relative who really did run away and join the circus. And, of course, there was the abyss of questions, mostly mine, about how anyone could simply hook up with a passing circus and pass himself off as a juggler. How does one fake juggling? And whom did he murder? (I searched for nineteenth-century murders involving jugglers in China, but the only thing I found was the story of a knife-throwing juggler who severed the carotid artery of his wife/model. He later told the judge he wasn't sure if it was an accident.)

We also wondered what had happened to those three other siblings of Papa Albert. My father asked his relatives in the Nilgiris; they assumed the children must have been sent to an orphanage. But why not Albert, my grandfather, the baby of the family? Did Julie, who was then a newlywed, simply decide to keep him and raise him as her own, and Florence as well? How did she choose whom to keep? We came to realize that discomfort with having a Chinese forefather was not the reason why John Abraham's identity had been kept hidden, or at least it wasn't the only one. John Abraham had apparently hidden it himself, running from his past all the way to India and up into the hills, and then running again, taking his secrets to his grave, wherever that was.

And that was the course that ensued for my father, and for me, to see whether a genetic trail could out him—if his own Y chromosome could connect us to a lost ancestry, to China, perhaps to the very corner of the country he'd come from, even if it was the scene of his crime.

In 1998, a year after my father made his second pilgrimage to the Nilgiris, the Y chromosome shrugged off its deadbeat reputation for good, proving again that it had a remarkable power to solve old family mysteries. On the heels of the *kohanim* report, a retired pathology professor turned to the Y to see if it could finally put to rest the endless whispers about a president and a slave girl.

Eugene Foster of Tufts University in Virginia had been talking with an amateur historian friend about the relentless speculation that Thomas Jefferson, America's third president and principal author of the Declaration of Independence, had fathered children with a house slave by the name of Sally Hemings. To complicate matters, Hemings also happened to be a half-sister of Jefferson's wife, Martha Wayles, born of a relationship between Martha's father and his slave mistress, Betty Hemings.

Sally Hemings is said to have been a fourteen-year-old latte beauty when she came to care for Jefferson's youngest daughter in Paris in 1786. Eventually she had six children, and rumours spread of an ongoing affair with her master. It was a point Jefferson never explicitly confirmed or denied, but one that many of Jefferson's white descendants felt had no truth.

Foster's historian friend thought that DNA testing of the descendants of Jefferson and Hemings might be the best way to finally answer the question. But, like Skorecki, Foster initially thought such a test would be impossible—that after the genetic shuffling of generations, any contribution from an eighteenth-century forefather would be too mixed or minute to detect. Then Foster heard from a biology professor that new work on the Y chromosome suggested such a test might be worth a try after all.

Since Jefferson had no known sons, it was not possible to use the Y chromosome of a direct male descendent of the president as a point of comparison. But Foster managed to collect DNA from a male descendant of Jefferson's paternal uncle Field Jefferson, working on the assumption that both men had inherited the same Jefferson Y chromosome from their fathers. Foster also took samples from a group of black men who might have descended from Jefferson's affair with Hemings.

In all, Foster gathered thirteen samples and delivered them by hand, with all the names removed and randomly numbered, to geneticists in England who were pioneering work on the Y, a team led by Mark Jobling at the University of Leicester. As it turned out, the Jefferson Y was a rare model. Comparing it to the male chromosomes of 670 European men and another 1,200 worldwide, researchers found no other like it. The only match they did find— and a perfect one at that, based on testing mutations at seventeen different sites on the chromosome—belonged to Sally Hemings's great-great-grandson, fifty-three-year-old John Hemings Jefferson, a direct descendant of Sally's youngest son, Eston. The match, verified by labs in at least three other universities, added the heft of science to 360 years of whispers.

It was not absolute proof of an affair; another Jefferson male might have fathered children with Hemings. Neither could the test reveal whether the alleged relationship between a president and his slave had been a tryst of hearts or of horrors. But given other evidence—Jefferson's comings and goings coincided with Hemings's pregnancies—it was compelling enough that even skeptics reconsidered.

The prestigious science journal *Nature* published the results in November 1998; in the wake of President Bill Clinton's "inappropriate relationship" with White House staffer Monica Lewinksy, the news had particular currency. The international media splash that followed made it one of the biggest science stories of the year. Once dismissed as genomic detritus, DNA's drooping don, the Y chromosome strutted into the research limelight like a locker-room braggart, flashing its enduring potential to kiss and tell. Two years later, the first company to offer personal genetic ancestry testing on the Y chromosome opened its doors, followed quickly by half a dozen others. All promised to reveal what a paper trail could not.

In Houston, Texas, Family Tree DNA was the first to market. It was founded in 2000 by Bennett Greenspan, a businessman who, as he told me on the phone one February night, had been an avid genealogist ever since he was a kid. "Some guys are interested in girls, some are interested in baseball," he said. "I was mainly interested in families."

Growing up in Omaha, Nebraska, surrounded by a large extended family, Greenspan often peppered his relatives with questions about his ancestry. They answered, but not before cocking their heads at a young boy being so curious about his roots. Even after he moved to Houston and started a photographic supply business, his enthusiasm to learn more about his family history never waned. Investigating his maternal roots eventually led him to Buenos Aires, where he found people whose names and stories suggested they might in fact be relatives. But with no paper trail to link their family to his, Greenspan assumed he'd hit a dead end. Then he recalled something he'd heard about how genetic testing had identified a modern-day descendant of Thomas Jefferson and revealed that *kohenim* men shared a bloodline going back to Aaron, the brother of Moses.

Like Dr. Skorecki of Toronto, Greenspan started reading everything he could find on those studies, on genetic anthropology and mutations of the Y chromosome. And, as with Skorecki, the research led him to Michael Hammer at the University of Arizona. Hammer's studies of the Y chromosome had continued at full pace through the late nineties, helping trace the origins of Native Americans in Asia, paternal lineages out of Africa and a genetic history of India's Hindu castes. His work on the genetic ancestry of Jews had also kept his name in the press, most notably when his first discovery helped to prove that a Bantu-speaking tribe in southern Africa had actually descended from a small group of ancient Jews.

The Lemba people had always had an oral tradition of Jewish ancestry, believing that many moons ago, a forefather named Buba had led their ancestors out of Judea. They also practised Jewish customs, including circumcision, honouring one holy day a week, and abstaining from consumption of pig-like animals such as the hippopotamus. But not until researchers from University College London found markers associated with Jewish ancestry was there proof. It turned out that some of the Lemba men even belonged to the highest caste of Jewish holy priests: they carried the very same genetic *kohanim* signature on their Y chromosomes that Hammer's team had identified.

When Greenspan finally reached Hammer by phone, he asked the scientist if a genetic test might prove the link between his family and the potential relatives he had discovered in Argentina. Hammer said it likely could, and Greenspan asked him if he would do the test.

"We don't do that," Hammer told him.

Greenspan persisted. "But could you do it?"

Hammer said again that he didn't do it, but he added, "Someone should do it. Someone should start a company like this because we get phone calls from crazy genealogists like you all the time."

Greenspan was forty-seven then, and having recently sold the family business, he figured he was the perfect someone. He also turned out to be perfectly persuasive, convincing Hammer, a career academic, to join him as an advisor in launching one of the first commercial efforts to bring genetics to genealogy. This included tests on mitochondrial DNA, which only mothers pass down to their children, and that great, lonely stump of malehood that is the Y.

Every man's Y tells a story. Someone, anyone, can send in a male's DNA sample and the lab can extract the Y chromosome, read its code and know where in the world that male's paternal line originated, all based on the mutations it carries. Within that code, two types of mutations matter most in tracing ancestry—the SNP and the short tandem repeat, or STR.

SNPs tend to reveal a man's more ancient origins, since each SNP is usually a unique event, a typo that pops up once in one man in history, often thousands of years ago—such as the first soul to sprout red hair. All males who harbour that SNP today are related to the original male ancestor who first carried it, just as modern-day redheads share a strand of common ancestry. Today's males continue to sprout new SNPs, but only those that have been around a long time have had the chance to spread widely through a population. So studying these older SNPs on the Y can reveal the geographic origins of a man's paternal line. The SNP is the mutation that says, *Aha, you may be able to sing "God Save the Queen" in your sleep, but your forefather was Arabian,* or *You may look like any other southern Italian but your forty-third-generation grandpappy ran with Genghis Khan . . . or ran from him . . . or maybe he was Genghis Khan.* Researchers have been mapping the various SNP mutations on Ys the world over, finding that these mutations differ by continent, a little by country, and sometimes dramatically within a country.

Men who share the same SNP mutations on their Ys are said to belong to the same haplogroup, the technical name for a very old boys' club whose members descend from the long-ago forefather who passed down the typos they carry on their Y chromosomes. It's a work in progress, but by studying mutations on the Ys of the world, researchers have identified common African haplogroups, Asian haplogroups, European, American, Micronesian and Polynesian haplogroups, and so on.

So the question was, to which haplogroup would my father's Y belong? Would Papa Albert's epicanthic fold and the scrawl of a French missionary be borne out in his biology? Did the Y he passed down to my father belong to one of the male-chromosome clubs of China?

Of course, even if we knew that, it would tell us nothing about the juggler's story. It's possible the juggler carried a SNP unique to his family. But generally, SNPs accumulate so slowly over time—over hundreds and thousands of years—that they are no help in figuring out what happened in 1905. To dig into the recent past, it's the other type of mutation, the short tandem repeat, that offers the most value.

A short tandem repeat (STR) is a place on the Y chromosome where a stretch of code is duplicated over and over—five, ten, twenty times or so—like a record skipping. It's the kind of genetic stutter mutation that happens far more often than a SNP, so much so that the number of times a stretch of code is repeated in certain places on the Y can actually be distinct to a family.

To figure out if two families are related to each other—the way scientists proved the link between Jefferson and Sally Hemings's great-grandson—they compare these STR markers, which they do by testing several places along the Y to see if two men share the same number of repeats in those places. The more places the number of repeats match, the more likely the two men are related and the more recently they shared a common male ancestor. A man whose Y matches your Y could tell you about his family history, and from it you could find out about your own.

And that's what it boiled down to as I discussed all this with my father: a kind of genetic dating game. Would we find a man whose STR mutations matched his?

The same year Greenspan launched his company, evidence of the Y's usefulness started piling up. A 2000 study by Brian Sykes at the University of Oxford found that men in England named Sykes, for instance, tended to share the same Y chromosome, even when they had no idea they were related. Sykes, a professor of human genetics, concluded that the Ys that did not match were due to cases of adoption or infidelity, or perhaps new mutations that had sprung up since the name Sykes first appeared in the record books back in 1300. But given that so many men in the twenty-first century still carried the Y of the original Sykes man seven hundred years later, it was, the professor noted, a testament to the fidelity of many a Mrs. Sykes.

In 2004, German scientists at the University of Göttingen reported similar results after testing the Y chromosomes of thirty-four men named Zierdt. The men came from three different families in Germany and the United States, and while one family line "revealed a deviant Y-haplotype," men from the two other families shared the same male chromosome. Two years later, Mark Jobling at the University of Leicester tested 150 pairs of randomly selected English men who happened to have the same surname, and found that nearly a quarter of them also shared the same Y.

The work was so compelling that it led to forensic interest in the Y chromosome, the idea being that a male DNA sample from a crime scene could point to the surname of a perpetrator if it matched other Y chromosomes in a database. Of course, for police investigators as well as for genealogists, finding a matching Y depends largely on the size of the database you have for comparison—the bigger, the better, whether you are looking for a serial killer or a cousin.

Since Family Tree DNA had been operating longer than any other company in its field, by 2006 it had amassed the largest Y-chromosome database—about forty thousand samples—and that number would grow exponentially in the following months. Greenspan's firm had forged an agreement to provide DNA tests for a massive and ambitious effort to trace the genetic history of the world.

In April 2005, *National Geographic* and IBM launched the Genographic Project, a $40-million, five-year effort to explain how humankind populated the planet. Its researchers needed samples from remote indigenous tribes that had long been isolated from the genes of outsiders, to glimpse how DNA looked in ancient times. But they also needed DNA from hundreds of thousands of people across all five continents to map the migration routes of modern humans out of Africa and beyond. In short, they needed huge public participation. So the Genographic Project began offering hundred-dollar mail-order ancestry tests and billed it as a bargain. People willing to swab and contribute to the project could learn titillating details about their deep roots, such as whether their ancient ancestors once dominated sea trade in the Mediterranean, painted on porcelain or were the first to domesticate horses.

The offer proved immediately seductive. Within a year of its launch, one hundred thousand people had mailed back their DNA kits, flooding the gene pool available for comparisons. At the same time the Genographic Project was attracting the kind of publicity a small-start up could only dream of—major network coverage, front-page articles, magazine features—convincing even more people to contribute their DNA to the genetic genealogy market. Maybe, just maybe, a long-lost relation of the juggler or the Captain was among them.

Our Family Tree DNA collection kits arrived from Houston just before my parents took off for India in January 2006. During their 1997 trip my parents had rekindled their relationship with the subcontinent, and India became a regular winter destination. My father had kept in touch with cousins he'd met, and corresponded regularly with Father Francis at St. Anthony's Church in the Nilgiri Hills.

Stephen and I planned to meet up with them in south India that March. I wanted to see where my father had been born and the hills where my great-grandfather had appeared and disappeared. And I hoped that while I searched for answers in the Nilgiris, the lab in Arizona would unearth them from my father's Y chromosome.

There was nothing flashy about the Family Tree kits; there was no fancy brochure, just a padded brown envelope with instructions and a consent form to allow the company to add your Y-chromosome results and email address to its database. But its two swabbing sticks were impressive—long wands with detachable jagged cotton heads to be stored and mailed, post-swab, in vials of special fluid to deter bacterial growth.

I arrived to swab my father the very day my parents were flying out for their three-month excursion. He was rushing between rooms, bundling stacks of his perfectly pressed shirts with rubber bands and looking for the keys to his suitcase. He stopped in midstride to swab where he stood. He hadn't quite made it to the recommended one-minute mark before he yanked the swab out of his mouth and thrust it at me like a relay baton.

"Good enough?" he said.

I nodded.

There was no toast raised to great-grandfather this time, no ceremony or solemnity as there had been with the first DNA collection. But then, there was a plane to catch. Some days the past just isn't as urgent as the future.

6

RETURN OF THE *CHOTA SAHIB*

A week before we left to meet my parents in India, I found tigers in the mailbox—three handsome Bengal cats lolling on the front of a postcard. It was from my mother. *Darling Carolyn*, she wrote. *The days are drawing closer for you and Stephen to be here and I realize you must be having kittens. . . . Whatever mixed feelings you have, you have to accept INDIA.*

"Having kittens" is my mother's favourite euphemism for a bout of high anxiety, known best to non-medical professionals as freaking out. I wasn't, but she did have good reason to suspect it. After graduation in 1991, Stephen and I had set off to experience South Asia on the proverbial shoestring, and India was the first leg of our journey. We had backpacks jammed with guidebooks, cameras and journals, and heads stuffed full of romantic notions. Stephen was going to make art with his Pentax. I was going to bond with my ancestral homeland—to eat mangoes fresh from the tree, buy a sari and dance on the sands of Juhu Beach, where my parents first kissed and our future began.

But we never did make it to Juhu, and the only dance I managed was a frenetic two-step to find a loo. On top of that, I developed a nasty psychological reaction to the anti-malarial pills I was taking each week; we took to calling them my "mefloquine Mondays," although they lasted well into Wednesday. It was a kind of PMS tinged with anxiety and paranoia—perfect travel companions for touring the blistering chaos of urban India, with its crowds, beggars, arrogant cows, an old man with betel-red teeth who squeezed my breasts at the market. I stumbled through it in a medicated stupor, clutching my money belt, my hermetically sealed water bottle and my chest.

But illness was only part of it. Even then I knew I couldn't fault an entire subcontinent for Delhi belly and bad side effects. The emotional pain of the trip stemmed from having high hopes of feeling like some prodigal daughter, a wayward soul returned from the diaspora, only to feel nothing at all—nothing familiar, nothing to recall the Sunday afternoon chronicles of my grandmother. I wanted to love India. Why didn't I love it? There were certain delights: the fine hospitality of a Sikh brigadier whose son worked with my father; seeing the Taj Mahal glimmer at sunrise; the camel fair at Pushkar; discovering what's special about special lassis and how to get back to your guesthouse after drinking one. Most people naturally assumed I was Indian, which only made the disconnect more acute. I was a counterfeit Indian in India, wrestling with the demons of identity.

When we finally left for Nepal, four weeks ahead of schedule, I said that was it for India and me. It had chewed me up and spit me out like a mouthful of paan. We were finished, an ill-fated couple with nothing but geography in common.

Even before my mother sent the tigers, all this had come back to me. But fifteen years had passed, and India had been locked away so long in my psychic vault of life's disappointments, it was as if someone else had taken that trip. Wasn't this one bound to be different? I was different. Also, we were heading to a corner of India we'd never been to before. "You can't visit the east side of Vancouver and say you've seen Canada," Stephen said. I skipped the anti-malarials and packed a few boxes of Imodium, sunscreen and sweaters for the hills. As I threw in a few DNA collection kits, it struck me that my mother was right. On some level, I had to accept India. It was in our blood, even if we rarely said so.

Ten degrees north of the equator, between the Western Ghat mountains and the Arabian Sea, the fabled state of Kerala hugs India's southwestern shore. Hindu legend has it that a warrior-saint saved it from the sea, chopping down greedy waves with the blade of his axe. This was not just any Hindu saint but Parasurama, an incarnation of the supreme four-armed god Vishnu, which suggests that Kerala has been a blessed strip of waterfront real estate since time began.

Travellers know it as a place of respite, a paradise of lazy beaches and backwaters. Ancients knew it as part of the mythical Malabar Coast, a living treasure of teak forests and lush hills that lured traders for more than five thousand years: Greeks, Romans, Arabs, Phoenicians, the Chinese. They came by boat and by caravan for its spices—pepper above all, the first black gold. But all this belongs to those foggy and often forgotten chapters of Indian history, before the Europeans arrived in the twilight of the fifteenth century. By then Cochin had become Malabar's hottest trading port, the queen of the Arabian Sea, and eventually the cradle of India's colonization.

Twenty hours after we left Canada and touched down in Cochin, the Indian sun packed a noonday sting at nine a.m. It roasted our heads as we emerged from the airport, pushing our luggage cart into a sea of gleaming white Ambassadors. Hindustan Motors started making the cars shortly after India gained independence, and they still look as if they have driven right out of the 1950s. We spotted my parents wedged between two of them, all high-beam smiles as they hailed us over to their taxi.

We fell fast into conversation in the back seat amid the chutney of Indian traffic, rumbling alongside oxen pulling carts, motorized rickshaws and trucks adorned with tinsel and pictures of Hindu gods. Gorgeous Indian women grinned down on it all from giant billboards advertising toothpaste, instant rice pilaus and cold creams to lighten the complexion.

We reached the Abad in less than an hour. It sits on a busy roundabout in central Kochi, as Cochin is now called, making it a perfect spot for any pedestrian with a death wish. It was a fine place, a clean, quiet hotel that my parents had made home base over the previous two months, getting to know the staff by name and by story. *Carolyn, this is Anthony. He's from Munnar, the hill station where they grow cardamom. He's getting married to a nice girl this weekend—an arranged marriage, but he likes her very much.*

We went to the beach that first day. After an early lunch and a jet-lagged sleep that swallowed the afternoon, the four of us took a city bus to the old district of Fort Kochi. We shared the ride with homebound commuters off the ferry from Ernakulum, Kochi's commercial district on the mainland. So many waterways run through and around the peninsula and its cluster of islands that people often call Kochi "the Venice of the East." More than a million people live in the area, but it suffers far less from the slum poverty and unemployment that plague other urban areas of the country. Not surprising, since Kerala is considered India's most socially progressive state, and its most literate: its women and children are the nation's best-educated. Malayalam is the main language, an ancient meld of Tamil and Sanskrit and one of fifteen languages that appear on the Indian rupee. But by religion if not by tongue, Kerala is a pan-Indian mishmash of Hindus, Muslims, Christians, Buddhists, Jains, Sikhs and Jews too, a tradition of mixing that owes a debt to its long history as the world's spice cabinet.

A short walk from the shore, the bus stopped in a dusty lot, where my father waved us over to a massive tree on the perimeter. "This has been here since I was a boy," he said happily, patting its trunk like the back of an old friend. "Isn't it a beauty?"

It was a banyan—elegant and intricate, India's national tree, the mystical strangler that starts life as a fig seed. Like Spanish moss, it's an air plant that germinates in the crevices of other trees and grows without need of soil. It can wrap itself so completely around its host that its limbs become indistinguishable from the tree underneath, as my father's banyan had. Aerial roots hung down and gripped the earth wherever they touched the ground, creating the illusion that it had not one trunk but many. To many it's a sacred tree—to Hindus, to Buddhists, and to Paul Simon, who sang about sleeping on its leaves in "Spirit Voices." Maybe it was the jet lag, but the song came back to me as I watched my father taking in the tree's splay of branches, considering the parallels between banyans and rootless people—our people—and whether our roots were more like those of the tree hidden underneath.

Dad walked us through his memories as we strolled towards the beach, pointing out the stretch of sand where he used to play as a boy, and in the distance, Napier Street, where he was born. He gestured to an open lot where young boys were playing cricket, remembering it as the parade ground where the British held their military drills. People used to say treasures were buried under that field, he said, and as a child he had always imagined that under his feet were trunks of gold and jewels the Portuguese and Dutch had stashed away.

It was the Portuguese who built the first European settlement in India, here at Fort Kochi. Fed up with the Arab monopoly over the spice trade, Portugal's King Manuel I sent Vasco da Gama to chart an all-sea route to India. He sailed around the bottom of Africa and back up again, reaching Malabar in 1498. He stopped north of Cochin, at the seaport of Calicut, bearing fabrics and washbasins for the local Zamorin ruler. But the gifts had all the allure of wilted flowers for the diamond-frosted Hindu king of Calicut, who kept servants dressed in silk and spittoons of solid gold. It took a second expedition and a string of bloody battles with Arab Muslims before the Portuguese gained a foothold, thanks largely to the Raja of Cochin, who was no fan of the Zamorin. It was the Raja who gave the Portuguese permission to build a factory in Cochin in 1500. Five years later, they were running the place.

But it's not the Portuguese influence that dazzles along the shore at Fort Kochi. As we neared the beach, the giant Chinese fishing nets came into full view, filling the horizon, a majestic row of cantilevered contraptions. Silhouetted by the sunset, they looked like giant stick insects with arms of teak and bamboo extended out over the water, suspending massive nets in midair. Locals call them *cheenavala*, and they have lined the coast for more than six hundred years. It takes at least five or six men to operate one, using an ingenious old system of ropes and stones as counterbalances to lower and lift the nets. Even as the fishermen stood around smoking and looking bored, there was something biblical in the simple, ancient art of it. Empty nets dipped gently down into the harbour's dark waters and rose slowly to deliver silvery thrashing mounds of pomfret, red snapper, prawns the size of a grown man's fist.

The nets, like the juggler, are something of a mystery. Some stories suggest they arrived with Chinese spice traders in the fourteenth century. Others say that China's famous eunuch mariner Zheng He introduced them a century later. I wondered if my great-grandfather had ever seen them, and if they had reminded him of home.

We stopped on the far side of the nets to take it all in. A soft breeze whispered off the water. My father's parents had met on this beach: Albert Abraham, a newly trained telegrapher from the Nilgiri Hills and Ena deCouto, from a long-established local family. My father's cousin Ralph Pereira, who produced a leather-bound volume on the deCouto history in Cochin, wrote that Ena's maternal grandfather used to buy fish from these nets on his way home from morning Mass. Often he would stop at his daughter's home to toss a fresh catch through her front door and keep right on going. Sometimes he had his cooks whip the fish into a curry he served to the poor, under a tarpaulin he pitched in his yard. I never realized until that evening just how close my father's family had lived to the harbour—witness to its colonial comings and goings, the birthplace of four hundred years of imperialism and, I suppose, our Eurasian ancestry.

In the weeks before we left Canada, I spent time at Toronto's reference library reading about the history of India's Eurasians. Most of what I knew, or thought I knew, had come by way of those kitchen chronicles—a history seen only through the grime of memory's window. I had always assumed that my Eurasian ancestors in India were the accidental by-products of imperialism—lonely white men in a land of brown women, slips of the colonial condom. But this was only half true. They were in many cases deliberate products of policies the Europeans enacted to further their aims, right back to the first fleets from Portugal.

On his second day in Kerala, da Gama described Indian women as being, "as a rule, ugly and small of stature" and Lisbon initially shipped spinsters to south India as it did sacks of chili peppers. But Portugal soon saw the benefits of a local bride. Its merchants wanted India's spices and its missionaries wanted India's souls; they pushed intermarriage as the perfect strategy. Indian women had to convert to marry Portuguese men and the children born of their unions would be raised Roman Catholic. Over time, whatever ties these children had to their mother's Indian roots slowly washed away, like so many footprints along the shore. As the Indo-Portuguese population swelled, so did Portugal's colonial coffers.

The spice trade had made Lisbon the richest city in Europe by the seventeenth century, and everyone wanted a cut. In 1663, with the help of the Zamorin, the Dutch ousted Portugal from the west coast of Malabar. A decade later the French began building a colony at Pondicherry, on the east coast. And all the while, the British were steadily expanding.

India had always been a political patchwork of kingdoms and colonies run by local rajas or sultans and whatever foreign powers had earned their favour. But Britain managed to gain the indulgence of the Mughal emperor Jahangir, son of Akbar the Great, the monarch of northern and central India and ruler of seventy million subjects. As one historian put it, next to him, Queen Elizabeth seemed like the mayor of a quaint hamlet. The British envoys laid more than washbasins at his feet, and in return, Jahangir was generous. He gave the first English sea captain he met the most beautiful girl in his harem (with a harem of eight hundred, he had a few to spare). Within a century the British had built factories, forts and settlements from Surat to Calcutta, turfed out the Dutch and made the royal-chartered East India Company the world's largest corporation. Men from all over the British Isles came to join the ranks of the Company's private army.

With a mantra of "trade, not territory," the British originally had no intention of building permanent colonies in India as it had in North America. They meddled in local politics only insofar as it served their financial interests. But eventually those interests included Indian women. After all, few English ladies were willing to make the long, hard voyage to the subcontinent. Those who did had to be wined and dined, and the soldiers wining and dining them had to be properly dressed—an expense the Company resented. Local liaisons were cheaper and far less trouble. Many English soldiers already had a local wife or lover, or both, a mistress or concubine gifted to them by the raja they served. The East India Company came to see these domestic affairs as a prime opportunity to literally grow itself a loyal population.

Like the Portuguese, the British began encouraging their men to marry Indian woman and to have children—the more the better. As a remarkable incentive, they offered money for the undertaking. In 1687, from its headquarters in Madras, the East India Company announced it would pay in gold—a minted pagoda—for any child born of a marriage between an Indian woman and a soldier of the Company. That was the equivalent of about five rupees at the time, a sum that reportedly grew to fifteen silver rupees per child. Some historians cast the scheme as Britain's attempt to legitimize the immoral affairs of its troops. Some Anglo-Indians have regarded it as proof the Brits once considered them such prized offspring that they rewarded parents for their birth. But whatever it was, the baby bonus really amounted to a crude experiment in social and genetic engineering: payment for a hybrid people designed to form a buffer between rulers and the ruled.

Everything went swimmingly at first. Anglo-Indians had the same advantages and social status as their English fathers. They were raised to be just like them, with English customs, English clothes, English religion, an English education provided at special English schools in India or, often, back in England. And of course they were fluent only in their father tongue, learning just enough "kitchen Hindi" to scold the servants. But like any unchecked experiment, it eventually ran amok.

Less than a hundred years after money was being offered for their birth, Anglo-Indians outnumbered the English in India. The Company suddenly cast them as a potential political threat, as the free mulattoes had turned out to be for Spain and France in the West Indies. Fearing rebellion, the English pondered what India's half-castes might be capable of, schooled as they were in the ways of their mighty white fathers. But it was a hollow argument. Anglo-Indians enjoyed the same rights as the ruling-class English; they had little to gain from warring against them. They were said to be "more British than the British." Historians say the truth had more to do with England's fears of losing out. As more Englishmen returned from India wealthy, more Englishmen lined up to go, believing that they, and their fully English sons, should have dibs on the best jobs, and the Company agreed. The only real threat Anglo-Indians posed was to English opportunities.

In the late eighteenth and nineteenth centuries, the Company imposed measures that, according to the Indian scholar V.R. Gaikwad, reduced Anglo-Indians "to political impotence and social degradation." They were sacked from administrative jobs, discharged from the army ranks and relegated to blacksmithing and beating the drums in military bands. They were forbidden to travel abroad for their education, effectively blocking them from any executive job. With time the policies became more draconian, denying Anglo-Indians the right to own or purchase land or to live more than ten miles outside a company settlement without high-ranking approval. Without land they could never farm, and without travel they could never trade, leaving them to scratch out a living in servitude to English officers or Indian leaders.

Yet despite it all, Anglo-Indians remained fiercely loyal to England, a motherland most had never seen. When Indians first revolted, in the Great Rebellion of 1857, Anglo-Indians fought alongside the British to put them down. When Britain took direct control over India's governance after the rebellion in 1858, ending the East India Company's quasi-administration, the Anglo-Indians had proved to be such loyal subjects that the new British Raj rewarded them with their own schools and preferential job opportunities. While Indians had to have a university degree to join the civil service, Anglo-Indians needed only a high school diploma. The policy—in place until 1919—proved to be an ingenious one, creating such a powerful disincentive to higher education that it shackled their futures to the ranks of government middle management.

Anglo-Indians became the officious, reliable pistons of the Raj engine, running its post offices, its customs service, telegraphs, police stations, buses and, most of all, its railways. In the late nineteenth century the Great India Peninsula Railway spread like ivy across the subcontinent. More than half of all Anglo-Indians relied on it for their livelihood, and their lives. They staffed its stations and outposts, as my Papa Freddie eventually did, making their homes in the colonies that sprung up alongside them, tight communities of pretty houses with gardens and gardeners, nannies and cooks.

But even as their economic prospects improved, their social status sank. In the late nineteenth century, the Suez Canal brought English women to India by the boatload, to join husbands or to seek one out, and they brought with them all the class and colour prejudices of the Victorian age. Charles Darwin's cousin Francis Galton published *Hereditary Genius* in 1869, the same year the Suez opened, launching the eugenics movement with its notions of racial purity and breeding gifted people like fine racehorses. In British India, Sir Francis's theories recast the half-castes as the spoiled fruits of a dreadful experiment. Ethnographers even set out with measuring tapes to gather evidence of the scourge, literally sizing up Eurasians as late as 1940.

"In colour the Eurasians afford, as is natural in a mixed race, examples of the entire colour-scale from sooty-black, through sundry shades of brown yellow, to pale white and even, as a very rare exception, florid or rosy," wrote Edgar Thurston, the prolific curator of the Madras Government Museum, in an 1898 monograph. "The product of alliances between British men and Eurasian women show the least signs of physical degeneration, and possess broader shoulders, hips and hands, greater chest girth, wider forehead, and more muscle as the result of re-vivification of the stock by direct British intervention. . . ."

High-caste Indians, meanwhile, tended to regard Anglo-Indians and Eurasians as mere lackeys of the British, born of low-caste unions on both sides—too low, in some cases, to even share the same sidewalk. In Cochin, the young deCouto girls used to zigzag along the pavement to throw their Eurasian shadows into the paths of high-caste Brahmins, delighting in the idea that it would force them home to bathe. My father's cousin Ralph wrote that Cochin must have had the cleanest Brahmins around. To many Indians, the Eurasians were "*chota sahibs*," the small bosses—in the worst light they were seen as "bastards of the Raj."

It was into this uncomfortable in-between world that my ancestors were born. Moulded by British policies that forced them to live as tenants, they clustered in city buildings and railway colonies like kids at a summer camp. They spawned their own customs, sports teams and social clubs and found their mates among their own, often at colony dances, where they developed their crush on

Johnnie Walker, the unofficial beverage of the British Empire. But they always made it to Sunday morning Mass, and home again for a nice biryani lunch.

Reading about their history made me consider, in a way I never had, the Anglo-Indian identity crisis. It was passed down, as surely as their genetic skein, from the railway colonies to the cold of postwar England and all the way across to Canada, where my grandmother tried, with good intentions on those Sunday afternoons, to pass it on to me. *"We're English. . . ." "But look at our tans, Nana."* And maybe to some extent she had. Not that I realized it then, but my frustration with India in 1991 was a very old family tradition—to feel connected yet never to belong.

We cracked open the Johnnie Walker in my parents' room that first night in Kochi, after the beach and a fish curry at the Abad. I talked about the things I'd learned at the library. My father recalled the curse of his dark skin when he was growing up, the pools where he was not allowed to swim, fair-skinned aunts who asked him not to mention that he was related when he went to visit. My mother spoke of the cloistered life she'd lived in the railway colonies, never socializing with the British or stepping inside the houses of Indians. The only Indians who visited their houses were the ones who came to clean them.

Neither of their paternal grandfathers had experienced this, not the Captain and not the juggler. It was their brides—the well-to-do Bridget Meek and the mysterious Mariamal—who had wedded these two very different men to the insulated world of the Eurasians, which is why they stood out among all the others within the melange of our family story.

We woke the next morning even before the muezzin wailed from his perch in the mosque nearby. I called Jade at home, where she was staying with my sister. We'd wanted to bring our daughter, but she was not quite three then, too young to be dragged through archives and up hillsides. Think of all the things she might put in her mouth, our doctor said. She had put her arms and legs around me when we said goodbye and whispered in my ear to bring her back an elephant.

Stephen and my father left for a long walk after we hung up. My mother and I, still in our robes, nursed a long pot of coffee in my parents' room.

"Thank you, Anthony," my mother said. "It's nice and hot, yes?"

"Yes, madam, very hot, very fresh," Anthony replied, his head rolling horizontally in that distinctive South Asian nod as he set down a tray with flowers and biscuits.

My mother looked relaxed, comfortable with the pampering, which took her back to days when a servant appeared every morning with something hot. Her DNA results had arrived before Stephen and I had left home, and as we drained our first cups I pulled them out. They had surprised me when I first read them back in Canada: 68 percent European, 1 percent Native American, 22 percent East Asian. Twenty-two—as though there had recently been a juggler on her side of the family as well. I was skeptical, convinced that the DNAPrint test was simply not precise enough to distinguish Central, East or even South Asian markers from one another.

But that morning, a mere rickshaw ride away from the Chinese nets and the harbour where half the planet had pulled ashore for millennia, the mixture of my mother's inheritance didn't seem nearly as strange as it did back home, where time and history are barely toddlers. In India, time seems like the sea—infinite, fluid, people flowing in and out, merging endlessly into one great body. The genome bears it out. The DNA of people in India and from India is a collage of the world, thought to be the most diverse outside of Africa. Who knows, maybe there was a recent East Asian ancestor on my mother's side as well, perhaps a Chinese silk wallah and a servant girl, a prisoner and a Hindu princess. But with no yarn to wrap around it, as we had with my father's East Asian tally, we let it go.

We fixated instead on the fraction that bolstered old suspicions: 9 percent sub-Saharan African. As soon as I read the figure out loud, my mother said, without a trace of doubt, "That's the Captain."

Even before we had her DNA results, or mine, there were clues to betray what's buried in our genes: my mother's full lips, cousins with variations of an afro. Her brother Basil's youngest daughter, Simone, has tresses like Diana Ross. I'd recently run into her at a bridal shower, where she told me she was dead keen to finally know the Crooks story. She pulled at a fistful of her spiralling hair: "Like, where did this come from?" she said. My mother's father had once asked the same question, telling her that when he was young, he could never even pull a comb through his hair.

Maybe it was the freedom of being so far from home, or simply having the luxury of a lazy morning, but my mother told me then, in more detail than she ever had, how my grandfather had abandoned his efforts to find out more about the father he never knew. It began in those bloody months of 1947 after partition tore India apart, violence breaking out between Muslim and Hindu, killing hundreds of thousands, leaving millions homeless and millions to migrate across the new border the British had drawn around Pakistan before their departure. Anglo-Indians were among them—600,000 scattered across the country—wondering if they should stay at all and, if they left, where they should go. Postwar England extended no carrot to the population it had fathered. Australia was refusing to accept non-white immigrants. There was a proposal, which never panned out, to resettle them in the Andaman Islands, a storied archipelago in the Bay of Bengal that the British had used as a penal colony. Anglo-Indians met in homes all over the country to discuss their options. My father joined a group that gathered at the local undertaker's. But my mother's father never attended any such meetings. He had his own relocation plan. He was going to pack up Nana Gladys and their seven children and sail to Jamaica.

Before independence, my grandfather had contacted the Registrar General's office in Spanish Town looking for information about the Captain. My mother said the search led him to believe there were Crooks relatives in Kingston, so he wrote to the pastor of an Anglican church there for help in making introductions. He was so convinced that his father's relations would welcome him with open arms, he had his family's passports stamped in anticipation of the voyage to the Caribbean and sold every stick of furniture in their living room to pay for the trip. "The velvet curtains, the brass jardinières, the settees—everything went," my mother said. "It was bare."

A reply finally arrived from Jamaica several months later. My mother never read that letter herself, but she heard enough from later conversations around the house to know what it said. The writer had insisted that the Crooks family had no Indian relatives. The letter accused my grandfather of being an imposter and warned, rather ominously, from what my mother gathered, against any future contact, assuring him that he would be most unwelcome, particularly—and this my mother remembered clearly—if his wife was white. "They must have been black," my mother said. "What else could you think?"

Australia was out of the question because my grandfather was brown-skinned. His alleged relatives in Jamaica, which was then a British colony, would tolerate no white skin, which would exclude my grandmother. Papa crumpled the letter and threw it away. He never spoke again of sailing to Jamaica.

Some months after that stark rejection, another letter arrived. This one was from New York, written by a man who shared my grandfather's name, Frederick Crooks. He introduced himself as a Jamaican relative—a cousin, my mother thought. He wrote that he had seen my grandfather's letter while in Jamaica, and he knew that the Captain did in fact have children in India. He had no children of his own, and he hoped that he and Papa might write to one another. My grandfather said he was no longer interested.

But I think he must have harboured some hope of future contact, because he passed the letter on to my mother. Having just begun her long, land-to-sea courtship with my father, she had become an avid letter writer. She was likely to take up the invitation to correspond extended by Frederick Crooks of New York, and my grandfather would have known that.

For the next three years my mother corresponded with the mysterious "Uncle Freddie" in New York. She wishes now that she'd pressed him for details of the Jamaican family story. But she was only seventeen then, and too caught up in her own affairs to be curious about a grandfather she'd never met. She filled her letters with small talk about the latest Bombay fashions and her boyfriend at sea. The New York uncle wrote to her about his wife, who had just graduated from university, and fascinated her with descriptions of the pencil skirts women were wearing in Manhattan.

In 1952 my mother wrote to tell him that she and my father were getting married, and in response he sent a bridal catalogue from New York. With it he sent money for her to order the wedding gown of her choice or, if she preferred, to buy one in Bombay. It was the first inkling my mother had of his wealth, though she never did spend his money on a dress. "How could I?" she said. "We had no settee in the front room, nothing to sit on. I gave the money to Nana and Papa to buy furniture."

Their correspondence trickled to an end after my mother got married. The move to England and motherhood left her little time to write. She regretted it, knowing that this New York uncle had no children of his own and seemed eager to maintain ties to her branch of the Crooks family. So she passed on his address to her younger brother Dennis, who, my mother understood, became his new pen pal.

It was Dennis I was to ask for DNA. My mother had five brothers who in turn had seven sons, which meant there were several potential men to provide a sample of the Captain's Y chromosome. But having fully evolved from reluctant donor to Director of DNA Collection Protocols, my mother believed it was only proper that Dennis, the eldest of the three surviving males in her family, should be the one to contribute. His Y could tell us what my mother's DNA could not: whether the Captain's paternal line could actually be traced back to Africa, whether his male ancestors—and ours—had arrived in Jamaica in chains.

We fell into our Kochi routine over the next few days, rising with the muezzin's alarm to make the most of the mornings before the sun drove us indoors. This was less of a problem for my father and me. We spent most of our days at the Santa Cruz Basilica, cooped up in a dark room the size of a closet. There are more magnificent churches in India, and beside the cathedrals of Europe it has all the grandeur of a country chapel. But I loved its ornate twin spires, its windows like portholes, its lemon-washed walls, all freshly painted as though they were expecting company. A team of labourers was laying stones for a walkway as we approached, their bare backs glistening in the sun. All through its history the church has invariably been in the midst of transformation. The Portuguese built it in the sixteenth century, the Dutch stored their arms in it and the British demolished it, only to change their minds and rebuild it in the nineteenth century.

My father was baptized at Santa Cruz and his parents were married there. So there was a chance that in the marriage register something, anything, might have been written about John Abraham, the father of the groom. We hunched over practically illegible record books, sweating next to a moody fan and watched over by a chipped statue of Saint Anthony and the hardboiled gaze of Cochin's last Portuguese bishop. Every ten minutes or so my father and I traded profound observations.

"Everyone here married their cousins."

"Look how many people died of worms."

"Worms and swelling."

"Swelling—is that a disease?"

We found nothing about the juggler (neither of the groom's parents were mentioned in the registry of Ena deCouto's 1921 marriage to Albert Abraham), but we did discover records of the maternal side of my father's family, dating back four generations. Swabbing may one day be to genealogy what the dishwasher was to domesticity—a sterile saviour of time and tedium. But taking the time to wash dishes by hand is occasionally therapeutic. So it was at the basilica.

As we came across familiar names, my father supplied the stories. Some of them stemmed from the research of his cousin Ralph, who had traced the deCouto line in Cochin back to Ramon deCouto, born about 1840 to a family of Indo-Portuguese shipbuilders in Ceylon, as Sri Lanka was then known. He was a light-eyed playboy who eventually fathered seventeen children with his wife, Joanna Fernandez. She was the daughter of a wealthy Indo-Portuguese family that owned fertile tracts of land near the old fort; the district still bears the name Fernandez Gardens. Joanna's father, Johannes Fernandez, adored his verdant acreage, but apparently he loved the horse races even more, and eventually he lost most of the property to gambling debts.

The gambling addiction ran in the family, as several studies have concluded that addictions do. My father said his mother's older brother, Edward deCouto, great-grandson of the track-loving Fernandez, was so virulently afflicted that, while he had once been a rich bachelor in Bombay, a civil engineer who made a tidy fortune on a dam in northern India, he ended up homeless. The "cotton figures" brought him down—wagering on the opening and closing rates of wholesale cotton in the Bombay exchange. When my father was a boy, Uncle Eddie often turned up at his house and Nana Ena would feed him, even when there was hardly enough money for my grandmother to feed her own children. She once pawned her jewellery to help cover living expenses and later gave Uncle Eddie the money to redeem it for her, but he never did. She lost it all, my father said, even her wedding ring.

They were all there in the records: my soft-touch grand-mother; my Great-Uncle Eddie; the marriage of Nana Ena's parents; her father, John deCouto, one of Ramon's seventeen children and once the personal physician to Cochin's maharaja, before he left to care for the poor in exchange for chickens and whisky. There was the doctor's bride, Isabella Vaz—best known as the iron matriarch Nana Bella—and her mother, Maria Leonora Snalleckz, whose family is said to have come from the Polish-Russian border. For all the stories those ledgers couldn't tell, they became more alluring with every find, a tangible paper trail of my ancestors, all in one cramped and jumbled closet of a file room.

One night the four of us set out to find Fernandez Gardens to see my father's cousin. "It's not really a garden anymore, but it used to be a beautiful one," my father said. "The pepper vines grew thick, right up to the entrance, curling around the trees, full of berries." We found our way there in the dark, walking along a busy thoroughfare until my father recognized a walled compound. We slipped in through a narrow entrance and followed a winding path where the prickly arms of shrubs and trees reached out in the pitch black, until light spilled from an open doorway up ahead. And there was Gladwyn deCouto, waving us in out of the night. "Uncle!" he shouted.

After so many days sifting through the lives of the dead, here at last was a living relative, and one who made his home on a parcel of land that had belonged to the family for three generations. I expected him to be much older, as if any relative still living here could only be from my father's time, but Gladwyn was in his early fifties. He was a second cousin, a grandson of Dr. John deCouto's brother. My father had first met him on shore leave in the 1950s, when Gladwyn was a child, and he'd called my dad "Uncle" ever since. They'd kept in touch through the years, both Gladwyn and his brother Dean, who also lived with his family in the old gardens.

Gladwyn has the same slim build as my father and is also an engineer. He had worked on the tugboats in Dubai, like many Cochinites, before an accident sent him home to a desk job. He ushered us into the small bungalow where he lives with his wife, Noella, a schoolteacher, their two teenaged daughters, Angel and Triana, and his wife's sister Yolanda. We sat on loveseats in their living room, drank orange juice, talked about our families and traded photographs.

Stephen noticed Gladwyn's large stack of country music albums near the stereo—Buck Owens and the Buckaroos and Vince Gill. Stephen grew up on classic country in Alberta, but it was the last thing he'd expected to hear that night in Fort Kochi. He and Gladwyn shared a good laugh, abandoned their juice for English beer and asked whatever happened to *Hee Haw*.

Eventually we discussed the reasons for our trip, why I was looking into the family's history and heading to the Nilgiris. I talked to them about DNA testing and wondered out loud if the deCouto Y chromosome might reveal more about our Portuguese heritage. Gladwyn said he'd be willing to contribute his DNA to find out. His only reservation was how I would get it: "Will you take my blood, give me a needle?"

"Oh no, just a swab of your inner cheek," I said.

Gladwyn smiled. "For sure, okay. Next time!"

Living where their ancestors had lived for centuries, Gladwyn and his family had never thought about delving into their heritage in detail, although they knew it was strikingly different from the majority of Malayali speakers in Kochi. Yolanda said her grandparents actually spoke Portuguese, and many of the songs they sang—that she still sings—are Portuguese songs. Angel and Triana, who both have long, dark hair and milky complexions, said that at their school, where they learn Hindi and Urdu and most of the students are Indian, they often face questions about their ancestry because of their colour.

"Your colour?" I said.

"Because we're fair," said Angel. "People ask, 'What are you?'"

We met them all again a few days later, after a Sunday evening Mass at the basilica. I'd never been to a service like it. It was March, but the Christmas lights were on, strung around pillars. The church was packed. The congregation spilled outside onto the newly finished walkway. The sermon of an invisible priest blasted over the audio system, crackling through the vastness of the historic old church as though it were being beamed from Heaven itself, competing with parishioners who prayed out loud with palms turned upward and outward.

Some women were done up in bright satin like disco queens; others were enveloped in jewel-toned saris. The men wore dress pants, some John Travolta–tight. After the sermon, from somewhere over our heads, a band began to play. I half expected a Bee Gees version of "How Great Thou Art," but the first bar screeched out of an electric guitar—a hardcore hillbilly twang that drifted down from the balcony as if the whole church had been lifted off its sandy south Indian base and set down in Nashville.

The congregation swayed and picked up the rhythm. Feet, theirs and mine, tapped in the pews. I've never been a big country fan, but something moved me, something amazing, perhaps spiritual, in that mishmash of a yellow church where my ancestors had howled as babies over the christening font, exchanged marriage vows and buried their dead. I felt blessed—I was knee to knee with pew upon pew of brown and beige people of Indo-Portuguese-Anglo-Dutch extraction. And I didn't even know yet that the lead guitarist was Alistair deCouto—another cousin.

We stood in the courtyard after Mass in the gentle embrace of the evening sun, chatting with Alistair, his wife, Anita, and Gladwyn's family about their plucky church band. Then we took off on motorbikes and rickshaws to the Shop 'n' Save near the fort to send emails from its Internet café and look for souvenirs. I bought Jade an India Barbie, a black-haired beauty in a royal blue sari with all the same physics-defying proportions as her Malibu cousin. Then we were off again, back to Fernandez Gardens, where Noella, her sister and the girls had spent the day preparing a feast of Indo-Portuguese specialties, with hand-ground fresh spices and fish hoisted straight out of the harbour: a pomfret fry with coconut and ginger, spicy noodles, a stinging vindaloo. I had a DNA kit with me to take Gladwyn's sample, but a buccal swab would have drained the soul out of the evening. Gladwyn played more honky-tonk and we drank more English beer and tried to coax Yolanda to sing to us in Portuguese.

I fell into a sweet sleep back at the Abad that night—the kind of easy slumber that comes when you finally make peace with a place.

7

INTO THE MIST

They appear out of nowhere, abruptly, like nature's own sleight of hand. One moment we were speeding along the plains of Tamil Nadu, and then suddenly they seemed to fill the sky, like a pod of humpback whales breaching to kiss the clouds.

It's true what they say about the Nilgiri Hills: the blue haze never leaves their sides. *Nila-giri* means "blue mountain" in Sanskrit, and legend has it that the haze inspired their name. But legends, like family lore, have different versions. Another says they were named for the rare blue *kurinji* plant that blooms on their slopes only once every twelve years. There's a tribe in the region whose members calculate their age by the appearances of its trumpet-shaped blossoms, and Tamil poems, two thousand years old, that say the bees that feed on their nectar produce a honey sweeter than any other. The bees are massive in the Nilgiris, the largest honeybees in the world. Rock bees, they're called; their hives hang down like giant tongues from the undersides of cliffs, hundreds of metres off the ground. Collecting honey from them is not a job for people who fear death. I don't know that my great-grandfather was a person like that, but he did do unusual things to survive—blowing glass, juggling. Perhaps an innate dexterity made him a natural at gathering honey in midair, from those busy bees that work even by moonlight, pollinating flowers.

The *kurinji* flowered in 1886, the year the juggler became John Abraham. It so happened that they were set to bloom again in 2006, when we went to follow the trail he had left beyond the reach of science, and the year that honey became yet another question about him. But we were five months too early that spring, so we saw only pictures of the periwinkle cloak they throw over the hills.

Of course, the Nilgiris are no more hills than the Atlantic is a pond. Crammed into a corner of south India where the Eastern Ghats meet the Western Ghats, the Nilgiris are a mountain range in their own right, more than two dozen peaks rising two thousand metres above the sea. Still, most people call them "the hills," as if they were as quaint and familiar as a nursery rhyme. But most of their history—and ours—they have been neither of those things.

It may be that the mighty who ruled in their shadow found nothing to tempt them, no riches to mine or towns to plunder. It could be that the jungle that fans out for miles from their base, full of tusks and claws, kept the curious away. For centuries, how to cross the hills and how to keep others from crossing them was all that mattered. No one paid the hills themselves much attention—not the tubby Hindu kings who pledged the highest peak to their goddess of wealth; not the Tippu Sultan, a.k.a. "the Tiger of Mysore," who used them as a lookout and finally surrendered them to the British in 1799; and, for a long time, not even the British.

When I ask about the circumstances that drew John Abraham to the Nilgiris, or how he lived while he was there, invariably my mother says, "What could we know? They were *hill people*." My father, when he describes the challenges his father, Albert, faced adjusting to life in Cochin, and later to the crowds and noise of Bombay, says, "Cities were a new world to him. You see, he came from the *hills*." The hills, the remote, inscrutable hills. Where people lived into their hundreds—or vanished.

Gladwyn had recommended a driver named Joseph, a tall, dark Keralan in his forties. He picked us up on a Monday morning in a polished white Ambassador. He wore a crisp white shirt and sported a thick black moustache that gave him the look of a seventies soap opera star, though he didn't much act like one. Quiet and shy, he kept a wooden rosary in his hip pocket that he rolled between his fingers whenever we stopped for gas.

Stephen, whose long legs were not built for Indian buses or back seats, sat up front with Joseph. They formed an easy bond, unfolding maps, studying the route north from Kochi. Joseph spoke Malayalam and a little English, but how little we couldn't be sure. Stephen inquired about mileage, diesel engines, and the peculiar honking protocol of Indian roadways (two for passing, one for changing lanes? for going too fast, too slow?). Joseph mostly nodded his replies and laughed.

We reached the jungle not long after the mountains materialized. The light changed instantly, reaching through the leafy canopy with golden fingers, scattering sun and shadows. We stopped to buy young coconuts from a lonesome roadside stall and drank from them by the car. The whole region, by decree of the United Nations, is one of the world's protected zones, home to tigers and the last remaining wild elephant population in Asia. Ours was the only vehicle in sight that afternoon. It was eerily quiet, except for invisible creatures that cawed and chattered near enough that I ignored the urge to pee. "You're a big funk, Carolyn," my mother said before she marched into the bush.

On the narrow road up to Coonoor, large signs warn of the hairpin bends—fourteen switchbacks my dad calls the "bloody bends" ever since he shoved his car around them in 1958. From a car you tend to miss the spectacular sights en route, the vertical forests and plunging gorges. But really, the only things crucial to see while driving up the mountains are the things coming down— a barrelling truck delivering labourers home to the plains, a maniac racing to reincarnation on a motorbike. In kilometres, the trip up is nothing. On the clock (and with a bladder full of coconut juice), it spans a Homeric age. But the train takes even longer. It's a steam-engine line the British dreamed up, confident that 2,100 metres of steep rock couldn't best their engineering prowess. They spent thirty-seven years debating technical proposals and another seventeen years building it. Just in time, perhaps, for it to become my great-grandfather's getaway train.

I couldn't be sure exactly when John Abraham left the Nilgiris, or when he arrived, just that when he did, the only way up was the bridle paths the Brits had cleared for their bullock carts, hauling velvet settees and ottomans, bone china and French champagne. The tropics were killing them—sudden fevers, malaria, typhoid, cholera outbreaks. Along with the subcontinent's freakish hazards, snakebites, tiger attacks, fatal falls from elephants, it was all enough to drive the British to madness and to drink, and never more so than in the summers, when it was hot enough to toast crumpets on a clothesline. Indian rulers often summered in cooler highland settlements, and the practice spread among the British like an epidemic. They set up more than sixty hill stations, from the Himalayas in the north to the Nilgiris in the south—the Hamptons of the Raj.

In those days it took ten hours to make it up to the Nilgiris' largest town of Ootacamund (now known as Udhagamandalam). Ooty, as everyone still calls it for short, is the second-highest peak in the range, and initially Coonoor was just a rest stop, a pretty perch at which to catch your breath. After the British introduced tea to its slopes, the population grew with it. We saw the legacy of that growth as we drifted into town: crowded layers of little pastel-coloured dwellings clinging to the hillside as if they'd been glued there as part of a grade-school diorama.

My father had us booked at the guesthouse where he and my mother stayed in 1997. We arrived to find that we had the whole two-storey building to ourselves. Sam, a bone-thin old man who minded the place, let us in. It felt as though it had been empty a long time. It certainly smelled like it had—a stinging combination of mothballs and insect repellent. We opened windows and rushed to pull sweaters from our suitcases, imagining how the homesick British must have shivered with glee up here.

My father went to call the only relative left in the hills, a distant cousin that he'd met back in 1997 when Aunty Flo was still alive. I heard him explaining our plans to meet up with Father Francis and, hopefully, find out more about John Abraham. Then for a long time he said nothing at all. Finally, he said, "Yes, yes, okay . . . I understand." Then he hung up a few moments later.

The relative, my father said, was expecting us that evening and had prepared a dinner.

"But she doesn't want any discussion about the family. She wants no talk of Chinese grandfathers or Indian mothers, or anything at all about ancestry."

"No questions?" I asked.

"No, no questions. She says she has standing in the community."

In this small Indian tea town the Abrahams had considered themselves mostly Anglo, and no good would come if any talk spread that they were otherwise, she had told my father.

"I suppose a DNA test would be out, then." I said.

"Oh golly," my father said. "I didn't ask her that."

I was half joking. DNA wasn't nearly as important on this trip as the memories people might share. But then all the relatives had told my father back in 1997 that there was nothing to tell, that they knew nothing. It was Julie's grandson Ron, visiting from Chennai, who had told my father, alone on that evening walk, that John Abraham had been a fugitive.

"I agreed that we'd say nothing about it," my father said. "We may as well keep the peace."

As Joseph drove us over to dinner that evening, through the hill town the British had built from scratch, it struck me that its social sensibilities might be stuck in the same century as its architecture, every Victorian brick an anachronism. It was no wonder that so few details about the juggler ever made it out of these hills. If this same inclination to deny even the possibility of having Chinese or Indian grandparents still prevailed in the twenty-first century, what was life like for a Chinese migrant to these hills a hundred years ago?

We passed a polite evening over a fine south Indian meal that first night in the hills, but we left as we came, in the dark. And before the night was over, it grew even darker.

Sam was waiting outside the guesthouse when we returned, posted at the front door like a stone-faced sentinel. He beckoned my father aside as soon as we climbed out of the car and whispered more words than he'd uttered since we'd arrived in Coonoor. As my father explained it, Sam had notified his boss that we were allowing Joseph, the driver, to stay in one of the empty rooms. Sam said his boss was unhappy about that, and he wanted my father to telephone him immediately.

My parents knew the owner from a previous visit. But their acquaintance made it only more galling to the proprietor that my father would put him in such an awkward position. He ran a respectable business, he shouted over the phone; he had a good reputation, and many friends, and all of it would be destroyed if he permitted a member of the servant class—even a Christian like himself—to sleep under his roof, in "the very same bed where very important executives slept!"

My father said he was shocked to hear such nonsense in this day and age. Joseph was a fine, decent fellow, he argued, and asked how the owner could even call himself a Christian with views like that. I doubted the owner heard any of it over his own roars. Fine, my father said, if Joseph couldn't stay, neither could we.

I don't know that Joseph understood everything said that night. But he absorbed enough to tell us that he had found a hotel in town while we were at dinner and that he preferred to stay there anyway. We told him that was ridiculous, that he would stay wherever we stayed. But he shook his head no, certain, I think, that we'd only encounter more of the same—certain because it was hardly the first time he had encountered it. We told him we were sorry. "It's okay," he said, and shrugged.

There's always been debate as to how the British managed to control India for so long when they were so dramatically outnumbered by the Indians. Some chalk it up to military might, others to the yoke of bureaucracy. But most agree that, with India's population so deeply divided by caste, by class and by creed, one group was always willing to side with foreigners to put another group down—Cochin's Rajah against Calicut's Zamorin, Hindu against Muslim, low caste against high caste. The Indian writer Khushwant Singh summed it up bluntly: "The English conquered India with the help of the Indians."

Even now, more than half a century after India's first constitution made it a crime to persecute people on the basis of caste and class, and when members of the lowest caste—the "untouchables"—have risen to become doctors, lawyers and even a president, discrimination still flows through the country like the Ganges. It irrigates villages where people can be sold like slaves or stoned for loving above their station. It trickles into the guesthouse of a mountain town to oust a workingman from his bed and make family history a taboo subject. It leaks into everything, even biology. Many Indians—and not just Hindus—see social status as a dictate of bloodlines, encoded not just in ancient scriptures but in their DNA. And the awkward truth is that thousands of years of social segregation have left a subtle and, some warn, dangerous imprint on the genomes of India.

A 2009 study by scientists at Harvard and the University of Hyderabad, the most thorough of the relatively few on India's genomes to date, concludes that all Indians alive today, regardless of caste, descend from a melding of two ancient peoples. One group, which the researchers called "ancestral north Indian," was a blend genetically close to Europeans, Middle Easterners and Central Asians. The other, which the scientists dubbed the "ancestral south Indian" line, was unique to the subcontinent. Those of high caste tended to have a higher proportion of the northern Eurasian lineage. People of low caste and the country's tribal peoples were genetically indistinguishable and both had a higher proportion of the distinct ancestral south Indian lineage. Researchers noted that there are towns and villages where the same families have lived for thousands of years without exchanging genes with one another because of the strictly enforced rules about marrying within caste. The work essentially describes India as a vast collection of small genetic caste-driven communities that sprang thousands of years ago from two tiny founding groups.

This social divide seems to show up dramatically in the Y chromosome. Other research has found that high-caste males are more likely to carry a Y-chromosome type common in Europe, particularly in eastern Europe but also found all the way north into Scandinavia. Known as the R1a haplogroup (one of many subgroups of haplogroup R), this Y was found in as many as two-thirds of the priestly Brahmins in certain regions of India, according to a 2005 study. It's unclear whether this chromosome was carried in by a Caucasian forefather or evolved in India and was carried out. But either way, Y-chromosome testing has taken off among Indians. Some eagerly seek a Brahmin lurking in their genes; others hope to confirm a high-caste marriage prospect. Like the priestly caste of Jewish *kohanim*, whose Y chromosomes can be traced back to the brother of Moses, Brahmins also believe that an unbroken line of male descent—the *gotra* system—links them to eight ancient sages from whom all Brahmin families descend.

In online chat groups, male Brahmins have embraced the Y chromosome as evidence of their supremacy over both women and all other castes. One man, identifying himself as a scholar, wrote that the inability of the Y chromosome to recombine with another chromosome was not a weakness but a strength, in comparison to the mercurial X, which mixes it up with every passing generation, "diluting the chances for super-intelligence." Another, posting to a different genetic ancestry forum, seemed to share this view:

> I am a Hindu Brahmin from South India [the "highest" caste in the Hindu system]. I belong to the R1a1 haplogroup. The genographic project traced my origin to Central Asia (Ukraine or thereabouts). I am surprised to see so many Slavs and Ashkenazi Levite folks also to be of the same group. I assume our ancestors were Central Asians who went separate ways and religions. I would be interested in knowing if anybody has more information along this line. . . . I read that Ashkenazi Levites have the highest average IQ in the world. It is a given fact that Brahmins have the highest IQ in India (though this group has not be [sic] tested on an average basis to compare to worldwide statistics) and Brahmins also do well in academics in India, USA etc. Do you think this is something to do with the R1a1 haplogroup?

Whatever stories the Y tells, they make up only a slim chapter of any man's genetic history. High-caste men may be more likely to carry a Y chromosome distinct from that of low-caste males, but most Indians, irrespective of caste, carry the mitochondrial DNA of a distinctly South Asian matriarch. Its presence is the genetic sword that strikes a fatal gash in the very heart of the caste system, proving that most Indians inherited their genes from both ends of their rigid social hierarchy.

Mitochondrial DNA, or mtDNA, as it's known for short, is an intriguing ring of genetic code that once belonged to bacteria. In the early stages of life on the planet, these bugs—along with their circular genomes—were engulfed by the cells that would evolve over eons to form humans. Now the genetic remnants of these bugs belong to us, repurposed as the machinery that human cells need to produce their power. Individual cells can carry thousands of copies of mitochondria, and unlike the double-helix genome that shuffles and recombines to make the next generation, the DNA within mitochondria doesn't change much. People who have the same mutations in their mtDNA sequences are believed to have descended from the same woman at some point back in time, and generally people inherit mtDNA only from their mothers. This is the result of one of biology's more bizarre quirks. Sperm carry mitochondria in their tails, and in the crash and bang of conception a sperm can lose its tail, and the father's mitochondria with it. And if a man's mtDNA survives, the egg destroys it. So it is egg, not sperm, that bequeaths mitochondria to the next generation.

Long before science realized the Y's potential, mitochondrial DNA was the first genetic thread to tie us conclusively into one human family—all the way back to the so-called mitochondrial Eve, who lived in Africa an estimated 200,000 years ago. She wasn't, like the biblical Eve, the only woman alive at the time, but she was the one whose female descendants survived to fan out and populate the world through an unbroken line of daughters. One of her female descendants was the founder of Haplogroup M, the mitochondrial DNA signature of the great matriarch of India. She is believed to have left the east coast of Africa some seventy thousand years ago and to have had enough daughters, who in turn had enough daughters, to eventually spread her mtDNA to roughly two-thirds of India's population. Hers is the legacy of generations of women who broke through social barriers to marry above their caste, however invisible that legacy remains.

I woke early to a chill and the rare Indian sighting of my own breath. I lay there for a while slipping into rusty resentments about India. Just when I had felt a sense of belonging, one night in the hills had made me feel like an alien again. I threw on a jacket and went outside to see where we had ended up.

It was a fine historic hotel, a former priory built a century ago, like so many buildings in Coonoor. The lobby was furnished with dark wood panelling and heavy doors; tapestries hung on the wall alongside the antlers of some unlucky beast. The guestrooms opened to a sprawling garden, and that morning its air was thick with the loamy smell of wet earth. There wasn't a soul in sight and the flowerbeds had yet to bloom. I walked along the edge of the garden, which jutted out over a mossy ravine. Below I could see the woods shaking off the night, haze rising like smoke, encircling cedars and pines, flattering the silvery trunks of eucalyptus. Almost none of these trees are natives of the Nilgiris. The British razed the old forests to build their homes and cook their dinners. They imported foreign species to replace them: blue gums and black-woods from Australia and, of course, English oaks. The mountains looked down on them all from a pale sky, appearing and disappearing behind their eternal veils of blue mist.

If my great-grandfather had been on the run, the gossamer beauty of these hills must have given him every reason to stop running. What a wonderful place to hide. He had that much in common with the British, since they were fleeing too—the heat, yes, but also the Indian masses. Up here in the nearly uninhabited wilds, they could mix almost exclusively with their own kind. They could create a compelling forgery of the English countryside, importing sheep to graze uphill of the elephants, stocking mountain streams with fish eggs shipped from Wales, and even pulling off regular fox hunts (albeit with the native jackal standing in for the fox and the occasional maharaja squeezed into jodhpurs). They could almost fool themselves. As India's viceroy Lord Robert Lytton once wrote to his wife, "I affirm it to be a paradise. The afternoon was rainy and the road muddy but such a beautiful *English* rain, such delicious *English* mud."

The hills became a home. A Bombay army lieutenant, Richard Burton, convalescing here in 1851, described Nilgiri society as "extensive and varied . . . among the ladies we have elderlies who enjoy tea and delight in scandal . . . spinsters of every kind . . .

from the little girl in bib and tucker to the full blown Anglo-Indian young lady, who discourses of her papa the colonel, and disdains to look at anything below the rank of a field officer . . . misanthropes and hermits who inhabit out-of-the-way abodes, civilians on the shelf, authors, linguists, oriental students, amateur divines . . . sportsmen, worshippers of Bacchus in numbers, juniors whose glory it is to escort fair dames during evening rides . . . clergymen, priests, missionaries, tavern-keepers, school-masters, and scholars, with *précieux* and *précieuses ridicules* of all descriptions."

Hillsides teeming with idle people, happy for any amusement to punctuate the day—it must have been the perfect destination for a travelling circus. That's what Aunty Julie told my mother forty-six years ago, that her father had come to the Nilgiris in a travelling circus. "A travelling circus? You're sure?" I'd asked my mother. "Not just an itinerant juggler going door to door?" To me it made a big difference in his story. Travelling entertainers, the lone-wolf sort who stopped at palaces and private homes, marched all over India, as they did in many Old World countries. But the travelling circus was a spectacle particular to the nineteenth century. The brainchild of British cavalryman Phillip Astley, it ballooned from modest horse shows with clowns and rope dancers into sprawling rosters of eclectic talent. There were troupes so large they travelled in their own rail cars, pushed and promoted by legendary lords of the rings—America's Phineas T. Barnum and James Bailey—but not just them. In India, a raja's horse master, Vishnupant Chatre, hit the road in 1880 with the first Great Indian Circus, featuring himself as the equestrian headliner and his wife on trapeze. They performed all over India for the British. The age of imperialism had whetted the public appetite for the exotic: Jumbo the African elephant, Japanese fire-eaters, Russian bareback riders, Afghan warriors.

It was possible that a circus company hired my great-grandfather in China. With its rich acrobatic history, China was a recruiting hotspot, and perhaps for jugglers most of all. In 1843

Barnum was reputed to have paid his Chinese juggler Yan Zoo fifteen dollars a week, more than many people earned in a month in New York. Maybe my great-grandfather landed a deal like that, one that took him all the way to the hills of south India, where there were paying crowds and jungles to pilfer of their elephants, tigers and monkeys. Barnum himself once raided the Nilgiris. The route book of P.T. Barnum's Greatest Show on Earth and the Great London Circus for 1884—just two years before John Abraham was christened in Coonoor—includes a list of acts in Barnum's "Ethnological Congress." This was described as "the largest collection of living human curiosities ever gathered together"; along with a Burmese dwarf, other "Distinguished Lilliputians" and high- and low-caste "Hindoos" were "Todas Indians from the Nilgiri Mountains of Southern India."

I half expected the list would lead me straight to a Chinese juggler named Chu. But the only mention of a Chinese member of Barnum's Ethnological Congress that year was a giant named Chang. I felt instinctively that this could not be him—the Abrahams are not tall people.

But who knows? It was possible, as everything seemed to be, and never more than on that crisp morning when we visited St. Anthony's, where the juggler had been reborn while the *kurinji* bloomed.

After I took a morning walk in the mist and ran up a hefty phone bill for the tonic of Jade's voice, Joseph drove us over to St. Anthony's, a handsome white church with blue trim and a red roof. Like everything in Coonoor, it sits on a precipice that overlooks the precipice below. A dozen locals were lined up outside the adjacent office to see the parish priest. He was a young man in a plaid shirt with a typical south Indian name, so many letters and syllables long that we took to calling him Father Alphabet. He laughed loudly at that. Father Alphabet ushered us into his large office, where the walls were papered with oversized calendar pictures of Mary and Jesus and where, by the desk, Father Francis was waiting for us.

He was built like a statue, sturdy and tall in his black shirt and clerical collar, with features that might well inspire a chisel: high cheekbones, full lips and a quiet, observant expression. He had been transferred to Ooty since meeting my father in 1997, but he had made the trip to see us here. My father had spoken of him so often over the years I felt as if I knew him. Father Francis knew about me too, and that I, like my father, had taken up the hunt for John Abraham. He understood why the mysteries of our ancestry would lure me here when my family had moved so far away from its roots. The distance alone would make anyone curious, he said. But it was not this way for hill people like himself, who had never left.

Father Alphabet retrieved the church record books from the 1800s and we opened them on his desk, turning the pages to John Abraham's baptism in 1886. My father had already recorded the details, but I wanted to see the entries for myself. I hovered over them, jotting details in my notepad while Father Francis explained how Christian missionaries had rained down like a monsoon on nineteenth-century India, giving Indians Christianity and Christian names.

Christianity was an especially easy sell among India's lowest castes. Missionaries often fed and sheltered them and taught them how to farm, and they often viewed conversion as relief from the heavy thumb of the Hindu caste system. The priest who christened my grandfather, Father Jacques-Denis Peyramale, was a member of the Paris Foreign Mission Society and a famously pious family. His first cousin Dominique was the priest who ministered to the young Bernadette Soubirous in Lourdes, France, during her visions of the Virgin Mary, and who raised one of Catholicism's most celebrated churches and shrines. His cousin in Coonoor left a more modest legacy: a Catholic school, a convent, and a hill full of converts.

It was presumably Father Peyramale who had filled out the baptismal register, and whose handwriting was only slightly more legible than a doctor's prescription. "What does this mean?" I asked, pointing at an unrecognizable word written under the column denoting caste or occupation. "It looks like *churumba* or *churumber*. What is that?"

Both priests bent down for a closer look, and then Father Alphabet shot back up. "Not *churumber*, Kurumba!" he said excitedly, adding something in Tamil to Father Francis.

"Ya, ya, Kurumba," Father Francis said.

After a lengthy exchange in Tamil with Father Francis, Father Alphabet confirmed. "There is no Tamil word *churumber* with a *ch*. There is only the word Kurumba, with a K."

"When I first saw it, someone told me it meant 'honey collector,'" my father said.

"Yes," said Father Alphabet. "*Kurumba* means 'tribal,' which means the native peoples, and they are honey collectors."

"The Kurumba are tribes of these Nilgiris—the natives," Father Francis added. "Even now there are Kurumbas in these hills."

"But why would a tribe be listed as our great-grandfather's caste or profession?" I asked.

"No, I think what it means . . . . He came here and he mingled with us," said Father Alphabet. "The Chinaman mingled with the tribespeople here and settled here."

"Maybe he collected honey with them," Father Francis said. "In the Nilgiris this is a very dangerous job. The hives are very high up in the mountains—from the cliffs they hang down."

"Do you think his wife could have been of the Kurumba tribe?" I asked.

Father Francis thought this was possible, but her name was Mariamal—a very common Tamil, not tribal, name, he said, meaning "Mary." But a lot of tribal people took a Tamil name, said Father Alphabet, particularly when they converted. Especially, they agreed, a name like Mary.

Why did we know even less about the juggler's wife than about the juggler? My father had never even heard his grandmother's name until he found it in these record books. Was she the Indian grandmother that our relative did not want to discuss? A tribal woman? Kurumba?

While everyone else hashed out the possibilities, I flipped again through the ledgers in search of details we might have missed about her. In the record of her marriage to John Abraham, age forty, the "Chinaman carpenter," she was listed as being seventeen and a spinster. Over the next fifteen years she and John Abraham had at least six children together, but Arokiam was the only child with a non-Anglo name. Perhaps, the priests thought, this was in keeping with the Tamil tradition of naming the first-born male after a grandfather, who presumably had been Mariamal's father.

John Abraham's profession was noted with every baptism. Whatever else he is said to have done for a living, he was always listed as a carpenter, even an "artisan Chinaman carpenter." If he did build, he must have had steady work during the British-led construction boom, but it was odd that Julie never mentioned his woodworking, only his glassware, his candied peel and his juggling. The final mention of my grandparents in the records appeared on December 14, 1907, when Mariamal, the "wife of John Chinese," died of a cold. She was thirty-five.

A few things about that entry haunted me: how young she was when she died; that after mothering six children, a "cold" killed her; that she was identified only as the wife of John Chinese, as if that fact alone distinguished her existence. I felt a pang of guilt as I realized that was what she had been to me all these years— nothing more than the juggler's wife. I had never seen my great-grandmother as a mystery in her own right. Even in my grade-school essay she was merely a pretty face in the circus crowd.

I knew the chances of learning anything else about Mariamal from the ledgers were as remote as these hills. I wasn't the first family researcher to hit the gender wall; like world history, family histories have traditionally been told along male lines, through the men who headed the households, held the property, fought the wars, sailed the ships. Women are relatively absent in historical paper trails. Women too rarely wrote wills or paid taxes, joined the military or owned property. More often they themselves were considered property.

There's an irony to this, in that humans as a species have more female than male ancestors. While it takes two to procreate, through human history more women than men—by some estimates twice as many—actually did procreate. Many men simply died before they had a chance to try; they were busy going about the risky business of hunting and fighting wars and sailing ships into the beyond. The fraction of men who did reproduce often did so with more than one woman, perhaps because one wife had died in childbirth and they took another, or maybe they were just greedy and had harems of eight hundred, like Jahangir. Regardless, they added more women ancestors to the collective family tree.

The robust longevity of female lines shows up in our mitochondiral DNA, which dates back, through an unbroken chain of mothers, to that genetic Eve of about 200,000 years ago. The Y tells a much shorter story, reaching back to the genetic Adam, who lived an estimated 80,000 to 130,000 years ago.

Unfortunately, as a tool to unearth recent history, mtDNA is a fairly blunt instrument. Its code mutates more quickly than the one-letter SNP typos that are used to define the world's ancient history and haplogroups on the Y chromosome. But it does not change as quickly as the Y's handy stretches of repeated code, the STR markers. Anthropologists are big fans of mtDNA for investigating "deep history," mining its molecules in men and women to reconstruct relationships between populations over great leaps of time. But for family historians trying to confirm relationships between people, its utility at the moment is limited.

It cannot reveal with certainty whether two siblings shared the same mother, only that they did not. Even two people with perfectly matching mtDNA will know only that they are descended from the same female ancestor, but she might have been around five years ago or five hundred years ago. Tracking the Y also offers the added bonus of having a surname that generally follows its descent through the generations. Find men with the same surname and you can prove their relatedness with a Y-chromosome test. Through most of Western history, however, a woman's surname changed when she married, making it much more difficult to track a maternal line by either record book or biology. My great-grandmother's maiden surname never appeared in the record books at all, if she actually had one. Not all south Indians did—particularly, I would think, if they came from an ancient honey-collecting tribe in the Nilgiris.

As we drove off from St. Anthony's later that afternoon, I wondered if Mariamal's mitochondrial DNA would connect her to the Kurumbas. Was their tribal matriarch different from the maternal line shared by most Indians? Who was still alive that carried Mariamal's, that I might test it? Not my father—he inherited his mtDNA from his mother. Papa Albert, my father's father, had inherited his from Mariamal, but it ended with him when he died in 1978. That great old centenarian Aunty Flo, who had no children, also took hers to the grave. Not knowing what had happened to Mariamal's mysterious other daughters, Mary and Annie, I was left only with the descendants of Aunty Julie, the eldest daughter, who had raised my grandfather.

Julie and her husband had six children, four sons and two daughters, none of whom were still alive. That meant my only hope of finding a sample of Mariamal's mtDNA rested with the children of Julie's daughters. One of these daughters was Bulah, who according to my mother married but had a rheumatic heart and died during the delivery of their first and only child, a daughter named Marion. As it turned out, Julie took on yet another child and raised Marion. My mother reminded me that I had seen Marion's picture. It was in the red tartan bag, in the package of black-and-whites from my parents' 1958 trip. Marion was a child then, as my brothers were, maybe five or six, with ankle socks and a bow in her hair. She is standing between my brothers, in front of Julie and my parents, looking sullenly at the camera, right here in these hills.

"So where is Marion now?" I asked my parents.

They didn't know. They weren't sure anyone did.

My parents flanking Aunty Julie in her garden in 1958. In the front row, Marion stands between Kevin (left) and Conrad, who had bumped his forehead in the car on the way up the mountains.

With all the talk of tribes that morning, I nearly forgot about the tea. But you can't forget the tea for long in Coonoor. It surrounds the town, cascading down the mountainsides onto terraced plantations of emerald green. My father always suspected that his grandmother had been a local tea picker. He's not sure how he came by the impression, but whenever we make Nilgiri tea back home, it's always steeped in the fanciful notion that we are brewing an ancestral crop.

The success of Nilgiri's nineteenth-century tea crops brought an unquenchable demand for labourers to pick it. Tea producers in China once trained monkeys to do the work. In India, in the Nilgiris, it was always women, and still is; their slender fingers are thought to be best suited to the task.

Dinesh Kumar, the son of a family friend, runs the Bengorm tea estate above Coonoor, and we took an ear-popping drive further up the mountains to see him that afternoon. He was waiting outside the estate's expansive bungalow in a ball cap and windbreaker to show us around the crops. We followed him down the road behind the house, where the tea grows in bushes, dense rows of irregular shapes fitting together like a dazzling jigsaw puzzle that goes on for acres, interrupted only by asphalt ribbons and the odd jacaranda tree. The armies of women who are hired to pluck it wrap their heads in brightly coloured scarves, just as they did in my great-grandparents' day. They wade chest-deep between the shrubs, removing the waxy upper leaves with a swift flick of the wrist and toss them into large burlap sacks slung over their backs, all in one fast, fluid motion. The top of each plant appears so perfectly flat it seems unfathomable that it was harvested by anything other than a blade. Dinesh looks out on this manicured geometry every morning while he does his five hundred jumping jacks on the back veranda. His wife and two children live in town and Dinesh sees them only on weekends; the rest of the time he lives here on the estate along with the tea pickers, who live in cottages nearby with their families.

We learned much about tea that afternoon, that each plant lives about ninety years and has roots that reach down six metres, and that tea grows quickest with the May rains. But it was what Dinesh said about the pickers that stuck with me. Many, he said, are women of the Nilgiri tribes, as they always have been.

We left Coonoor for Ooty the next day, found rooms at the Holiday Inn and drove over to the cathedral to meet Father Francis and, it turned out, his entourage. There was Charles, his assistant, who made the priest's appointments and his lunches; and George, a young local contractor who turned the priest's many charitable ventures into bricks and mortar; and sweet Father Vincent, just twenty-three and yet to earn the stripes of his own parish, who said off-hour Masses and zoomed around the hills on a motorcycle with "only God as his helmet."

We sat around the large kitchen table in the rectory, talking again about this business with the Kurumbas and the tribes. Father Francis felt we had to see the Kurumbas for ourselves, convinced that once we saw how African they looked we would know there was no familial relationship. "They are looking like they have the Negro features," he said. "If your grandmother or grandfather was Kurumba you would see it in your daddy."

Would we? The genome is like a thick deck of cards, and the further back the ancestor, the fewer cards he or she contributes to the deck. I had never picked out Chinese features in my father, but I had seen them in Papa Albert. Father Francis was certain of his theory, however, so we took off en masse deep into the hills to test it.

The Kurumba reserve is nearly invisible from the roadway, a tiny village of tin-roofed huts around a courtyard of concrete, fenced off by a high wire perimeter fence that keeps the jungle out. Children came rushing from all corners as we climbed out of our cars, boys wearing shorts and polo shirts and girls dressed like cupcakes in frothy synthetic frocks, as if they had been waiting all afternoon for a party to start. They giggled shyly and kept their enormous dark eyes trained on their feet until they saw Stephen, tall and white, and his video camera; then they took turns waving in front of it. No one appeared to speak English. There was a lot of nodding and smiling and hand gestures.

Unprompted, the children assembled in a semicircle. After some half-broken exchange of words, Father Francis announced they were going to sing for us. And they did—in high, sweet voices in a tongue we'd never heard. We dug in our bags for something to offer in thanks, but came up with only a few pens and a protein bar, which they took happily and ran off delighted.

If this band of Kurumbas was descended directly from Africans, nothing about their appearance suggested it. Even Father Francis was surprised. "They are looking like Indians," he said.

I visited the Nilgiri library that afternoon, in a downpour of cold English rain. It was another portal to the past, all its colonial trappings intact: plush old velvet curtains, Victorian mouldings, heavy bookcases that stretched to high ceilings, bearing leather-bound volumes and rare first editions. In one corner was a grand wingback chair where an elderly English man in a tweed jacket was hidden behind a copy of *The Independent*.

I settled in at a long mahogany table with memoirs and travelogues of the nineteenth century that convinced me we had at least read the church record correctly. *Kurumba* was often spelled with a C in those days, as *Curumber* and *Cooroombah*. They are one of about half a dozen noted tribes in the Nilgiris, the best known being the buffalo-worshipping Todas. With their surprisingly fair skin and storied descent from a mysterious Scythian community of Iranians, Todas are said to be the most studied tribal group in the world. Even the Prince of Wales came to check them out when he visited India in the 1870s. The anthropologists who led the tour had tried to coax the Todas out of their huts by telling them the prince was a very wealthy and important warrior, with many houses and many soldiers. Yes, the Todas had responded, but how many buffalo does he have?

The Kurumbas distinguished themselves by being the most mysterious of the Nilgiri tribes, beguiling tricksters of the woods. The name itself may come from *kurumbo*, the Tamil term for mischief. "Shy woodsmen and sorcerers who kept to their old ways . . . deep in their jungle home," according to a 1968 National Geographic publication called *Vanishing Peoples of the Earth*. They lived off what they could forage or grow, wove baskets, painted bright landscapes on the walls of crude temples, cremated their dead and worshipped the ghosts of their ancestors. But it was their use of magic that fascinated and frightened other tribes and foreigners: their charms and incantations to treat the sick, their exorcisms, their uncanny ability to tame wild beasts, the elephant especially. This impressed the British, who relied on elephants to help clear the old forests for their tea plantations.

Like many indigenous peoples, the Kurumbas' way of life fell prey to modernization. Deforestation and tea cultivation forced them from their woodland homes and into poverty. Collecting and selling honey became one of their more lucrative ventures; no other tribe is as well known for besting the dreaded rock bee, and the Kurumba name became synonymous with it. They often reached the cliffside hives by climbing forest vines twisted into long rope ladders, one end tied to a tree or rock above, the other held fast down below as the man made his treacherous ascent. One comb could yield as much as forty kilos of honey. Traditionally the Kurumbas worked in teams of two or three, often the husband and brother of one woman, insurance that both men had every incentive to make sure the other returned alive.

Had my great-grandfather worked in such a trio? Did he disappear into these woods fleeing a murder charge, and then the circus, to hide and collect honey with the Kurumbas? It strained credulity to think the tribe would have admitted an outsider to its ranks, let alone one as foreign as a Chinese circus juggler. But maybe it was his alien status that bonded them, or maybe he'd already met Mariamal in town and she introduced him to her people, and also to the church where they were married nine days after his conversion.

We dined on speculation that last night in the Nilgiris, over masala fish and Kingfishers with Father Francis and his friends. Somehow it was my mother's ancestry in India that came to dominate the conversation. Her mother, Nana Gladys, was born in south India, about five hours east of the Nilgiris, in Trichy. The city's official name is Tiruchirappalli, but for a mouthful of reasons people rarely call it that.

Father Francis started it. He asked if we planned to head there next. He wanted to join us, he said, to help access any church records we might need. Stephen was hesitant—five hours to Trichy and then nine hours back to Kochi, where I still had to meet up with Gladwyn and collect the DNA sample he'd promised. And of course we had a plane to catch in three days.

How sad, my mother said, to come all this way and not stand in the church where her mother was baptized. She admitted that she knew nothing of the city, how long her mother had lived there, whether the family had any significant history there. Still, it was a shame to be so close and not at least see her mother's birthplace.

My father agreed. My mother had been a good sport while we'd been consumed with tracking his side of the family. We ought to go, he said.

I saw that my mother could be persuaded to skip Trichy, but I could also see the bruise it would leave, that we had been so close to her mother's birthplace but never visited. I understood her desire. She wanted a sense of the place, to see it, to breathe it in. That's what had brought me to the Nilgiris and what had brought my father to these hills in 1958, when he had a young family to pack up and move to England.

I looked at Stephen. He was worried about the time the trip would take, but his sense of place, of origin, ran as deep as any tea root. The day we got married in Ontario, his father had reached out from the pew and pressed a fistful of Alberta grain into his palm. It was a symbol of growth, of reaping what you sow, and also the late harvest that had held up our wedding. But the wheat from their fields was also a powerful symbol of place and history, the earth he came from. That he understood completely.

Trichy was an instant reminder that we'd spent most of our trip shielded by the serenity of the Indian countryside. Sitting on the banks of the Kaveri River, it is a sprawling ancient urban centre that pulses with people and traffic. We'd been there less than fifteen minutes when we lost sight of Father Francis's bronze Ambassador, and our bearings. Stopping to ask for directions to the cathederal, where we were sure we'd find him again, we spotted a faded old sign pointing the way to the Railway Colony. My mother got out of the car. "Nana's family must have lived here," she said, walking off to see if there was anything left of the place.

After Madras, Trichy was the most important city in the south under the Raj, and once home to a large Anglo-Indian community. At St. Mary's Cathedral we discovered that Anglo-Indians had been buried in their own cemetery, and all the church records related to them were kept in separate ledgers. It took no time to pinpoint my grandmother's christening in the record books, where we also happened across pages of Rouses—not one or two, but dozens.

"See there," my father said to Stephen. "We come all this way and we find your relatives."

"Great," I said, "so long as they're not related to *our* relatives."

It was too hot to walk far in Trichy that afternoon. Even blinking felt arduous. The locals stood under sun umbrellas and kept to the shady side of the street. Yet Father Francis, a native of the cool hills, seemed oblivious to the temperature. Even as the perspiration sparkled at his temples and rolled down his face, he was keen to stop and buy bananas. The others had gone off to shop and explore, so I strolled with him over to a fruit stall, where the vendor held up a small bunch. Father Francis took one, turned it over in his hands and peeled back its skin. He broke off an inch of its creamy flesh, slipped it into his mouth and chewed slowly. Watching his jaw move up and down in the heat was slightly hypnotic.

Finally he swallowed, nodded and handed a few rupees to the vendor, who passed him the whole bunch. We began to walk again.

"So what do you think about your ancestors?" he said. "You think your great-grandpa was Kurumba, or your grandma?"

I told him I didn't know what to think. But I suspected the church record meant something, that he'd had some connection to the Kurumbas. From what we knew, he was at home in the hills, making a living from what he foraged, and maybe he had somehow learned some of that from tribespeople. I asked Father Francis if he found it odd that any of us should care at all about a great-grandfather who had abandoned his children.

"What else could he do? He had to leave," he said.

"Why?" I asked, astonished.

As a widower he would have wanted his children to be educated, he explained. But with no one but him to look after them, he could not go to work to earn the money to send them to school. "If he left, he knew the Church would take them in as orphans and educate them."

"Was that how it went?" I asked. "The Church only provided an education if both parents were gone?"

Usually, he said, that was the case.

"If that's true, it must have been an awful decision he had to make," I said.

"Very hard, yes."

The priest's explanation rang true when I recalled stories about my grandmother pleading with Church officials to reduce tuition fees so she should keep all her children in school. The priests had agreed, so long as her children made the honour roll. My father never lost the sense that marks could make you or break you.

I had never thought of the juggler that way, as a practical man who left so his children might have a chance at a better life. It would explain why Julie never had a bad word to say about him after he disappeared. It also cast him as a relentless slave to pragmatism, that he would do what he had to do to achieve his ends. In that way, my father—who would take a shot of amoebic dysentery to get shore leave, send his new and pregnant wife home to India alone, and embrace genetic ancestry testing from the get-go—would seem to possess a streak of the juggler.

We ended the day at one of the oldest rocks on the planet, Trichy's famous Rock Fort Temple, a massive, mystical boulder that dates back more than three billion years. No one can say what evolution it has witnessed, but people have long revered its proportions and secret perspectives. By the seventh century two Hindu temples had been carved into its interior. One is devoted to the supreme god Shiva, destroyer of the universe and the ego, the other to the elephant-headed Ganesh, lord of beginnings and deity of wisdom, pushing the faithful to see beyond the physical form to the spiritual. It was fitting that we ended up there when I now had all my hopes pinned on the physical—the testable, collectible genes of my ancestors—to answer the metaphysical questions of origin and existence.

The shrine to Ganesh sits on top of the rock, which stands as tall as any cathedral spire. The only way to reach it is to climb, barefoot, up its steep and well-worn 370 steps. My parents took a pass to bargain hunt with Father Francis in the bustling bazaar at the rock's base. Stephen, Charles and I made our way up the cool stone stairs with the temple crowd. When we finally reached the entrance to the shrine, it was dark inside. At first I couldn't make out the creature in the shadows. Once my eyes adjusted, I could see that it was a live elephant, handsome as far as elephants go—even, I imagined, without the pink jewels and swirls painted above its eyes.

"Go," Charles said, nudging me forward. "Go, take the blessing."

I wasn't surprised that the assistant to a Catholic priest was urging me to take part in a Hindu blessing. Religious divides seemed irrelevant inside a rock crammed with every stripe of humanity, and the next thing I knew I was kneeling before the massive animal, staring at its toes while its powerful trunk found the top of my head. I felt a gust of breath and then a soft, firm tap on my crown and the damp spray of a snort.

Anyone can receive the blessing of the temple pachyderm for a few rupees, which the elephants are trained to collect with their trunks. It's nearly as common as incense in south India. But at the end of that long day, near the end of a journey I once said I'd never make, in search of some connection to an ancestry we'd never known, it meant something to take part in that ancient Hindu ritual. It may have been a sacred rite to long-forgotten ancestors, before we, like so much of the world, split from our tribes and our gods. The symbolism of the act was powerful to me all the same, maybe even spiritual on some indefinable level—to feel small and vulnerable inside this big, timeless rock, on my knees before a beast that could crush me with a sneeze—the six-tonne pet of the Kurumbas; the workhorse of the British; an icon of wisdom, memory, India and, of course, the circus.

8

HIC SUNT DRACONES

I t was in my inbox the night we landed back in Toronto. Sandwiched between a joke about what women *really* want and a bulk offer of Viagra, I found my father's Y-chromosome test results. After years of speculating about the possibility of Chinese ancestry, it was now, apparently, mere clicks away. I followed the message prompts to a screen that read: "Dudley . . . Welcome to your Family Tree DNA personal page."

The greeting led to a series of options for viewing my father's results—by the actual markers tested, by close genetic matches or by haplogroup. Haplogroups are not usually a huge draw for genealogists, since they say more about a man's deep roots than his recent history, but there was nothing I wanted to know more. Confirming my father's Y-chromosome haplogroup could confirm (or overturn) what we'd read in the church records in Coonoor and what I as a child had seen in the features of my grandfather.

Haplogroups reflect the genetic trail early humans left behind as they departed Africa and fanned out around the globe. The precise origins and path of each group are still a matter of intense research, and opinions evolve as scientists uncover new Y mutations. But what seems well established is where in the world each haplogroup ended up.

Scientists of the international Y Chromosome Consortium have named each major haplogroup after a letter of the alphabet.

Haplogroups A and B, for example, are the oldest; they are found almost exclusively in Africa, the cradle of humanity and home to the genetic Adam, the man from whom all men alive today are believed to be descended. Haplogroup C seems to have emerged relatively soon after the first modern humans left Africa, migrating along the Arabian Peninsula and into India. It is one of the signature Ys of the subcontinent, but it spread far and wide from there, so that today it can also be found in Australia, Southeast Asia, East Asia and the Americas. Group D is thought to have sprung up in Asia some sixty thousand years ago; its subgroups appear today in men of Tibet, Japan and the Andaman Islands, and in about 10 percent of Thai males.

Haplogroup E is prevalent in sub-Saharan Africa and among descendants of those brought as slaves to Europe and the Americas. F is the group that corresponds to the second great migration out of Africa; the largest haplogroup in the world, its founding father is thought to be the super-granddaddy to nearly all the world's non-African men. Then there's G, common in the Caucasus region, but with a reach that extends from southern portions of Russia and Ukraine and down into the Middle East, and H, prevalent in India but also popping up in Kurdish men, Syrians and Serbians. On it goes through the millennia to M, a genetic fixture among men in Southeast Asia, and the confusing N, present in East Asia but also Finland, with its origins still being debated.

Then there is O, the dominant haplogroup of East Asia—and, as I discovered, the haplogroup to which my father's Y chromosome belongs. The best research from the Genographic Project concluded that Haplogroup O is so common in East Asia that a staggering 80 to 90 percent of men in the region belong to it. But in western Asia, Africa, Europe and the Americas, it is practically non-existent.

No one knows exactly where the story of O begins, only that it seems it first appeared somewhere in the region of modern-day

China before the last ice age, about 20,000 years ago. Hemmed in by mountains and ice, the hunter-gatherer ancestors of O moved eastward and at some point along the way a boy was born with a unique blip on his Y chromosome: it was missing a tiny string of genetic code. By virtue of a random copying error, five base pairs—five molecular building blocks—were deleted. Scientists now refer to this as mutation 175 (M175), the genetic hiccup that defines Haplogroup O. Every one of the hundreds of millions of Asian men who carry it, my father among them, is a direct descendant of that prehistoric boy who lived when woolly mammoths still roamed the planet.

Of course, O has a wide reach through East Asia, which might suggest that my great-grandfather could have been Indonesian or Korean, or possibly Japanese. But the lab had gone one step further. Based on my father's markers, they determined that he belonged to a distinct subgroup of Haplogroup O known as O3. The founding father of O3 was a descendant of O born sometime within the past ten thousand years, after his ancestors had wandered further south and east across the continent, spreading their signature Y as they went. As well as the missing code of M175, this boy also carried a new mutation on his Y, a typo that changed a T to a C—now dubbed mutation 122. This was the hallmark of Haplogroup O3, and, as the lab report noted, "one of the main lineages of China."

And there we had it. My father's Y belongs to a main lineage of China, the paternal line of more than 50 percent of all Chinese men. In some areas of the country it's more than 80 percent.

Neither of the mutations associated with O and O3 are known to have any medical implications. They certainly appear to have no ill effect on the ability to reproduce. The prolific patriarch of Haplogroup O3 fathered enough sons, who also fathered enough sons, to leave a legacy of another five hundred generations of sons that now account for more than half the males in the largest population on the planet.

That this one man's Y spread like the wind through what is now China had much to do with timing. Researchers suspect its emergence coincided with the rise of agriculture, that profound turning point in human history when farming triggered an unparalleled festival of procreation. No longer were so many males dragging home bison, dying young and distributing their Y wherever the hunt took them. Now they were settling down, tilling fields, taming livestock, sowing and reaping—both crops and children, who grew up to raise more crops and children—fuelling a fecund cycle that ensured the O_3 Y chromosome would live a long, long life in the region. Men who carry it are generally considered to be descendants of China's first rice or millet farmers.

I couldn't get enough of this. My father's DNA had finally provided proof that my great-grandfather was, that *we are*, that *I am*, in part at least, Chinese. And wasn't that something—that we could follow John Abraham's trail up into the Nilgiri Hills or into the microscopic caverns of a cell swabbed from the inside of my father's cheek, and end up at the same place—China? It's true that the O_3 haplogroup is common in other East Asian countries, and modern men who carry it can of course be found as far away as, well, Mississauga. But on the balance of probabilities, in the context of everything we'd seen, heard, read, my father's biology had substantiated our story, lent a whiff of credence to my grade-school essay and the juggling of tennis balls and my nephew's shiny hair. Oh, I was smitten with the science that jet-lagged morning, pumped up on caffeine and optimism.

It didn't last. My father's Y had confirmed his Chinese roots, but knowing his haplogroup told us sweet nothing about the man John Abraham had been, where in China he was from or why he had left—both his country and his children—or where he had gone. The best genetic hope of piecing that together was to find a man whose Y chromosome closely matched my father's, an unknown relative who might be able to tell us things about the family we never knew. He might be able to reveal our true name, for starters, or which province of China John Abraham was from. Perhaps he'd even heard tales of a long-ago great uncle who fled China in a travelling circus. This man would not only have to share my father's O3 haplogroup—as about, oh, half a billion Chinese men apparently do—he would also have to share my father's haplo*type*. It's a haplotype that has the potential to reveal events of the recent past, since it involves those short tandem repeats, STRs, the kind of mutations that spring up more frequently than SNPs. The number of repeats—known as alleles—can be as specific to the paternal line of a family as a surname.

I had ordered a twelve-marker test on my father's Y, which in 2005 was the commercial standard starting point. It meant the lab would count the alleles at twelve different places along my father's Y chromosome. Each of these places refers to a specific address on the Y chromosome, so it's a bit like taking a neighbourhood census, stopping at a dozen houses and counting how many people live in each one. The numbers in my father's results represented something like digits on a lottery ticket. The question was whether it was a winning ticket: Did anyone else out there share those numbers? Did any other man's Y match my father's twelve markers? I drew a breath and clicked the link to view results by Y–DNA matches.

In the winter of 2006, Family Tree DNA had the Y-chromosome test results of 65,000 men available for comparison. Whenever the lab completes new tests, it cross-references the results to find potential matches in its database. Most people who take the test sign permission forms allowing their name, email address and country of their oldest known male ancestor to be released to men with matching Y chromosomes. But for my father's Y there was not a one—no other Y in the system had the same twelve alleles.

I shouldn't have felt as deflated as I did. I knew it would be a long shot to try to find a relative in a random volunteer database of 65,000 strangers. Nearly a third of the Ys on file at the time belonged to unique haplotypes, meaning they had no matches either. In that light, my dad's Y was just one of 19,000 lonely Y signatures in the database.

There was hope. Exploring the report about my father's recent ancestral origins revealed that four men in the database had Y chromosomes with ten out of twelve markers in common with my father's. One man was from China, another from Tajikistan and two from Taiwan. But all four were listed anonymously: no family names, no email addresses, no notes on their ancestry—all details I had submitted with my father's DNA. Why had these four men declined to be contacted? Perhaps if I increased my father's testing to analyze twenty-five markers, or even thirty-seven or sixty-seven—which the company had begun to offer—one of them would prove to be an even closer match, which might tempt him out of hiding. Could testing more markers reveal one of them to be a cousin after all, even if they had failed to match perfectly on the first twelve markers tested? I would have to call Bennett Greenspan at Family Tree DNA for answers. But first I had to call my father.

I asked my dad once why he wanted to be Chinese. It was summer and we were in my parents' backyard. My father was roaming about collecting branches to construct a trellis for the runner beans he grows every year. I was picking their mulberry tree, up a ladder with my head in the branches and my mind wandering, thinking about how un-Chinese my father actually is. Aside from having a slight build, he doesn't really look Chinese; he doesn't speak a word of Mandarin or Cantonese and has never expressed an interest in learning the languages. He's a lover of history and geography but I've never known him to be particularly a student of Chinese history. He does have his Chinese friends, takes Chinese medicine from time to time and enjoys Chinese food, even though he is no fan of chopsticks.

And so, that afternoon from up in the tree, I asked. "Hey, Dad, how come you want so badly to be Chinese?"

It was a query out of the blue, such a jarring non sequitur that I assumed it would take at least a moment to process. But my father answered instantly. "They were a people," he said.

"A people?"

"Yes, they have an identity. We never had that."

When I called with the news about his Y chromosome, my father laughed in a way that made him sound younger, energized. "Oh boy, this is wonderful," he said. "Wonderful! I'm absolutely delighted." I wished I'd driven over to deliver the news in person, but I could imagine the look on his face.

It wasn't so much that belonging to a Chinese haplogroup was unexpected—at that point, finding out that he *didn't* carry a Chinese Y chromosome would have been the real shock. But the scientific confirmation, the power of his own biology to reveal a truth he had so long suspected, had a profound effect on my father. Some weeks later, he put his thoughts on paper in a letter to me.

When you told me that science had proven that my Y had been traced to China—a rush of emotions held me captive—elation, relief, vindication, emancipation.

Yes, emancipation—from doubts of my paternal heritage, and relief—it explains the uncanny affinity I have always felt to the Chinese kin and culture.

My mind was awash with recollections stemming from this science-based authenticity.

I thought of my childhood in Jubilee Building in Bombay, a walled compound housing mainly Anglo-Indians and Eurasians. I used to ask Mum why the aunts had called Dad a Chinaman, but she did not reply. My father would never be drawn out. . . . When my youngest brother Mark was born, his features indicated Chinese. Still Mum would say nothing. I always asked her about it—how much did she know? Not much I presumed. I would take Mark out in the pram for walks and face questions on his Chinese features. I was a teenager at the time and my proud reply would be that I was taking the son of the Chinese Emperor out for a walk. In those days, I was watching a serial every Saturday at the local cinema with Flash Gordon and Ming, who was the evil Chinese genius endeavouring to kill my hero. That's all I knew of China then and the mystery only deepened as no further information was forthcoming from anyone in sight.

Now we know. We are Chinese. My grandfather was Chinese. Though it only makes me question more so, why do we keep (should we keep?) the name Abraham? We now have a justifiable claim on the name Chu. I have even discussed it with Mum, changing the name, aligning our identity with the evidence in our bloodline. Mum said it was a nice idea, but too complicated now. She said, "Why? We are all happy with children and the children have children now. . . ." So now I just hope to be back one day in the province my grandfather hailed from and that maybe the scientific way will lead me there.

I had no idea how keen my father would be to adopt our original Chinese surname until after I read his letter. By 2006 the Abraham name had been his for eighty-one years, and our family's through five generations and counting—more than a century. At what point does a reinvention become the real deal? And just how real was the Chinese name we saw in the record books? Even if we assumed that a fugitive would give his true name, what was written there by the French priest was unclear. Was it Chu, Atchu or Atchoi? More than half a dozen different Chinese surnames, represented by different Chinese characters, could also sound like "Chu." I'd read up on some of them in the ancient Chinese text *The Hundred Family Surnames.* Over a thousand years old, the index ranks Chu eleventh out of more than five hundred common surnames in the country. If my great-grandfather didn't carry the Chinese equivalent of Smith, it was something close to it. Yet as my father saw it, taking a Chinese name would mean staking a powerful and public claim to the kind of cultural identity he'd never had.

But what surprised me most about my father's letter was the heaviness I felt after I read it. As wonderful as it was to have been able to present him with this small gift of ancestral knowledge, I suddenly felt the burden of his expectations. My father hadn't intended this, of course, but reading about his "elation" on the heels of a genetic test made me worry that I, or the mere prospect of this new science, had raised his hopes too high. I was struggling to keep my own in check, and my father, in what he often describes as his "bonus years," had a lifelong dream hanging in the balance.

Days passed and turned into weeks, and weeks into months. Except for the four anonymous men, the lab turned up no more matches, not a single one. Impatience festered into a glum funk. I moped around the house like a lovesick teenager waiting for the phone to ring. That there should be not a single match for my father's Y—a measly twelve-marker doppelgänger for a chromosome that apparently originated in China, the most populated country on earth—seemed especially cruel. Bennett Greenspan could hear it in my voice.

"I think I've hit a dead end," I told him when we next spoke. "Could it be that my father might have matches, or closer matches, if more or different markers were tested and compared?"

"No," he said. "There's no reason to test at a higher resolution at this point." Each marker on the Y chromosome mutates at a different rate, he explained, and the twelve markers used in the test are among those known to mutate most quickly. In that way they're valuable in helping to connect two men within a recent time frame. So without a match at twelve markers it would be pointless to test more, unless there was another man to compare more markers with. "See?" he said. "You can't accuse me of trying to upsell you!"

The only thing I could do was be patient, he added, and wait—wait for more people to be tested, wait for the database to grow, wait for a match. He realized it could be frustrating. Here he was, the founder of this genetic genealogy company, eager to learn about his paternal history and the origins of his Greenspan line, he said, and he had no matches either. Bennett had collected the DNA of nearly four dozen men named Greenspan or variations such as Greenspon and Greenspun. He'd found that several of these men had Ys that matched some of the others—three distinct Greenspan lines, in fact—but none of them matched his own. He'd begun to suspect that his grandfather was not actually a Greenspan at all. "Perhaps he changed his name at some point," he said. "I've never been able to find my great-grandfather's name on ship passenger lists."

I told him we didn't have a solid surname to track with my father's Y, only that church records suggested it was some variation of Chu. Then I asked him about the four men in the database who had ten markers in common with my father, the men from China, Taiwan and Tajikistan. Could I learn their last names and perhaps see if they would be open to further testing for comparison?

But Bennett said that wouldn't be possible. The DNA from those men had been collected during research field trips that Michael Hammer of the University of Arizona had made with his team to Asia. They were anonymous participants in anthropological studies, he said, which is why they had no ancestral profiles or contact information. "What's your father's haplogroup?" he asked.

"O3."

"Oh," he groaned. "There are very few samples from Asia." Most of the DNA in the system was from North Americans with European ancestors who had immigrated a few hundred years ago, he said, folks wanting to go back across the pond to discover their roots in the Old Country—England, Ireland, Scotland, Germany, France. "They're the ones who have really taken this up with fervour," he added. "There's a man named Bailey who is on a mission to test every Bailey he can find. Genetic genealogy is a western European sport."

That phrase stuck with me long after we hung up—a *western*

European sport. I took it as Bennett's attempt to lower my expectations as diplomatically as he could. In other words, if genetic genealogy takes as long as golf to catch on in China, I could be waiting the rest of my life for a matching Mr. Chu, and almost certainly for the rest of my father's.

On old maps of the world, medieval cartographers often drew images of serpents and other mythical creatures to label distant, unexplored territories. But on the beautiful copper Lenox Globe, crafted in France in the sixteenth century and housed at the New York Public Library, the words HIC SUNT DRACONES appear, a Latin sentence famously translated as "Here be dragons." The words are etched near the coast of East Asia, a warning as much as a confession that what lies here lies beyond the boundary of knowledge— an uncharted land. Genetically speaking, the East is still a lot like that: from the Western perspective, *terra incognita.*

The effect has been most pronounced in matters of medicine. Several studies have found that many Western drugs don't work the same way, if at all, in East Asians, particularly heart-related drugs. In 2002 the Japanese government passed a law that allows drug companies to sell their products in Japan only if they have been successfully tested on Japanese patients. Just before our trip to India I'd written about new research from China showing that nitroglycerine, one of the oldest and most common heart drugs on the market, likely offers no medicinal benefit for up to half of all East Asians. Doctors have prescribed it for more than a century to relieve the crushing chest pains of an angina attack. But Jin Li, a well-known population geneticist at Fudan University in Shanghai, reported that 30 to 50 percent of East Asians carry a genetic trait that blocks the body's ability to process the drug.

If scientists were just getting to the genetic root of crucial medical distinctions between Asians and Caucasians, how long would it take for genetic genealogy to cross the East–West divide? It occurred to me that Jin Li would be a worthwhile person to ask.

The forty-year-old scientist was then splitting his time between Shanghai and the University of Cincinnati, and also between medical concerns and research on the genetic history of China. He'd recently joined the Genographic Project as its chief investigator of East Asian populations, contributing to the very bank of knowledge that had revealed the history of my father's Y chromosome.

I caught up with Professor Li (or Felix, as he prefers) by phone at his university office in Shanghai on a spring afternoon in 2006. I told him about my mysterious great-grandfather and the results of my father's Y-chromosome test, and lamented that there seemed to be so few East Asian Y chromosomes available for comparison. Was genetic ancestry testing catching on in his country, as it is in the West? I asked him.

"I don't think most Chinese are aware of the possibility of doing it," he said. "But this is something that we are trying to do, to make them aware."

Felix had a thick accent and an even thicker sense of humour. It's not that Chinese families are not interested in genealogy, he stressed—quite the opposite. "Most families have, or had, their genealogy all laid out in a book. In Chinese we call [genealogy] *pu*. But it sounds terrible in English—*pu*! But Chinese love *pu*!" He laughed uproariously.

The histories of many Chinese families disappeared from view after the country's civil wars and the 1960s Cultural Revolution, he said, which aimed to "smash the old world." There were exceptions; some families still had their records of ancestors dating back hundreds and even thousands of years, most famously the descendants of Confucius.

The Confucius family tree is considered one of the oldest in the world. The Confucius Genealogy Compilation Committee was then in the midst of the fifth revision of the 2,500-year-old Kong family tree—Kong being the surname of the famed philosopher, whose rich legacy includes more than three million descendants. The Kong tree was last revised in 1931, and this time, for the first time, the committee had decided to include female descendants along its branches. Felix hoped they would soon add genetic testing as well. He was working on a movie, he said, "using a Confucius pedigree as sort of an example to show people how powerful genetic tools can be to identify the ancestry or ancestors of the people." The Beijing Genomics Institute was also stepping up to offer Y-chromosome tests on Kongs for 1,000 yuan, the equivalent of about $125.

Felix said the Chinese are ideally suited to pursue genetic ancestry testing, especially with the Y chromosome, since the Chinese have used surnames for so long. In Europe, surnames emerged around the twelfth century; by then China's book of common surnames was already two centuries old. Being able to wed an ancient surname with a Y chromosome offers the chance to piece together an unparalleled early history of China's population. What's more, Chinese families rarely changed their names. "To do so would have been an insult to an ancestor," Felix said. *Unless*, I thought, *they were on the run from a murder charge or decided to convert to a Western religion.*

For the most part, Felix said, people changed a surname only if it was similar to the family name of the ruling emperor. As a sign of respect they would adopt another name, and then revert back to their original name when the emperor changed. This happened in Felix's own family. "My last name is Jin, which means 'gold,' and I know that about one thousand years ago my ancestors' last name was Liu. But the emperor's name at that time was [similar] and it would be offending to keep your last name, so you have to change it. Of course, most of the people, after the emperor died, changed back to Liu. Apparently my ancestors were very busy with something else and forgot to do that."

"How do you know what your ancestors were called a thousand years ago?" I asked.

"It's in the Family History Library in Salt Lake City, Utah. I have my genealogy there, or rather they—the Mormons—have my genealogy there. I really appreciate what those Mormons did," he said. They had sent a crew to record the genealogies of China through whatever documents they could find. "The Mormons love *pu* more than anybody!"

Yet, for all the *pu* in China, Felix suspects that genetic ancestry testing will be a tough sell. Genetics is controversial in China, he said, and his work is controversial, clashing as it does with the traditional ideas of what it means to be Chinese. For starters, Chinese culture holds that the Chinese have been a distinct people for some five thousand years. But his research, based on thousands of DNA samples from regions across Asia, suggests the Chinese population emerged much more recently than that. "The Chinese became Chinese probably about two thousand, at most three thousand years before present," he said.

But even more contentious is who contributed genes to that effort. The Chinese have a strong belief, based in part on the skeletal remains of Peking Man, a 750,000-year-old fossil unearthed in 1923, that they evolved into modern humans—from *Homo erectus* to *Homo sapiens*—in their own native corner of East Asia, separate from other populations. But Felix is a leading proponent of the out-of-Africa model, arguing that the genetic record he has studied shows that the Chinese, like the rest of the world, descended from Africa. Based on Y-chromosome studies of thousands of men throughout the region, he concluded that modern humans migrated out of Africa and into Southeast Asia some sixty thousand years ago, and from there they moved into southern China. (East Asia's Haplogroup O3 also carries the telltale mutation of Haplogroup C, considered one of the first migrant groups to leave Africa.)

The Chinese may have evolved with distinctive physical characteristics, but other populations have nonetheless contributed their genes to the mix, Felix said, including Caucasians. DNA samples taken from people in the northern part of China especially, he said, show "a great deal of Caucasian DNA. . . . I was very much surprised, and when it comes to light, I think a lot of people will be surprised." He argues that the Chinese cannot be considered genetically unique. The Han Chinese, the country's largest ethnic group, have traces of "multiple nationalities or ethnic groups . . . *Chinese* is not a genetic entity, it's a cultural entity."

His words made me think of my father. Without any cultural tradition connecting him to China, a single chromosome had proved to be such a powerful link that he wanted to adopt our long-forgotten Chinese surname. Felix was finding that even his fellow scholars had a hard time separating culture from genetic identity. That very morning he had shared his research in a talk he gave to colleagues.

"How did people react?" I asked.

"Not well," he said. "One professor came to me and told me I had just created [the idea] of Chinese hybrids, and that probably would be offending to everybody."

Yet despite these initial reactions, Felix had high hopes that curiosity will drive more Chinese to try genetic genealogy. He had a plan, "a dream," he said, to assemble the entire genetic genealogy of China; he had already, in 2006, analyzed more than twelve thousand Y chromosomes in the country. He was starting to explain that he'd been talking with Mike Hammer and Bennett Greenspan about offering Family Tree DNA testing in China when I realized that Felix already had what I needed: a database teeming with Chinese Y chromosomes.

"Felix, do you think I could send you my father's DNA sample and you might be able to cross-reference it against the database you have?"

"Yes, I can do that," he said. "But you should send the sample to my office at the University of Cincinnati. If you send it to China, I don't know what the customs people will do with DNA."

With our DNA in the Houston database and my father's Y on its way to Felix's office in Cincinnati, I developed a new relationship with my email account. I have never dated by Internet, but I imagine it feels a lot like the months that followed: waiting for a compatible prospect to appear in the inbox, a man with all the right alleles. Late one night in the summer of 2006, as I was on my way to bed, the message landed, its subject line reading: "Y-DNA 12 Test Match 12 for 12." Suddenly I was wide awake.

> An exact 12 marker match has been found between you and another person in the Family Tree DNA database. You and the other person match in all 12 loci. If you share the same surname or variant, this means that there is a 99% likelihood that you share a common ancestor in a genealogical time frame. If you match another person without the same surname or variant, you still probably share a common ancestor, but this ancestor most likely lived in the time before surnames were adopted.

The match was not with my father's Y chromosome but with the sample I had collected from Gladwyn deCouto, my father's honky-tonk-loving, motorbike-riding cousin in Kochi. When I took Gladwyn's DNA sample, I was wondering if the deCouto Y chromosome he carries might biologically point the way back to Portugal. That this first match was not with my father's Y but with the paternal line of his mother didn't matter much to me at that point. Even after my conversation with Felix, I had been losing faith in the whole process, but here was proof, in principle at least, that it was possible to find someone in the world with a Y chromosome that looked like one of ours. His name was James Theodore List. He had provided an email address and reported that his oldest known male ancestor came from Germany.

Gladwyn also had nine out of twelve matches with two other men of German ancestry, and also with men from Hungary, Ukraine, India, Mongolia, the United Kingdom and Indonesia. Men from Lithuania, Belarus, Israel, Italy, Kazakhstan and Uzbekistan had turned up with eight markers in common. The founding father of the deCouto Y had apparently left a wide legacy. The lab pegged it as belonging to Haplogroup J2, a male line that emerged somewhere between four thousand and nineteen thousand years ago in the northern portion of the Fertile Crescent. This man's male descendants then followed the spread of agriculture through the Middle East, around the Mediterranean, into south-eastern Europe and West Asia, and also south into India, seeding their Y wherever they went.

Some research suggests that J2 is the haplogroup of a third of Sephardic Jews and nearly a quarter of Ashkenazi Jews. In fact, many of the Y chromosomes of Judaism's high priests, the paternal line of *kohens*—the ancestral line that launched the age of genetic genealogy—are also members of J2, and some have also been found to be members of J1. (Actually, researchers have found that markers once thought to be exclusive to the *kohanim* can also be found in other populations, and not all of them Jewish.) J2 appears in India almost exclusively as one of the Y haplogroups of upper-caste men. It turns out that J2 is not as prevalent in Portugal as it is in Italy, where about 20 percent or more of men carry this Y type, in the southern regions especially. But J2 still includes about 10 percent of Portuguese men, making it entirely possible that the deCouto Y sailed into Cochin in the cells of a Portuguese explorer, merchant or missionary. How, I wondered, did it fit in with the story of Mr. List?

I drifted off to sleep that night making a mental list of the questions I wanted to ask him, wondering how personal my questions could be to a new-found relative. Was it best to stick to basics—*Where was your grandpa from? When did he leave Germany? Why did he come?* Or would I ask about culture, religion, colour—*Dear Mr. List: Are you brown? Do you like Boney M and spicy food? Buck Owens? Johnnie Walker ... ?*

As it happened, the very next morning, Mr. List made the first move.

```
Greetings,
I am informed by familytreedna.com that
you [Gladwyn deCouto?] and I share an
exact match of 12 DNA markers. I assume
this is a follow-up to the National
Geographic Genomic Program process to
which I subscribed to trace my genetic
heritage. I am very curious about this
match, and would be most interested in
sharing backgrounds. I know the lineage
on my father's side back four generations—
to Bavarians who migrated to Michigan
around 1840. The genomic project says I
share genetic material with southern
Italians, and about 20% of Spaniards.
Please let me know your connections with
the project and any information you think
is relevant.

Jim List
```

Greetings. I loved that, one earthling reaching out to another, linked by our nucleotides. But Bavaria? Michigan? How about Lisbon, or Goa? The company had warned as much: if you don't share the same surname, your common male ancestor likely lived before the advent of surnames, eight hundred years ago or more. The chances of Mr. List and I finding a common forefather were remote.

I wrote back telling Jim List about Gladwyn and my project. I explained that we believed the deCouto line originated in Portugal and that we could trace it back in India four generations, to a Ramon deCouto, born 1840. I told him Gladwyn lives in an old port city on India's southwest coast and that Kochi had always been a magnet for traders, explorers and adventurers.

He was astounded: "Before the DNA analysis, I always assumed my background was pretty one-dimensional on that side. The only hint of a broader gene pool for the family was a vague family story of migration from Hungary to Germany in the Middle Ages." He told me he lives in Maine but that his father and most of his relatives live in Michigan. He said his mother is a Swede from Minnesota, and added, "Now I would really like to know what her mitochondrial DNA would show!" With so much to discuss, we made plans to speak by phone.

A week after I first connected with Jim List, I ran into a surprise guest at my parents' house. Ralph Pereira was in town, a first cousin of my father and the one who had compiled the book on the history of his mother's deCouto line. An affable, adventurous man, a pilot and world traveller, Ralph is tall and still powerfully built for a man of seventy-two. His book had been invaluable when my father and I were combing through the records in Kochi, and I asked him what had made him so keen to compile it.

After his family left India for England in the 1950s, they often faced questions about their heritage, so in an effort to anglicize their identities they changed their name from Pereira to Williams. But with his dark skin, Ralph said, the new name only invited more questions. "Tell them your grandfather was Welsh," his mother would advise. Ralph eventually felt that the entire family was running from its true identity, constructing a reality that hid any traces of India. So he set out to reconnect with his Indo-Portuguese heritage, changed his name back to Pereira, and began his family research.

As we sat down to the lunch of lentils and chili fry my mother had prepared, we realized that we had at least held on to India's cuisine, passed down to all of us by Indian grandmothers whose identities had otherwise been lost. I told him that Dad's mtDNA test result, which I had arranged at the same time as his Y-chromosome test, backed that up. The lab had found that my father's maternal line belongs to Haplogroup M, as I thought it would, M being so ubiquitous in the subcontinent that it can also be found in India's tribes, including the Kurumba people. Even though my father had not inherited his mtDNA from the juggler's wife, his ancient maternal line may well hearken back to the common female ancestor they shared. M represents an unbroken line of mothers that reaches back to the earliest migration out of Africa, some seventy thousand years ago.

I told Ralph that this was his maternal line as well, because he and my father descend from the same maternal grandmother. Telling him, I realized that the genetic tests on my immediate family had personal relevance far beyond it. My father's mtDNA test result was also Ralph's test result. And it occurred to me that whatever I learned of the deCouto Y would be of interest to all the deCoutos. So I told Ralph about the match between the Y chromosome of Gladwyn deCouto and Jim List of Maine. "I have no idea exactly how we are connected," I said. "List's paternal ancestors came from Bavaria, and before that, maybe Hungary."

"Ah, Hungary!" Ralph said instantly. "Well, there it is, then."

"There it is?"

"Yes," he said. "There is a well-known connection between Hungary and India: the gypsies of Romania and Hungary originated in India."

The Roma people appeared mysteriously in eastern Europe about nine centuries ago. People called them "gypsy" from the mistaken belief that their dark hair and skin suggested an Egyptian heritage. But nineteenth-century studies concluded that the Roma language and its many dialects reflect ancient forms of Hindi and

Punjabi; and, as with Indians, the Roma adhere to a strict caste system. Still, some scholars have argued that speaking the language of a particular place or practising some of its customs is not definitive proof that biological roots lie in that place. After all, the nomadic and culturally diverse Roma defy any narrow definition of a population. Without a written account of their history, the question of the Roma's origins had remained unresolved until the genetic record began providing firm answers.

Studies through the 1990s, many of them led by a Bulgarian scientist named Luba Kalaydjieva, show that Europe's eight to ten million ethnically diverse Roma actually descend from a small founding population. Their diseases tell part of the story. Roma suffer high rates of unusual genetic disorders such as spinal muscular atrophy, crippling Charcot-Marie-Tooth disease and a metabolic disorder that makes them prone to cataracts in the first weeks of life. To geneticists these conditions are symptoms of a "founder effect"—evidence that a population has sprung from a relatively small number of individuals, making the mutations they carried more pronounced in their descendants. The effect is exacerbated if the founders' progeny tend to marry among their own, as they do, say, among the Amish, or are geographically isolated, as was the case in Newfoundland and parts of Quebec.

The disease-causing mutations that Roma carry are also prevalent in India, but in few other places in the world. Based on this, and on Y chromosomes and mtDNA samples from more than a thousand Roma and Indian subjects, scientists estimate the founding Roma population left northern India eight hundred to a thousand years ago and may have numbered fewer than a thousand people. Maternally they tend to belong to mtDNA haplogroup M—the same grande dame grouping as my father. About half of all Roma men carry a Y that belongs to Haplogroup H, prevalent among India's lower-caste men and seldom seen in big numbers outside India.

Interestingly, an estimated quarter of Roma men also carry a Y that belongs to J2, the same haplogroup as Gladwyn deCouto of Kochi and Jim List of Maine. Could anything in world history connect those dots? How did a quarter of Roma men end up with a Y chromosome prevalent in the Middle East? One theory suggests that the low-caste forefathers of the Roma people were caught up somehow in the eleventh-century Muslim invasions of the subcontinent. Another suggests that Muslim conquerors captured the Roma's founding population in northern India and took them back home as slaves to the Middle East, from where they eventually made their way into south-eastern Europe, including Hungary, where Roma males with a J2 Y chromosome can still be found.

Could that be the connection between Jim List's family and mine? Did a long-ago male ancestor give rise to one male descendant who made his way into Hungary and another who ended up in Portugal, where he produced a son who would make his way back to India as a mercenary, explorer or missionary? Was it a bloodline connection to an eleventh-century Muslim invader that we shared? The only thing we could say with confidence was that we would never know. Our common ancestor had lived before surnames were invented, making it near to impossible that any paper trail could lead us to him.

Jim List and I finally spoke with each other in June 2006. We'd had a couple of weeks to ponder just how far the genetic family can extend, and it had only made both of us more curious about the other. Jim was fifty-six, the father of two, a biologist with a special interest in nature preserves and coastal research, and he'd always had romantic notions about his heritage. "I thought I detected an epicanthic fold in my eyes," he said, referring to the upper eyelid skin fold usually associated with East Asian populations. "I thought maybe it was my mother's ancestors' wild Viking roaming that brought that into the bloodline."

We laughed and Jim said, "Oh yes, I've had a lot of romantic notions." When he read in a magazine about the National Geographic–IBM effort to trace the genetic history of the world, he decided to take the test. "The first thing I learned was that my ancestry, maybe ten thousand years ago, came from the cradle of civilization in Mesopotamia and we were agricultural—which is a bit of a disappointment."

"What were you hoping for?"

"Well, being a romantic, I wanted to be the line that went straight north [from Africa] to the steppes and became the first ones to tame horses. I guess I had nursed this fable of the Hungarian and the Mongol and the epicanthic fold and all that."

I began to suspect that nursing romantic notions about ancestry ran in the family.

"Now I've been constructing a whole different history," he said, "since I read that I share ancestry with twenty percent of southern Italians and ten percent of Spaniards."

He'd only done the one genetic test, and ours was the only match so far. I asked if he'd shared the news with his family.

"Oh, yeah, I told my mother," he said. "My mom was wary of it. She doesn't understand how one can tell you have the same DNA as someone living one thousand years ago. So she's still curious, but I tried to explain to her the different proteins of the DNA molecule and how they combined and recombined, and the Y chromosome and all of that, but she thought that was still a little far-out."

I asked Jim how much he knew about his Hungarian ancestors, wondering if he'd ever heard of "gypsies" in his bloodline, but he told me he only knew details dating back to 1840, when his great-great-grandfather Johann Adam List arrived in Michigan from Germany. "He came from a community near Nuremberg that decided the Indians needed missionaries. Rather than just sending one or two, they decided to establish a whole community and, through their example and support, to advance the Indians in their spiritual well-being," he said. "But my great-great-grandfather was not a preacher himself; he was a carpenter and an architect, a craftsperson. So they established a farming community. It's one of the larger tourist attractions in Michigan now. They adopted all the building standards, so it's all still very Bavarian."

Our Portuguese ancestors may have gone to India for similar reasons, I said, to spread their culture and Christianity to the Indians of South Asia. But as far as we could tell that was the only common element in our stories—two forefathers who left their homes on a mission to faraway lands—and in all likelihood, we agreed, that's probably all we'd ever know.

"Yeah, well, the Y chromosome is one out of forty-six [of our chromosomes], so it doesn't say a whole lot about your genetic makeup. But it does tell you your shared ancestors—that's still pretty neat. I had never thought, until this, exactly where the family had come from, other than maybe they'd come from Hungary to Germany," he said. "I guess I had never reflected on the fact that they had to get there from Africa somehow, and the idea that I was Mediterranean at one time was a new one."

I decided to ask Jim what he looked like, wondering if any physical feature hinted at the Middle Eastern–Mediterranean ancestry his Y chromosome suggested. He told me he'd been blond as a child, as his sons had been, but all their hair had darkened as they got older. He'd already sent me a picture of himself, he said, and just before we hung up we promised to keep in touch.

The match with Jim List was bittersweet for my father. On one hand he found it fascinating that one family's Y chromosome could match another, entirely unexpected family, but disappointing too, that the Y was not his own, and so did nothing to reveal more about his roots in China.

It was my mother who was most taken by it. She wanted to know all about Jim List, why he'd taken such a test, how he'd felt to learn he had a match with a man in India. Surprised, I told her, just as we'd been to learn we had a distant relative in Maine— Gladwyn, too, when he'd heard by email.

"Family from Germany and Hungary!" my mother said. "That's a new one."

I told her about the picture Jim had emailed, standing next to his son on his graduation day, beaming. He did look slightly swarthy to me, or perhaps just well tanned. He had lost most of his dark hair and if I looked closely I could see the traces of an epicanthic fold. But, I said, I'd never pick him out for a relation.

The match was just a shred of shared genetic code, but its significance for me was much greater than that. Our pursuit of the juggler had stalled, my father's Y having apparently hit the other great wall of China, but Jim List had boosted my optimism. Maybe we would have better luck with the male chromosome the Captain passed down. Maybe we could find a good match with the Crooks Y.

Sometimes you have to be careful what you wish for.

9

GENGHIS CROOKS,
OR WHO'S YOUR DADDY?

They say there's one in every family—a keeper of the record. This is the relative, often north of sixty, who can say where Mum's mum was born and knows the church where she was baptized, when Great-Granddad died and the names of his parents, and the Irish village they fled to keep from starving. Chances are, somewhere in the keeper's house is an overstuffed drawer or a box or two brimming with birth and death certificates, old travel papers, photographs and photocopies. In my mother's family, the keeper happens to be her younger brother Dennis. He is the eldest of the surviving Crooks males and the uncle my mother felt I should ask for the official contribution of the Crooks Y chromosome.

Before we left for India in 2006, when I began gathering dates and places involving Captain Crooks, Mum had said instantly, "Call Dennis. He'll know." And he did. He knew the captain's date of death and the day he married Bridget Meek in Bombay in 1903. He knew the name of the cathedral where they wed and the names of Bridget Meek's parents. All of it seemed to be right there at his fingertips.

That he should also be the one to contribute the Captain's Y was a terrific coincidence, since Dennis was rumoured to have a link to the family's Jamaican connection. He had taken up the correspondence with the mysterious New York uncle my mother used to write to, and apparently the uncle had named Dennis in his will. It's been a running joke in my mother's family for years—that Dennis had conquered the Caribbean and was sitting pretty on a secret Jamaican stash. I wondered less about the inheritance than what he might have learned from this uncle about the Captain's family.

The first time I called him about it, Dennis told me he was pleased to know that someone else was taking up the torch to look further into the Crooks history. My mother had talked to him too, specifically about the DNA test. One afternoon Dennis and her other brothers, Basil and Charles, dropped in at my parents' place, and they had all teased Dennis about being "the chosen one." With his willowy frame and aquiline features, he'd never looked like anyone else on the Crooks side of the family, they said, and his DNA would finally reveal all. They all had a good laugh at that, my mother said.

I'd wished my grandfather were alive to test. It would have been a sweet thing if his DNA could provide the sample that would illuminate the father he never knew. My memories of Papa Freddie are among the earliest I have. In England my mother used to drop me off at her parents' house while she went to work, and I'd plant myself beside my grandfather for hours. He suffered so severely from rheumatoid arthritis that he could hardly walk without his canes. We made quite a pair; he couldn't move and I couldn't stay quiet. I'd jabber on, plucking the thick veins on the back of his hands like banjo strings until desperation, I think, would finally drive him to manoeuvre his false teeth to the end of his tongue and scare me out of the room.

My grandfather died in November 1971, exactly a year before we left for Canada. I wondered how he would feel about trying to find our roots in Jamaica. From everything I'd heard, he grew up idolizing the legend of his father: a ship's captain, a life-saving hero of the high seas, the recipient of a royal commendation. Papa Freddie harboured such a strong affection for the sea that he was instantly fond of my father, who wore the stripes and brass buttons of the merchant marine. My parents had met at a Royal Navy dance and it didn't take long for my grandfather to give the young Mr. Abraham approval to waltz away with his eldest daughter.

My father knew all about Papa's dream to sail to Jamaica, after independence from Britain put the Anglo-Indians' future in doubt. My grandfather had shown him the passports he had stamped for the family, and told him he planned to settle on his father's sugar plantation. Yet no one knew if the Crooks family in Jamaica actually did own a plantation. Maybe the Captain was like the juggler—a master of reinvention, docking in India desperate to bury his past. But my grandfather obviously believed it. Through the online archives of the British Library, I found a reference to a letter he had written to Sir John Colville, the former governor of Bombay, dated February 21, 1948, just six months after India gained independence. The letter turned out to be only one in a correspondence involving my grandfather and Colville, who had also acted as viceroy and governor-general of India up until 1947. Finally I could read about my grandfather's aspirations in his own words.

> *Your Excellency,*
> *I have the honour to address these few lines to you for your kind and sympathetic consideration and guidance.*
>
> *You who have served as his Majesty's representative out in India are fully conversant as to the prevailing conditions and outlooks of the Anglo Indian community.*
>
> *I am at present serving in the GIP Railway as an Assistant Station Master at Poona Station and have on frequent occasions officiated as Station Master, Kirkee, where I have had the honour of meeting you and her Excellency on several occasions.*
>
> *I am a married man with a very large family of seven children, whose future outlook in this country is frightfully dismal.*

Hence I am anxious in their interest of taking them away from here to my father's country, where his people at this present moment are abiding, and that's in Kingston, Jamaica. Which unfortunately I am unable to undertake doing on account of financial circumstances.

My object in addressing your Excellency is to crave your help and guidance (which you have with kindness and sympathy extended unto my fellowmen) in securing for me the necessary passages.

I may enlighten your Excellency that I had appealed to the Joint Repatriation Officer, New Delhi, for their necessary help and assistance on the grounds to me having been a long standing member of His Majesty's Auxiliary Force, India, which your Excellency is aware of that every Anglo Indian has served most faithfully and loyally. This unfortunately was denied me on the grounds to me having no War Service. But it is a recognized fact that every Railwayman did his duty during the War, a fact which your Excellency will agree with me, is almost as good as having served in the War.

I tender unto your Excellency my most humble apologies for encroaching upon your most valued time and crave that you will enlighten me at your earliest convenience, as I am anxious to get away as early as possible.

I am,
Your Excellency's
most obedient servant
F.W. Crooks

My grandfather's request triggered a flurry of notes from the staff who reviewed the mail to Sir John, who had become Baron Clydesmuir of Braidswood after his return from India. In some memos, officials noted that since my grandfather had not served directly in the war, he could not be entitled to military assistance for passage to Jamaica. Another official pointed out that it could be politically unwise to help him, since the Anglo Indian Association of India was not officially sponsoring any emigration schemes. On March 15, 1948, Lord Clydesmuir replied to my grandfather that he would continue to make enquiries, but said, "I fear there is little that I can do at this end. . . ."

Clydesmuir's rejection obviously did nothing to deter my grandfather. He went on to sell the living room furniture. One way or the other, he was going to get to Jamaica. But then that mysterious reply from Jamaica arrived, with its accusations and warnings, and suddenly changed Papa Freddie's mind.

While I waited for the chance to collect the Crooks Y chromosome, I began researching the family the old-fashioned way—on the Internet. We had every reason to believe that the Captain, unlike the juggler, had left us his true surname, and having a name to trace is the lifeblood of genealogy. Knowing his Chinese family name, Jin Li had been able to track his ancestry back a thousand years.

In Britain, surnames appeared only after the Norman Conquest of 1066. Even then they didn't become common until about the fifteenth century, as they trickled down from monarchs to the masses. Surnames allowed rulers to keep track of and tax those they ruled. When Napoleon invaded the Netherlands, he decreed that every Dutch citizen had to have one. The public mocked the bureaucracy by calling themselves things like Naaktgeboren, meaning "born naked," and Piest, which means "to urinate," under the sadly mistaken assumption that the practice would never last.

In many European countries the etymology of surnames is more predictable. People were often named after their fathers, such as Johnson or Williamson, or they were named for their trades—Baker, Mason, Miller—or where they lived—Woods, Hill, Buxton. The more entertaining varieties were drawn from nicknames or personal traits, even though the modern-day Mr. Daft might say otherwise (it once meant "mild-mannered"). Naturally, I wondered if Crooks had once meant something other than swindler.

The British surname database suggests that Crooks was a Gaelic name originating in Ireland, with an unknown etymology. Other sources, including the Irish-based surname database, peg it as Viking, derived from the old Norse term *krokr*, meaning "bent," "hooked" or "corner." According to the *Collins World English Dictionary*, by the twelfth century *crook* had entered Middle English; it referred to the curve of any hooked instrument, such as a shepherd's staff, or even the bend in a winding stream. The earliest references to it as a name seem to apply to an ancient family in Scotland—where Vikings invaded in the eighth century—and then later in the north of England.

Even without looking, I knew Crooks was a common surname in Jamaica. Sprinter Charmaine Crooks, a five-time Olympian for Canada, hailed originally from Jamaica. The retired English football player Garth Crooks has Jamaican roots. And, in one of my earliest Internet searches, I came across the website of a British author by the name of Paul Crooks who also has Jamaican ancestry. His website promoted his first novel, *Ancestors*, based on the thirteen years he'd spent tracing his family history. It fictionalizes the story of the author's third-generation grandfather, who was snatched as a child from West Africa, sold into bondage in Jamaica and put to work in the cane fields of the Crooks Cove estate, a sugar plantation on Jamaica's north shore. The boy's life and his struggle for freedom were imagined, but apparently Crooks Cove itself was no fiction.

Paul Crooks's website describes a 763-acre estate that had grown to more than twice its size by the early 1820s, home to nearly two hundred slaves who lived in the shadow of a big house on the hill. Its original owners were said to be among the Europeans who had been given plots of land by Oliver Cromwell in the seventeenth century, when Britain began to colonize the island. The Crooks family named their plot after themselves, and in mass baptisms they also gave the Crooks surname to many of the slaves they owned.

I took stock. A Jamaican plantation that bore the Crooks name jibed with the rumours of our ancestors being wealthy Jamaican landowners, and it was in operation well into the nineteenth century, maybe even at the time my great-grandfather was born. I ordered the novel online and made a mental note to ask Dennis if he'd ever heard of the place.

On a hot afternoon in June 2006, I visited Uncle Dennis for the long-awaited swab. He and my Aunty Merlyn live near my parents in one of those seventies subdivisions of low-rise back-splits with wide driveways and perfectly square lawns. When I was young, we'd gather there on Christmas Eve, when the snowbanks could be as high as the cars and the Crooks clan celebrated my grandmother's birthday. No one knew then that Nana Gladys had actually been born three days before Christmas Eve, but it wouldn't have mattered. It was her favourite night of the year—the whole family around her, a lavish spread of curry and rice and cousins. My grandmother would wear one of her fancy frocks and take her throne in an overstuffed chair in the living room, the ice in her crystal tumbler of Bacardi tinkling, just like the hidden medals she wore. "My son Dennis," she'd say, "play some Jim Reeves!"

I rang the doorbell. No one answered. I waited a minute or two and rang again. The front curtains were drawn. Had I mixed up the day? Had my uncle changed his mind? Forking over DNA can make anyone uncomfortable; my own brother had declined. But then I heard footsteps and the door opened.

"Sorry, darling, the bell's not working," said Aunty Merlyn with a wide smile.

The drapes had been pulled tight to keep out the sun and the dim coolness of their house enveloped me as I stepped inside. "Uncle Dennis is downstairs watching the World Cup," she said. "He's been glued to it today."

My uncle popped up a moment later and we shared a hug and a kiss on both cheeks. We settled in the living room, where my aunt set out a plate of homemade cheese straws and my uncle opened a bottle of wine. I told them how this family project had begun to consume me, what with the testing and the trip to India and the Internet searches. Dennis, the record keeper, understood completely. He told me about his own recent breakthrough: locating the daughter of Nana Gladys's long-lost sister in New Zealand.

I took that as my cue and began fumbling to explain how DNA can also connect a person to long-lost relatives they didn't know they had. I started by comparing DNA to a record that shows how all modern humans descended from Africans; I was partway through when I decided to back up and talk about how DNA made us all human in the first place. But instantly that seemed too abstract and too long a story. It was ridiculous, really, to be nattering on about primordial ooze and single-celled organisms while nestled on a plush sofa with a glass of wine. Just how informed do people have to be to give their informed consent? I wondered.

I stopped, took a gulp of wine and switched gears. "Okay, so basically we were all black once, until we spread out all over the planet and morphed into different colours and characteristics. And the Y chromosome, which only men carry, can tell us a lot about that history." At that moment I was grateful that the story of the male chromosome is, like the Y's size, fairly simple and compact. I explained how the Y is passed from fathers to sons with distinctive markers in its code, and the markers are like the genetic signature of a male lineage. They can reveal where in the world a male line originates and can also link you with a potential relative, if you can find a man with the same markers on his Y chromosome.

"I tested Dad's Y chromosome and it shows that his grandfather was Chinese, which we had suspected but never knew for sure," I explained. "So it could be that the Crooks Y chromosome could reveal something about the background of Captain Crooks, who also left us with certain mysteries. The Crooks Y could tell us where, beyond Jamaica, his father's line came from. The Captain would have passed it down to Papa Freddie and he would have passed it down to all his sons."

"I don't think my grandfather was really born there—in Jamaica," Dennis said, surprising me. "Maybe he just stopped there and his real business was in Bombay. His birth certificate says Jamaica, but I don't know if that's correct."

I hadn't known there was a birth certificate. "The only official document I've seen was a brief death record. It just listed the Captain's age and the cause of death as beriberi."

"I think I have a copy of his birth certificate in one of my boxes," Dennis said, and offered to dig it out.

I told him that Mum certainly believed her grandfather had come from Jamaica. She had always told me that Papa Freddie believed that too, that he had gone to extremes in trying to get the family there after India's independence.

Even if the Captain had not been born in Jamaica, Aunty Merlyn said, turning towards Dennis, "There was that uncle who used to write to you, right?"

"The one with whom you corresponded?" I interrupted. "Mum said she passed on the address for you to write to him after she got married."

"Yes," Dennis said. "I was about sixteen or seventeen when I picked up the correspondence."

Dennis said he always called him Uncle, and that, like both the Captain and my grandfather, his name was also Frederick Crooks. He used to write encouraging letters from New York urging Dennis to study hard and do well in school. "His letters always arrived from 492 Hancock Street in Brooklyn, with a single U.S. dollar enclosed to pay for the return postage."

The uncle once wrote to Papa Freddie as well, explaining that he and his wife had no children and asking if he could adopt Dennis. Of course, Papa never entertained the idea, but the young man and the mysterious uncle continued to correspond. Only after the uncle died in the late sixties did it become apparent that he had been looking for an heir.

"It was a maid who telephoned me," Dennis said. "She said she had found a bankbook with my name on it." From what he understood, the uncle had started a successful gas business in Jamaica. But it turned out that the uncle's wife—"a Clarice Crooks, I think"—had named her own nephew as the beneficiary.

"There was money and property, and this nephew was to be the heir of all the inheritance," Dennis said. What's more, the funds were in a Jamaican bank and could not be taken out of the country.

"We spent more on lawyers than anything else," Merlyn said. "We didn't get a penny."

"That's too bad," I said, realizing that all the years of jokes about my uncle's island fortune had been just that. Yet clearly the Crooks family had some wealth, so maybe there was a plantation after all. I asked my uncle and aunt if they got to know the Crooks relatives in Jamaica during their ordeal, but they said they hadn't.

I told them about the old Jamaican sugar plantation I had read about online, called the Crooks Cove estate. It was located in the northwest part of the island, I said, owned by whites and worked by slaves.

Dennis had never heard of it. "To the best of my knowledge, Papa's relatives were in Kingston," he said, but beyond that he knew little about them.

"Well, you have to think that somewhere along the way the Crooks ancestors descended from slaves brought over from Africa," I said. "Mum's DNA test suggested some traces of sub-Saharan African ancestry."

"It's true," Dennis agreed, "there must be something to it. My father had the kinky hair, Simone's got it. . . ."

I told Dennis there was a chance he might carry a Y chromosome that suggested our Crooks line originated in Africa, the way my dad's had led us to China. But I also told him I doubted that would be the case. "As far as these things went in history," I said, "it was almost always the white man with the dark woman, don't you think?"

I gave my uncle the consent form and he spent a few moments reading through it.

"So you'll have to brush against your inner cheek for about sixty seconds," I said as I opened the package and passed him a swabbing stick. "Then do it again with a second stick on your other cheek."

My uncle opened wide and I tried to keep my eyes trained on my cellphone clock. Jiggling a stick around in your mouth seems like fairly personal business. I'd seen enough to decide that you can tell something about a person by the way they swab. There's the laissez-faire technique perfected by my sister, the casual up-and-down brushing motion of a swabber whose mind might be a million miles from the swab—nothing to hide, lose or gain. Some do it tentatively, as if one errant thrust could pierce the cheek. It seems furtive, betrays a certain reluctance, as it did that first time with my mother. But I saw none of that with my uncle. He swabbed with vigour, in long, firm, deliberate strokes, as though he were chasing the very last cells of a bloodline.

I didn't make it out of the subdivision before I felt compelled to pull over. On the passenger seat beside me, sloshing about in my purse, was the Crooks Y chromosome, passed down through the generations to my uncle from my grandfather and the Captain before him and . . . who before that? A man owned by another or a man who owned men? I reached into the padded envelope, pulled out the two vials and checked that the lids were screwed on tight. I held one up to the light. It looked like nothing, just a nub of white cotton. Yet it contained a code that could end a century of speculation. I did not think to consider that it would unleash even more.

In his sobering volume *Y: The Descent of Men*, British geneticist Steve Jones estimates that the world's men copulate fifty billion times a year. Globally they release 200,000 billion sperm per second, and for all that effort produce just five births. Women of the world drop only four hundred eggs for the same result. But it's not how many seeds you have to sow, it's whether you can sow them at all. And since most men didn't through history, it whittled down the variety of Y chromosomes that got around. In 2004, Mike Hammer's group at the University of Arizona published evidence, based on the limited diversity of the world's Ys, that relatively few men had fathered the world's population. And those men who did win at the mating game sometimes won big, leaving enough male descendants to populate a large chunk of the planet.

It helped to think about all this when my uncle's DNA results arrived. Six months had ticked by without a match for my father's Y chromosome. That the deCouto Y turned out to have even a single match felt like a minor miracle. Yet I opened Dennis's results to see that the Crooks male chromosome had matched up with 350 men right out of the test tube—350! Whoever our common male ancestor was, he had been a very busy man. I imagined the Crooks men in my family dining like kings on this news.

The lab had found that Dennis's Y chromosome belonged to Haplogroup R1b, the most common haplogroup in Western Europe, the club to which more than half the continent's men belong. Its origins are unclear, but men of R1b are believed to descend from the first modern humans to populate the continent. I realized that my uncle's high number of matches had much to do with the fact that many men of European descent had offered up their Ys for testing. It was, as Bennett said, a western European sport. Apparently we were now in the game.

Not only did the Crooks Y belong to Europe's most common haplogroup, Dennis also carries the most common pattern within it, the so-called Western Atlantic Modal Haplotype, defined by six markers that are most common among men from western Europe. Scientists suspect it saturates the region because it was caught up in a "genetic bottleneck," which occurs when something kills off such a large swath of the population that only a few people are left to sire the next generation. The best evidence at the time suggested that this Atlantic haplotype emerged about ten thousand years ago as Stone Age populations waited out the last ice age, perhaps around the Fertile Crescent. When the great thaw finally arrived, the survivors kicked off a dramatic population expansion as farming also took off. The markers of the Atlantic haplotype are prevalent from Spain in the south to western Scandinavia in the north. In parts of the British Isles more than 80 percent of men bear its signature.

As I read the results, I felt an unexpected sense of kinship with the continent of my birth. I'd always felt that my being born in England was little more than an accident of travel. England was the place where my parents had stopped on their migratory route from India to North America—albeit for twenty-two years—and we'd soaked up certain cultural trappings such as baked beans, Benny Hill, that sort of thing. But Blighty had proved an uncomfortable motherland for many of my relatives, a place where they tried desperately to fit in with their not-so-white complexions and singsong accents. My brother Conrad was five when he arrived in London with my parents, fresh from living like a small prince in Bombay. They moved into a flat above a pub where people used to call him "chocolate drop." The first thing he learned there was how to fight.

Yet now, through the prism of the Crooks Y chromosome at least, our time in England was recast less as a stopover than a return to the ancient fatherland where one branch of our ancestral tree had sprouted. Way back when the world was still half-frozen, a forefather of ours was there, shivering in a cave and doing his considerable bit to populate the planet. There was little doubt now that my great-grandfather, in his paternal line at least, was not of African descent. As the proxy for the Captain's Y chromosome, Dennis's seem to bear the crystal-clear imprint of a white man.

By process of elimination, whatever African ancestry the Captain had passed down to us, his European Y suggested it came by way of a woman. I had always suspected it would. Wherever European men went in the world, from South Asia to South America and the Caribbean, they came, saw and copulated. In 2003, a study of eight hundred men from the University of Puerto Rico found that 70 percent carried the Y chromosome of a European forefather; yet most of them carried the mitochondrial DNA of an Amerindian or African female ancestor. I had no reason to think the story would be much different in Jamaica, just seven hundred miles away, or in any society where one group dominated another. In the United States about a third of African-American men carry the Y chromosome of a European male ancestor, largely because of the sexual politics of slavery. In Iceland the Y chromosomes of men tend to lead back to the Vikings, but their mitochondrial DNA comes from the Scottish and Irish women those Vikings kidnapped a thousand years ago. The Y is a hidden record of history's winners and losers, a short volume on the sex lives of powerful men—you lead, you breed.

In 2003, researchers at the University of Oxford published a paper estimating that in Asia today, some sixteen million men carry the Y chromosome belonging to the paternal line of Genghis Khan. The legendary leader of the Mongols, born in 1162, had several wives and mistresses and is said to have fathered more than forty sons as his armies conquered a continent. In turn, his sons sired dozens of sons of their own. Their particular Y signature, which belongs to Haplogroup C, can now be found at a remarkable 8 percent prevalence rate across sixteen different populations from the Pacific to the Caspian Sea, an area that corresponds to the boundaries of the old Mongol Empire. Still, Peter Underhill, a leading Y chromosome geneticist at Stanford University, told me it's a stretch to think that every one of the sixteen million men who sport this particular Y is a direct descendant of Genghis Khan. These men could just as easily be descendants of the Khan's brothers, he said, or cousins, or even Mongol men from the same village. Most likely, he felt it was a very common Mongol male line that went through a recent genetic bottleneck.

Still, the Genghis Khan phenomenon was the first in a string of reports about the remarkable reproductive success of history's rulers. In 2005, British scientists estimated that 1.5 million men in north-eastern China and Mongolia may have descended from Giocangga, whose Manchu grandson founded the Qing Dynasty that ruled China during my great-grandfather's time, from 1644 to 1912. A year later, a study from Trinity College Dublin reported that about three million Irish men share the same Y as the fourth-century warlord known as Niall of the Nine Hostages. The male chromosome of the tribal king, whose Ui Neill dynasty dominated Ireland for more than five hundred years, also lives on in about one in ten Scottish men and about 2 percent of New Yorkers with European ancestry.

Who knows, maybe the founder of the Atlantic modal haplotype was a prehistoric king, a hero who led his people across miles of frozen tundra, or maybe he was reviled as a tyrant who killed off his competitors as his clan bedded down in the caves. As it was, all I could do was stretch the bounds of my imagination as I scanned a sample of his impressive genetic legacy: the 350 names of his descendants, and my new genetic relatives. Their countries of origin included Poland, Cuba, England, Wales, Scotland, Austria, Russia, Puerto Rico, Jamaica, Canada . . . and on it went. They were named Kennedy, Bondelier, Zucco, Guttendorf, Saliceti, Collins, McDaniel, Hershberger, Ellis, Turcq, Barlow, Rodriguez, Ford . . . and on I read through an unalphabetized telephone book until one entry stopped me cold—Meek. Kenneth Everett Meek.

The name jumped off the screen. Meek was the maiden name

of Nana Bridget, my great-grandmother, Papa Freddie's mother, the Captain's wife, the pint-sized conjurer. That was bizarre. Dennis has a Y that matches the Y of a man named Meek?

Based on mathematical models from the University of Arizona, Family Tree DNA had stipulated that an exact twelve-marker Y chromosome match between two men who share the same last name suggests a 99 percent likelihood of a common ancestor in a genealogical time frame. Did this Kenneth Meek and Dennis share a Meek male ancestor? Was there some unknown connection between the Meek side of the family and Uncle Dennis? No Crooks appeared on this list of 350 men, but here was a perfect match between a Meek and the Crooks uncle who had never looked like a Crooks.

Oh God, what had I stumbled into? Had my uncle been fathered by a Meek man? Had Nana Gladys stepped out on my grandfather? Had my tinkling-with-holy-medals, guided-by-glow-in-the-dark-Mary grandmother cheated with one of her husband's Meek relatives? No, that was crazy.

But then I started to think about my grandmother in more than two dimensions. She was complicated, defiant, independent, but nothing could soften her like the attentions of a man. She blossomed like a peony in their presence. Well into her eighties she would stay up half the night watching love stories on television, even when they played in a foreign language. Nana could recall the name of every boy who had courted her, and as a widow she had a parade of suitors. I pictured her all dolled up in a flaming red polka-dot dress, on her way to the pub to share a drink with Mr. Priest, a silver-haired beau who used to pull coins out of my ears. "Go to sleep, my girl," Nana would say with a wink, as she disappeared out the front door.

A few years earlier I had written a long newspaper feature that suddenly felt utterly prophetic to me that August night. It was all about genetic research inadvertently exposing the widespread infidelities of women. Stephen Scherer, a prominent geneticist at the University of Toronto and the Hospital for Sick Children, had been telling me about the logistical hurdles of running large population studies when he mentioned how often they find that the man listed as the father of a child turns out not to be.

"Really?" I asked. "Often?"

At least 10 percent of the time, he told me. They'll be doing a study on cystic fibrosis, for example, collecting DNA from the afflicted child and both parents, and find the father doesn't carry a CF gene. Yet to develop the disease, a child has to inherit one copy of the CF gene from each parent, meaning that Dad couldn't possibly be the biological father. Other geneticists gave me a similar estimate, that roughly one in ten of us is not fathered by the man we believe to be Dad. A British survey conducted by the University of Manchester between 1988 and 1996 came to the same conclusion. "Pedigree errors" or "false paternities" is what researchers call these incidents—technical jargon for the unwitting number of us who are chips off someone else's block.

If there was any doubt left in the twenty-first century that women are somehow biologically driven to single-mate bliss, that females are built for monogamy or that mothers rarely mess around, the genomic age was killing it. Researchers have found that false paternities cut across all cultures and socioeconomic classes. Scherer told me they can wreak such statistical havoc on a genetic study that "people have made careers designing software to catch these kinds of things." I asked him what they do when they do catch them.

"We toss the samples," he said.

Was that what I should do now? I wondered. Toss this result? Abandon it? Start again?

If you factor a 10 percent false paternity rate into attempts to trace ancestry, it could easily snap entire branches from a family tree. At that moment I had no way of knowing if it actually was a false paternity, only that I could not ignore the possibility. How could I draw any conclusions about the paternal history of the

Crooks line if this wasn't the Crooks Y chromosome? How could I know if it belonged to Europe's dominant haplogroup or revealed anything about the Captain's origins if I could not be sure that the Y I had collected from Dennis had actually been passed down by my grandfather?

My mother was in Mexico with my brother Kevin when Dennis's results arrived. I was grateful for her absence. My father would be much less likely to give me an earful for entertaining the possibility that her mother had been unfaithful. I called and asked him to meet for dinner on the weekend. Then I called my sister and told her everything. "What do you think?" I said.

"Well, I don't think it's impossible," she said. "But I don't know that I would tell Mum."

The three of us met at a Chinese restaurant that Saturday night. It was a busy spot. Armies of servers whizzed between tables with giant platters above their heads. We huddled over bowls of rice and kung pao chicken and I started at the beginning. I explained that Dennis had a Y that belonged to a European haplogroup and that he had 350 exact matches.

"Wow, 350?" my father said, with a tinge of envy.

Yes, I said, but this was also a problem, because one of those 350 men was named Meek.

My father raised his eyebrows.

"It might not mean anything," I said. "It could be sheer coincidence, because those twelve markers of his are just so common in Europeans, that Dennis's Y just happens to match the Y of a man named Meek. But there is also a chance that it isn't a fluke. He had no matches with anyone named Crooks. There's a chance that the match exists because Dennis actually is a Meek, and at some point there was . . . an infidelity . . ."

The word hung over the table like a plume of steam. My father got a faraway look in his eyes. "Do you know the name Earnest Meek?" he asked.

It sounded familiar, but beyond that the name meant nothing to me or my sister.

Earnest was the younger brother of Nana Bridget, Dad said. He had never married, and for a while he lived with Nana Gladys and Papa Freddie in their home outside Bombay.

"When would that have been?" I asked.

Dad didn't know the dates but said my mother was small at the time. "Earnest was the handyman, you see."

"The handyman?" Christine and I groaned.

"Yes. He did things around the house while Papa was working," Dad said. "Nana was quite fond of him."

Fond. Oh my.

It absorbed us, what to do next. For the rest of dinner we discussed and debated through pots of tea and fortune cookies. (Mine said, "Time heals all wounds." Sure, I thought, until DNA splits them open.) Should I test more markers on Dennis's Y chromosome and see if he still matched with this Meek fellow? But then I would have to contact this Mr. Meek to see if he'd be willing to have more markers tested as well. I should reach out to him anyway and ask about his background.

Should I simply collect DNA from another Crooks uncle and see what it showed? If they didn't match the implications would be profound and potentially catastrophic—for Dennis and for both his sons, my cousins. And how would I explain wanting another sample from another uncle? Mum's other brothers already knew that Dennis had given me his DNA. *See, I'm just not completely convinced that Dennis is a Crooks, Uncle, so if you don't mind just sticking this in your mouth. . . .*

We worried about my mother, whether she would be angry and hurt, horrified at the mere suggestion her mother had been unfaithful to her father. Or maybe Mum would know something to extinguish the suspicions. I remembered a story she had once told me about Nana Gladys's mother, Josephine DaSilva, actually giving away one of her children to a sister who was unable to have children of her own. Josephine had ten, and it was her fifth child, a son, whom she gave to her sister Louie. If that son had ever had his DNA tested, he would have learned that he did not carry the Y chromosome of the father who had raised him. Tragically, the boy ended up dying of a mysterious infection at the age of five, Mum said, leaving her Great-Aunty Louie child-less once again. I wondered if such a story might explain the Meek match. Had my grandparents quietly adopted the son of a Meek relative? But then, if my mother knew about something like that, she would never have sent me to Dennis to collect a sample of Crooks DNA.

In the days that followed the arrival of Dennis's DNA results, memories of my grandmother haunted me. I had the strange sen-sation that she was listening to the internal dialogue running through my head.

I had not envisioned hauling this kind of skeleton out of the genetic closet. I imagined the waves of posthumous judgement that would attach to her memory, accusations she could never counter. And what right would anyone have to judge? My grand-mother was just seventeen when she married my grandfather. He was twenty-four, a railway guard, introduced to her by an older sister. She called him Mr. Crooks all the while he courted her, even on their wedding night. Who knew the circumstances at play in the most private relationships of her life? At the same time I felt guilty for thinking her capable of it. She was my grandmother, the one who smothered me in her roundness and slept beside me in her bed, even when I was covered with measles.

One afternoon I was typing at the computer, trying to cap-ture this swell of emotions, and the letter O suddenly went ber-serk. On its own, as though it were being depressed by a stubborn accusatory finger, row upon row of Os appeared on my screen—hundreds of them, filling the page. I changed the battery in the keyboard. Stephen changed the keyboard. Nothing helped. I called my sister, a purveyor of custom software and the family's twenty-four-hour technical assistance provider, and asked if she'd ever heard of this kind of glitch—rampant wilful O syndrome. She hadn't ever. The letter O behaved when I wrote emails, I told her, but each time I returned to this chapter, ruminating on Nana's possible tryst with Earnest Meek, ooooooooooooooooooooooooooooooff it would go again.

Science reporters are not supposed to believe in ghosts. Faith in anything that can't be measured or weighed or poured into a test tube, grown in a petri dish or swished about in a centrifuge is generally considered to fall on the pseudo side of science. But having grown up in the deep woods of superstition, I've always been a bit ambivalent about their existence. Of course the brain is a powerful machine, full of quirks that can fool you and make you feel things that aren't there, a dazzling CPU that can draw rapid-fire connections between a smell and a memory—or a computer malfunction and the supernatural. So maybe it was inevitable that as I meddled in the affairs of the dead I would collide with one phantom of the mind or another. Even my pragmatic father had his own eerie confrontation, when his camera jammed as he tried to photograph his grandfather's records in Coonoor.

But my grandmother had been a true believer. Bridget Meek's spirit-stalking used to upset Nana Gladys, not because she thought it was nonsense but because she was worried her mother-in-law's next-world communing would invite some long-lost soul to take up residence in their house. After my grandfather died, Nana Gladys was so convinced that his spirit lived on in their house in England that when I stayed with her as a child, she used to tell me that Papa was up there in his study. It was a small room with a hardwood floor, a desk, a chair and a bookshelf. It hadn't been touched since his death, and Nana swore that sometimes she could hear him creaking about, looking for this or that. I crept in there once and stood in the centre of the room, waiting for something to happen. Nothing did before fear eventually got the better of me and I ran out.

Thirty years later, I think I understood what my grandmother meant. She simply felt his presence—and she felt it powerfully, just as I was feeling hers.

IO

THE TROUBLE
WITH BEING EARNEST

In the fall of 2006 I flew to Houston, Texas, where Family Tree DNA was holding a conference for people running genetic ancestry projects. It was designed to help family historians interpret DNA test results, unveil the latest discoveries and provide a forum for people to share their experiences. For that reason alone I was keen to get there. If the false paternity rates run as high as 10 percent in the general population, I assumed I would find someone else who had stepped into a dilemma like mine, someone with insights or advice to offer.

I finally asked my mother about my uncle's test result a couple of weeks after she returned from Mexico. I had stopped in for a visit and she was telling me about her trip, describing the sixteenth-century shrine in Guadalupe where Roman Catholics gather in the millions, and the church built where roses had bloomed in the middle of winter.

I said, "So, did Dad tell you?"

"Tell me what?"

"Dennis's results came back."

"Yes. Dad said there was some confusion."

"Yeah, it's confusing."

I laid it all out in detail: that Dennis carried a very common European signature on his Y chromosome, so common that he had 350 exact matches right off the bat. None of those men were named Crooks, I told her, yet here was this perfect twelve-marker match with a man named Meek. "So the question is, did Dennis really inherit his Y chromosome from a Crooks man? Or was it from a Meek man?" I said. "Do you know what I mean?"

Of course she did. My mother got that same distant look in her eyes that my father had when I first told him. "Who is this Meek that he matches?" she finally asked.

"His name is Kenneth Meek and he lives in the U.S.," I said. "His online profile says his ancestors came from Scotland." I told her I wasn't sure if I should contact him to find out more, since it wasn't my aim to find out if Dennis matched a Meek, only whether the Y chromosome I was testing actually belonged to the Crooks line. "It may just be a coincidence, but it's an uncanny one when there were Meeks on one side of our family," I said.

My mother said nothing after that, and I filled the silence with statistics, describing the research I had done on false paternities and how surprisingly common they are. But then I realized that was probably no comfort at all, and so, for a while, neither of us said anything.

There was a picture of my grandmother over the living room chair where my mother sat, a large family portrait. It was taken a few years before Nana died. She's sitting in the middle of the front row, looking every bit the snow-haired matriarch, surrounded by three generations. She's wearing a blue dress and an unusually broad smile—my grandmother had often censored her smiles after she got her dentures. I had an absurd urge to walk around the room to see if her eyes followed me. But then my mother started thinking out loud.

"We had a big house in the railway colony," she said, "and Earnest Meek came to stay with us."

"Earnest?" I had deliberately not mentioned the name to my mother, but there it was at the tip of her thoughts, just as it had been for my father.

"Yes, Earnest was Nana Bridget's younger brother. We were small. We were living in Sholapur," she continued. "Earnest had a top job in the railway but he came to live with us after he retired."

"Why? Was he broke?" I asked.

"No, he had pots of money. He was just very frugal, and we had the space and he was very fond of Nana. He was a big help to Nana."

"But he wasn't so fond of Papa?"

"Papa never liked him."

"Never liked him . . . . Why?"

"I don't know. There was coldness between them—I don't know why, really, but I sensed it. And Uncle Earnest never seemed to give Papa much credit for anything."

My mother thought it might have had something to do with the Captain. Somewhere between moves to different railway colonies, Papa had lost the papers confirming his father's royal commendation, and Uncle Earnest held a grudge over it. "Those papers would have helped to repatriate the family to England, and Earnest thought Papa had just been careless with all that."

"Was Earnest married?"

"No. All sorts of relatives had tried to match him up, but he never married."

"He must have been much older than Nana."

"Yes, but he was very fit, very stylish. 'Eat a lot of garlic,' he used to say. 'It will keep your skin pink.' In fact he used to tell me off for not wearing nice slippers in the house. You know, with the hot weather I didn't wear anything on my feet."

"Dad said he was a bit of a handyman."

"Well, he just used to be around the house because he really admired Nana. He had a lot of compliments for her: how she took care of all of us, then still found time to put on her white shorts and go off to play tennis. He used to help her out sometimes, give her money to outfit the boys."

"Do you think Nana had an affair with him?" There, I'd said it.

"No, of course not!" Mum shot back. But her conviction faded as suddenly as it appeared. "Well, I don't know. . . . I was a child. Funny, everyone has always said Dennis is so much like the Meek side—his features and even his ways. That day they were all here, Basil and Charles were teasing him about it."

"Well, he carries Meek genes no matter what," I offered. "Papa's mother was a Meek, so maybe he inherited a big dose of her genes. Just look how much my DNA seemed so much more like Dad's than yours when we did that first test."

Mum was far away again. "Nana loved to go out when she was young. She loved to dance. She organized so many of the railway dances," she said. "Papa never liked to dance."

There didn't seem much to say after that. My mother may as well have told me Uncle Earnest was a first-class foxtrotter.

"Well, that's the bottom line then, isn't it," I said. "I can't assume this is the Captain's Y chromosome. I have to test another Crooks male, or it may be that I'm not researching the Crooks history at all. If that Y matches with Dennis, then we can be confident that it is the Crooks chromosome. If it doesn't . . . Well, let's not think about that right now."

"Go to Basil," my mother said. "Basil said he would do it. Just tell him you need it."

I didn't have a chance to meet up with Basil before I left for Houston. But there would be no pushing the matter out of mind. As soon as I checked in at the airport hotel hosting the conference, I noticed the name of the restaurant just off the lobby: Basil's Tavern. Just what I needed—another weird coincidence.

I've been to many science conferences over the years: massive events devoted to AIDS, small workshops on cancer, microbiology meetings predicting the comeback of measles and plague, gatherings of fertility doctors exploring better ways to make babies in a lab. But I had no idea what to expect of this one, or whom to expect. The seats had sold out like tickets to a rock concert. More than two hundred people had signed up, most the self-appointed heads of surname projects—gathering and comparing the Y chromosomes of men with the same or similar surnames to see how, or if, they are related.

The delegates milled about the registration desk the first morning, picking up their tote bags and nametags as they do at any conference. Except the tags at this one carried not only the name of the delegate but every surname that delegate was researching. This meant people spent more than a polite moment staring at each other's chests looking for a familiar handle.

Many were seniors, several wore hearing aids and at least two had brought their knitting. The only people much younger than me were technicians at the lab where the samples are processed— and they are processed by the thousands. Max Blankfeld, Family Tree DNA's head of marketing and operations, told the crowd that when the firm launched in 2000, about ten DNA kits a month used to trickle in. Now, six years later, it was at least three thousand a month, and some months it was double that. Together with the Genographic Project, the company had processed 220,000 DNA samples, and that very week, the Y-chromosome database was expected to hit 81,000 entries. About 5,000 were anonymous research samples, but more than 75,000 had arrived by post, from people just like us sitting in the audience.

Mine was no solitary march into the genetic past. It was a pilgrimage—thousands flocking to the shrine of science, just like the faithful to Guadalupe, looking for . . . what? Answers? Peace? Did we all have mysteries to solve? The most devout could toss out highly technical terms with the ease of an expert, debate the relative mutation rates of short tandem repeats versus single nucleotide polymorphisms, and speak in knowing terms about the Y's tricky palindromic arms. They were an impressive bunch.

It may be that retirement had fuelled their hobby, as it did with my father. It may be that age heightens the desire to confirm one's place in the human continuum, to be cast in the larger pageant of life on the planet. But it was Bennett Greenspan who warned everyone that DNA can write a script full of plot twists. I had spoken to Bennett on the phone at least three times by then, but I'd never seen him in person until that morning, bounding onto the stage, bald, glasses, a wiry fifty-four-year-old firecracker in jeans and a purple tie, arms fluttering up from behind the podium as he spoke.

"Like you," he said, "I'm a genealogist, interested in bridging the gap between anthropology and genealogy." The crowd loved him. Applause nearly drowned out his words. He talked broadly about the ethical challenges of DNA testing, having people agree to be tested, the issues related to privacy—not just when someone publishes test results online, but also when a test inadvertently reveals someone's identity. The Y-chromosome database had grown so large, he said, that a fifteen-year-old American boy was able to track down his anonymous sperm-donor father with nothing more than a swab and the Internet.

Bennett talked about the power of genetics to match people with their families, but also, he said, "the discomfort of finding that two people who should match don't match." Or, I thought, finding that two people who shouldn't match do. Either way, it suddenly seemed as if Bennett was speaking directly to me, letting me know that the whole *What did my Nana do?* phenomenon was par for the genetic course. In fact he estimated that events of mistaken paternity run as high as 1.5 percent per generation. Then he offered the story of Buford, from Arkansas.

"People from Arkansas and Texas don't typically need genetic tests," he joked, "because they all have the same DNA." But Buford, in his eighties, was curious. Traditional sources of genealogy had already revealed to him that his paternal grandfather was born out of wedlock back in 1859, followed by a brother in 1865 and two other children. Then Buford decided to give DNA testing a whirl and discovered that, while the male descendants of his grandfather's brothers had matching Y chromosomes, his Y was a mismatch. Instead, Buford found that his male chromosome matched perfectly with a perfect stranger—at thirty-seven markers. When Buford looked for that man's surname in 1850s census records, he found that it belonged to a nineteen-year-old male who had lived near his great-grandmother when she was also nineteen. This man, who later died in the Civil War, had apparently fathered Buford's grandfather. The test result shook Buford to the core, Bennett said, "to find out, at that stage of his life, that he is not who he thought he was."

I thought about my uncle's case. If his Meek match held, if he turned not to be a Crooks, it was much more dramatic than the truth Buford had uncovered. Buford's mistaken identity made him a mismatch with his cousins. In my uncle's case, it would be with his own brothers. I wondered how I would feel to discover, out of the blue, that my father was not my biological parent, that my siblings were half-siblings. Would it shatter me?

The number of men with Y chromosomes that matched my uncle's at twelve markers kept rolling in like the tide. Hardly a week passed without the arrival of a new message informing me of yet another perfect score with the possible Crooks chromosome. The list had soared to four hundred when I left for the conference, but none of them were named Crooks. At the same time, the sheer volume only made my father's languishing Y seem more frustrating.

As Jin Li had suggested, I had sent my father's DNA down to his lab in Cincinnati. But there had been no word since then. In the meantime I continued my own search for a Y that matched my father's. Free online databases had sprung up, allowing people to upload their Y-chromosome test results and compare markers with people who had been tested by different companies from any-where in the world. But not one of them produced a match.

Family Tree DNA had established Ysearch.org, which, with

its ties to the Genographic Project, quickly became the largest of the online genetic databases, with more than nineteen thousand Y test results on hand that summer. I checked it often, hoping that somehow a genetic cousin had suddenly added his East Asian sequences to the fold. Initially I had searched for the perfect twelve-marker match for my father. But as the weeks wore on, I became less fussy, until one afternoon I found matches with four men at eight markers. Two men were from China, one was from Japan and one was a man by the name of Huy Ton-That, from Vietnam, who could apparently trace his history back more than a thousand years. His oldest known ancestor was Nguyen Bac, born about 939 AD. On his profile page he said he had tested with the Genographic Project, and he included his email address for anyone interested to get in touch. I wrote to him instantly.

```
Hello,
I realize this is a long shot, but your
Y-DNA results match 8 out of 12 with
my father's line, which we had always
suspected led to somewhere in China. I
am wondering if you know of any family
connections on your side to China—
and I thought it might be worth checking
since, impressively, you have a name and
date for a paternal ancestor as far back
as 939.
I would be very interested in making
contact.
Regards,
Carolyn Abraham
```

Two hours after I sent the message, Huy Ton-That had replied from his home in Miami with an exuberant subject line: "Hello Kin!"

Hi,
Good to hear from you! From history and
genealogy I could date my family line
back to 900s AD (to Nguyen Bac, the "Nation-
Establishing Duke" of Vietnam). My family
name is Ton-That but the original name
is Nguyen (long story). Yes, we are the
descendants of the last imperial dynasty
of Vietnam (The Nguyen Dynasty) and that
is why we have records of our family dating back to the first known ancestor
Nguyen Bac.

    Nguyen Bac is suspected to be one of
the descendants of a Chinese "Nguyen" who
came to VN after the Chinese colonized
VN in 111 BC. Our M-122 type somewhat
confirms that we are from China. Thanks
for writing. Bye!
Huy Ton-That

He was right. It was almost too much to digest. But I felt it
again as I had the first time, when a bloodline suddenly materialized between Kerala and Maine and Gladwyn deCouto's Y brought
me to Jim List. It was a rush. Another piece of a very old puzzle
had been pulled out of the past. But it seemed a stretch to make
much of it. It was only eight measly markers, a bond I presumed
to be rice-paper thin. However, it was something, a tiny link in the
chain to China when there had been nothing for months, and even
more intoxicating because it suggested we had a connection, however faint, to royalty. Royalty! *Why not quit now?* I thought. *It's such
a happy ending.* With the entry of a few keystrokes at Ysearch.org,
my kin rose from rice farmer, fugitive and circus act to distant cousin
of a ruling family. It was pathetically clichéd and yet . . . deliciously
romantic. For a few minutes I felt like a Vietnamese princess.

Of course, math diluted the thrill. Back in 2002 the *Atlantic Monthly* carried a memorable article by Steve Olson titled "The Royal We." It offered up the theory, based on some clever modelling by Yale University statistician Joseph Chang, that everybody is a royal, that all Europeans descend from Charlemagne and that all people the world over can trace a family line back to Confucius and Nefertiti. The logic flows from the notion that all of us—from kindergarten teachers to kings—share a common ancestry in the fairly recent past. Since the number of ancestors each of us has increases exponentially with every generation—two parents, four grandparents, eight great-grandparents, sixteen great-great-grandparents, etc.—you need look back only a few hundred years to find that collectively we have more ancestors than there would have been people on the planet. Under this theory, everyone can boast of blue blood in the branches of their family tree, because there is but one tree.

Mark Humphrys, a computer scientist and genealogist Olson interviewed at Dublin City University, rejected the idea that this somehow undermined the joy of a royal find for a family historian. He argued that while everyone has a common ancestral past, each path back to the past is unique. The reward, he said, was in reconstructing that path. "You can ask whether everyone in the Western world is descended from Charlemagne, and the answer is yes, we're all descended from Charlemagne," Humphrys said. "But can you prove it? That's the game of genealogy."

If math offered one sure shortcut to royalty, genetic testing provided another. With a mere swab, a Y chromosome or mitochondrial DNA test can indicate in a matter of weeks if one belongs to the same familial branch as Marie Antoinette, King Sweyn II of Denmark, Genghis Khan and so on. It was a key selling feature for every genetic genealogy firm opening up shop. The Crooks Y chromosome—if it was the Crooks Y—belongs to the same R1b haplogroup as England's Prince Philip, Prince Charles and Princes William and Harry, the sixteenth-century English king James I, Norwegian kings Haakon VII, Olav V and Harald V, three fifteenth-century Swedish kings, the Romanovs, and at least four kings of Greece. And every one of the many millions of men in the East Asian Haplogroup O3 who carry the same M-122 mutation as Huy Ton-That, and every one of the many millions of women and men related to those men by blood, can also claim a familial connection to Vietnam's last dynasty. My father just happens to be one of them. How sobering.

Except that my father toted more than just the M-122 mutation on his Y. He shared eight of those fast-moving markers with Huy's family signature, which suggested that our link to the regal clan was by degrees even closer. Maybe we shared a common ancestor five hundred years ago, or maybe it went back to a grandfather of Nguyen Bac from the first millennium. It still boosted my spirits to discover the partial match, as it did my dad's when I told him he was a distant genetic relative of a "nation-establishing duke."

"My goodness me," he said. "That's amazing news, just amazing. I'm chuffed! I'm feeling so Chinese these days. . . . We have no real details of my grandfather, but we have confirmation again of the Chinese history, and the trail hasn't ended yet."

In our great fishing expedition for a matching Y, finding Huy Ton-That was like a promising nibble for my father and me. It was just enough to keep us hopeful that patience would pay off. At the conference I managed to grab a moment with Mike Hammer to ask him if he, like Bennett, thought it was a false hope.

As one of the world's leading Y-chromosome experts, the University of Arizona geneticist had the aura of a rock star down in Houston, and he looked the part—boyishly handsome, thick auburn hair, wearing jeans and a leather jacket. Hammer also had a reputation for being terribly hard to reach. Reading coverage in the press about his various discoveries, from his studies on the genetic Adam to the telltale Y marker of the *kohanim* caste, I suspected the professor wasn't entirely at ease with his brand of science's becoming a recreational tool for the family historian. His work had helped pave the intersection of molecular genetics and the masses, but few academics are comfortable in the commercial world, and perhaps they are even less so in the direct-to-consumer milieu. Bridging the gap between anthropology and genealogy, as Bennett put it, might be a legitimate aim, but it's a messy one. When genealogists talk about the "distant past," they're usually referring to the centuries before surnames were adopted. To the anthropologist, that's like last Wednesday.

Even Hammer's talk at the conference had more to do with the value of the Y in forensics than in family studies. Still, as the chief scientist for Family Tree DNA, he did politely field questions from enthusiastic hobbyists over the salad-and-sandwiches lunch. And when I finally caught up with him on a break in the conference room, he seemed genuinely interested in my story, particularly the bit about the Chinese great-grandfather and my father's result suggesting his Y belonged to the O3 haplogroup. His eyes lit up in a way that suggested, *Aha . . . now here is something we can prove. . . .*

An O3 designation was unusual at the conference, and confirming a haplogroup is grounded solidly in the science of mutations, unlike the softer efforts used to predict when two men share a common male ancestor. Hammer even offered to test my father's Y to confirm that it was in fact an O3 designation. But I was most anxious to learn about my father's closest matches, I told him, which appeared to be only with men whom he had sampled on research trips in East Asia. Was there any chance that I could learn more about those men? None, Hammer replied, confirming what Bennett had told me about the anonymous donor samples. I asked him how long he thought it might be before enough Chinese DNA flowed into the public data banks to offer a reasonable chance of a near match.

Hammer shrugged and smiled sympathetically, in a way that put me in mind of the looks you get at the Delhi bus station when you ask what time the express from Agra will arrive (*Maybe today, maybe tomorrow . . .*). "It could take a while," he said. "A long while."

I envied my fellow delegates with their big family projects, their having detailed histories of ancestors dating back three or four centuries, assembled with the help of documents and DNA. I was a neophyte among them, with a lonely Y on my father's side and a dubious Y on my mother's. There were 3,642 group projects registered with the company that fall, averaging twenty members each. Some were as small as my own but others involved the DNA of dozens, and in several cases, hundreds of people.

A retired doctor from Tennessee had enough DNA data to fuel a half-hour PowerPoint presentation on the Y-chromosome haplotypes of the McLeod clan. Other men and women took the stage and described how DNA had grown their family trees, while knitting needles clattered throughout. At lunch I met Maria Plummer, an unassuming woman from the Midwest who manages the DNA of people named Smith—*Smith!* Her name tag said "Smith Worldwide." I marvelled that she had time to eat. But Plummer told me her group was not as large as I imagined, because the original Smiths project of seven hundred members had split into the Smiths of the southern U.S. and of the northeastern U.S., which also included Schmidts, Smithes, Smyths and Smythes. But since there were Smiths who matched neither of those groups, Ms. Plummer had started Smith Worldwide.

So it was that Walker was the largest surname project that fall, with about 380 members. The Williams group was running a close second, headed by one of the youngest delegates at the conference, Adrian Williams, an energetic thirty-six-year-old software developer from Missouri. One night after the conference, I spoke with him on the phone. Despite having a day job and five children, Adrian managed to devote long nights and any other hours he could spare to his hobby. He was a genealogy junkie, he said, and had even designed Internet tools to record, track and compare the DNA results of men in the Williams project. Every few weeks, men named Williams were sending in their DNA, and his project was growing at a steady clip of about a dozen new members a month.

I asked Adrian why he thought so many people—people who might never have spent a minute researching their ancestry—felt suddenly compelled to find genetic relatives. "We're lonely," he said flatly. "Families are so fractured, and we're all caught up in this rat race and in the process we kind of lost our identities. I'd much rather talk to a cousin I never knew I had than to a complete stranger. We don't want to be so lonely anymore."

Adrian had good reason to start young. His parents divorced when he was three, his father won custody of him and his mother disappeared. At the age of twenty-one he started looking for her, and after he found her, he went on to investigate his history on both sides of the family. His efforts had taken him all the way back to 1638. His earliest known male ancestor was a Roger Williams. "But I don't know where he came from, and that's the problem," he said. "In colonial America there were literally thousands of Williams who came across the pond . . . and one of the hardest problems of a U.S. family researcher is getting back across the pond."

That's the big draw of DNA for many American genealogists, he said—the hope that a genetic match can bridge the gap between the Old World and the New. "But so far," Adrian continued, "the British aren't exactly jumping on the bandwagon. They don't understand the predicament of Americans. We're immigrants and they're not, and they generally aren't as interested in their genealogies as they are in their geographies. I guess their thinking is, *I don't need to know about my cousins in the U.S.* For them it would be working their trees forward to find living relatives, some branch of their families that went off to the colonies."

The transatlantic disconnect hasn't discouraged genealogists in North America. They just kept recruiting and testing, recording and analyzing—the Williamses, the Walkers, the Smiths, the

McLeods. There were quips about packing swabbing kits before toothbrushes when they take trips, and the powerful temptation to pluck hairs without permission or steal coffee cups still wet with saliva. There was a bioethicist from the Hastings Center in New York who felt compelled to rein everybody in, arguing from the conference stage that there should be boundaries in this fledgling field, or at least a serious discussion about how to set them. Originally from New Zealand, Josephine Johnston was a wisp of a woman with a coffee-brown bob. She stood behind the podium and teased the delegates, telling them she "understood a thing or two" about them and their desires to get to the bottom of tantalizing family tales, however they could.

When I interviewed her later, she told me she had been preoccupied with the recent controversy that had erupted around DNA testing of the Melungeons, a mysterious mixed-race population with roots in Tennessee, Virginia and Kentucky. "Melungeon" was a derogatory label slapped on their dark-skinned ancestors, a number of whom were known to sport an extra thumb. In 2001, Brent Kennedy, a University of Virginia professor of Melungeon descent, collected DNA samples from more than 130 fellow descendants. Testing confirmed Native American, African and European ancestry, among others. The study angered some, who felt it had gone ahead without defining who qualifies as a Melungeon; others were riled to hear the tests had apparently proved they were part black; still others were offended that anyone should consider them Melungeon at all. And almost everyone was frustrated that the results were not published in a peer-reviewed journal where they could be properly scrutinized.

Johnston said the Melungeon study had made her determined to caution the conference crowd that afternoon. "I wanted to remind everybody that the information from these tests can be powerful and it can have an unpredictable impact, and that genes are only one aspect of what we can consider to define ourselves," she said. People attending a genetic genealogy conference might lean toward "genetic essentialism," she thought, and be more likely to see DNA as the core that defines family relationships. "But families have always been about much more than genes."

It may have been her thick Kiwi accent or the good-natured finger wagging from a wee referee, but everyone accepted Johnston's counsel with good humour. Just before she left the podium, she turned back with one last bit of advice for the DNA hunters present: "Don't do anything in the nighttime that you wouldn't do in the day." I assumed it was a far-fetched admonition, even for this lot. But later I heard a talk by a woman who proved me wrong.

Roberta Estes was one of the first people to use DNA to investigate family history. Even before surname projects existed she was sending samples to commercial labs, trying to solve mysteries on her father's side. He'd died in a car accident when she was seven. Her story stuck with me, in part because she had a hell of a stage presence—a big-boned, no-nonsense brunette from Michigan with relatives who sounded like they'd stepped out of a Mark Twain novel. There was Uncle Buster, who told her, "I don't care about DNA. . . . I am who I am," and Hard-Cider Jack, deep in the Tennessee hills, and John Y. Estes, who walked from Tennessee to Texas—twice. Roberta's intense commitment to her genealogical pursuit made her stand out, even in an auditorium full of family-gene hunters. She spoke seriously of exhumation and had actually secured an estimate (around $20,000) for digging up her father.

Roberta told the audience she knew her desire to dig up her dad probably sounded extreme. "But let's face it," she added. "We're all more than curious. If you're just curious, you wouldn't be here." She had spent thirty years researching her paternal line, and DNA testing had only broadened her ambitions. She was running about twenty surname projects, submitting DNA from hundreds of recruits, including samples from hair follicles and a stamp licked by her late grandpa. Roberta had all sorts of lessons to share, but the most striking for me at the time was how often she had stumbled upon false paternities. She had even coined her own term. "Undocumented adoptions," she called them. "Because these people were adopted, whether Daddy knew he was adopting or not." The phenomenon is so prevalent, she said, "I really, really encourage you not to test close relatives." Too late.

At a workshop on ethics, people agreed that discovering a false paternity is the number one problem genetic genealogists face—to tell or not to tell? The desire to take a DNA sample without permission ranked as number two. Yet, as Josephine Johnston told me later, there are no clear rules that apply to DNA tests given or taken for recreational purposes. In research, scientists often tell participants they cannot share individual test results, only the conclusions of the project as a whole. "But when it comes to family members, I don't see how you could enforce that—not giving individual results," Johnston said. "If you tell them you won't give them their results, they're probably not going to give you their DNA."

On top of that, Johnston said that since a genetic test result could affect those related to the person being tested—parents, siblings or children—it is fair to ask if all those people should be asked for their consent as well. "But," she acknowledged, "that's probably not feasible." As it is, the issue is not covered by any law or regulation, only by what actions are morally defensible. Ideally, people running a project should inform everyone willing to give his or her DNA about the possible outcomes, warning them in advance how often a man will learn he carries the Y chromosome of someone other than the father he knows. That way, she said, at least they receive fair warning and give *informed* consent before they swab.

Adrian Williams told me he is always up front about the potential for family secrets to fly out of the test tube. Many of the Williams men he recruits to his DNA project are strangers to him, footing the bill for their own tests, and he feels they deserve to know everything their money might buy them. "If you don't want to know, you better not ask," he said.

So when one of the Williams men in his project turned out not to match any other Williams man, but instead to have the same twenty-five markers as a man named Clark, Adrian called them both and said, "Hey, you guys are related." Their perfect match held at thirty-seven markers, and even at sixty-seven. When the Williams man had his brother tested, he found they carried two different Y chromosomes. "So [this Williams] goes to his mama and his mama says the test is wrong. But he keeps at her and keeps at her, and then she told him that the summer before her wedding, she had a beau named Clark. He was actually ecstatic to know," Adrian said.

But what if the people you test are not strangers? What if they are family members providing their DNA only because you, their curious niece, have come calling? What then?

Basil's Tavern was packed at dinner. I shared a table with three other conference delegates, an adventurous elderly couple from California who had driven to Houston in their RV, and a helpful woman from Tennessee. Together they had clocked decades visiting archives and wandering around old cemeteries before DNA testing came along. By dessert I was telling them about the disturbing match between my uncle and a man with a name all too familiar. I asked them what they would do. All of them had the same perspective: they said they would never tell a relative if they discovered he was fathered by a man other than the one he knew as dad.

This is just a hobby, they said. It hardly merited destroying a life. The woman from Tennessee said the chances of discovering a false paternity are high enough that as standard practice she collects at least two Y-chromosome samples to represent one paternal line. "If one turns out to be different than the other," she said, "I never tell a soul."

Besides, they all agreed, it's not blood that defines family relationships. So why mess with a family if the blood says something different? The Y can kiss and tell, but we don't have to. It was the same tack geneticists usually take when they come across a false paternity in their research, I told them—toss the sample and say nothing. A few years before, when I interviewed Cheryl Shuman, director of genetic counselling at Toronto's Hospital for Sick Children, she had told me that lawyers and ethicists advised them that maintaining family peace was in the best interest of the child, that any test result challenging that should be disregarded as "uninformative."

By the second day of the conference I began to suspect that my fears over my uncle's paternity were premature. Perhaps they were even unfounded. DNA tests are not infallible, and neither is the way in which they might be interpreted. Bennett had acknowledged as much in his opening remarks. He told the story of Tom Robinson, a mild-mannered Florida accounting professor vaulted into a moment of fame that summer after a British testing company found that he appeared to be a direct descendant of Genghis Khan. "From Bloody Conqueror to Guy with Calculator," one headline said. "Khan Be Too Careful," said another.

A movie company bought a ticket to fly Robinson to Mongolia to feature him in a film about the legacy of the fearsome warrior, and the Mongolian ambassador to the United States promised to hold a reception to toast the Khan's new-found descendant. But it turned out that, while Robinson shared a similar pattern of repeats on his Y with Genghis Khan, he did not belong to the same haplogroup. Oxford Ancestors, the original testing company, had checked his chromosome only for short tandem repeats, the markers that mutate so often it's entirely possible that two unrelated men from different parts of the world, and from different haplogroups, might have a similar pattern. Robinson himself had grown suspicious, since he had always thought his ancestors came to the States from England. Sure enough, a second test with Family Tree DNA found he did indeed belong to the same European haplogroup as the vast majority of those taking ancestry tests.

"And what group is that?" Bennett asked the audience. "R1!" the delegates hollered back, with all the exuberance of a Pentecostal congregation. Europe's R1 haplogroup is thought to be at least thirty thousand years younger than the Khan's C3. Not only did Robinson not descend from Genghis Khan, he didn't even inhabit the same branch of the human family tree. Robinson's story was not unique. From what I gathered, the wily code of the Y chromosome can be a master of mischief, particularly among those belonging to Europe's dominant haplogroup—as my uncle did, and as we did if he actually turned out to be a Crooks on his paternal line.

With the size of their surname projects and the passion they put into analyzing hundreds of Y-DNA test results, many group leaders had real-life examples to prove how quickly the male chromosome can mutate, even from one generation to the next. Some of its markers are prone to shifting so rapidly that Roberta Estes dubbed them "the naughty alleles." Naughty, she said, because they appear to make a mismatch of people who should match perfectly—fathers and sons or brothers—causing headaches, if not heartaches. Bennett noted that certain fast-moving markers are most likely to differ between a father and his youngest son, particularly if that son was conceived when Dad had gotten on in years. Over time, it seems, the biological mechanisms that preserve coding in the Y simply wear out, just as they do in other parts of a cell.

So even if it looked as if my uncle had a perfect match with a Meek man, there was a chance it wasn't as perfect as it looked. Observations also suggested that R1b men like my uncle seem to have a particularly high risk of so-called accidental matches. The pattern of repeats is just so prevalent among Europeans that it can suggest a family connection between two men who may not have shared a common ancestor for thousands of years. This, I heard, was especially true if the Y carries the signature of the Western Atlantic Modal Haplotype, the most common set of markers among men in western Europe. In fact Family Tree was then estimating that at least two out of every hundred western European men carry all twelve of its markers, and they warned that anyone belonging to it—which meant, apparently, me via my uncle—should start the testing at twenty-five or even thirty-seven markers, to rule out accidental matches between two men.

Is that what the Meek match was—an accident, a fluke? Was it just quirky happenstance resulting from a genetic signature so ubiquitous in western Europe that a Crooks man and a Meek man could look like close relatives when they were not? Maybe the twelve markers they shared could be blamed on a naughty allele or two, or maybe it was a ghostly remnant of a common ice-age ancestor. Maybe infidelity had nothing to do with it.

The more I heard at the conference, the more convinced I became that the Meek match could be like our supposed Native ancestry—a red herring. Before I rushed out to collect Basil's DNA, I decided I would bump up the testing on Dennis's Y chromosome to thirty-seven markers and see what happened to the Meek match then.

II

CAUGHT IN THE WEB

Men, men and more men. Every other day brought a new man to my inbox. Emails alerting me to yet another fellow with a perfect twelve-marker match with Uncle Dennis started to feel like spam. But I opened them all in case one of them was a man named Crooks. This went on for weeks, until finally, at the end of January 2007, my uncle's new test results came in.

Bumping up the number of markers tested on his Y chromosome from twelve to thirty-seven had whittled down his ever-growing list of matches with the finesse of a chainsaw—from more than five hundred men to four. Just four, and not a Meek man among them. I realized that Mr. Meek, like most of the other men on the original list, had probably not been tested beyond a dozen markers, but I was content to let that lie for the moment, to dismiss him as one of the flukes I'd heard about at the conference in Houston.

The men who did match my uncle exactly at twenty-five markers were named Barlow, Hollingsworth, Hart and Lomax. Their names had the ring of a venerable old law firm when I said them out loud, all marble and mahogany, and as British as they come. They were all close matches; Hart was off by only one marker, and the others by two. Our paternal lines must have intertwined at some point. That each man had a different surname suggested a common forefather from before surnames came into common use. But so many matching markers—nearly three dozen—seemed to suggest a more recent connection.

Trying to estimate when two men shared a common ancestor is one of the most complicated aspects of genetic genealogy. DNA alone simply cannot provide a concrete date; only a traditional paper trail can reveal that. Even when two men match perfectly at twenty-five markers or at thirty-seven (different companies test different numbers), whether they share a common surname or not, figuring out when they shared a common male ancestor is an educated guess, based on the idea that you can calibrate a molecular clock by knowing how often mutations occur. On the Y, different markers mutate at different rates, and some much faster than others—like the naughty alleles Roberta Estes described in Houston—apt to change even between one son and the next, blurring the genetic line between brothers. But researchers have established the varying mutation rates for various markers on the Y chromosome and how often each one is likely to change per generation. So by comparing the Ys of two men, marker for marker, it's possible to come up with a time window of probability. The more markers tested, the less likely there will be false positives suggesting that two men are related when they are not, or false negatives that suggest two men are not related when they are.

Two men who share a marker known to change quickly are more likely to have had a common forefather more recently. If two men have a mismatch on a marker known to be as stable as the pyramids, the time back to a common ancestor is greater. If the mismatch is slight—say one man has a marker where the sequence is repeated twelve times and the other man has a repeat of eleven—that's a single misstep in favour of a more recent family connection. Thankfully, most DNA-testing companies provide a special calculator that factors all these variables into an equation and does the math for you.

In the case of my uncle's match of thirty-five out of thirty-seven with Melvyn Lomax, for example, the calculator predicted an 80 percent chance of a common male ancestor within the past eight generations. The odds rise to 89 percent that our common forefather lived sometime within the past twelve generations, and if we reach back twenty-four generations, the chances jump all the way to 99.7 percent. If you put a generation at twenty years, the results suggested that at the outside, Mel Lomax and my uncle shared a forefather who lived sometime in the past five hundred years. That wasn't just post–ice age; that was post–Middle Ages. It was something, finally, to work with.

The time frame to a common ancestor was similar for all the men in my uncle's quartet of well-matched Ys. But that was all that could be said about it without swapping details of our known histories. Once the emails started to fly, I learned that Hollingsworth, Hart and Barlow were all Americans who had spent years researching their ancestry, all with the aim of tracing their forefathers back across the pond. They were fairly certain their paternal lines led back to England, and none of them had any known connection to Jamaica.

I came to know Mel Lomax best. He was a retired police sergeant living in Hervey Bay, a small seaside city north of Brisbane, Australia. Mel went by his mother's surname of Lomax, but his father's last name had been Ainsworth, and Ainsworth, he told me, was also the name of the hamlet in Radcliffe, in northwest England, where he was born. Radcliffe was historically part of Lancashire, and Mel felt that was the county that connected us all, the place where our paternal lines converged. He'd spent more than thirty years researching his ancestry in Lancashire, where the surnames Hollingsworth, Barlow, Hart and Crooks had been kicking around for centuries. I remembered reading that one of the earliest references to the Crooks surname could be found in the north of England—in Lancashire in particular—and now DNA was leading me to the very same region.

That we all had different surnames didn't surprise Mel. As he described it, back in the twelfth and thirteenth centuries, just after surnames were introduced in England, people often changed their names like petticoats, especially if it gave them a leg up on a piece of land, entitled them to a certain position or status or improved their marriage prospects. The Crooks and Ainsworth families, he told me, had connections to the region's famous Pilkington family, a powerful clan of knights and nobles. One Katherine Ainsworth had married Robert de Pilkington in the fifteenth century; their son Alexander, who inherited the estate at Rivington, married a Katherine de Crook, daughter of Richard de Crook of Whittle. Mel included links to websites so I could read more about them, and I did, burrowing into a rabbit hole of medieval dealings and marriages involving the Crookses of Lancashire.

Founded in the twelfth century, around the same time that surnames were introduced in England, Lancashire was a county of green and grit, with rolling hills, pastures and farms but also quarries, mills, mines and shipbuilders, especially around Liverpool. Long before it was known for its football team or that little band called the Beatles, Liverpool was famous for its port. Nearly half the world's trade was passing through by the early nineteenth century. And it may be that nothing did more to build its shipping business, and the city itself, than the slave trade. Ships dropped anchor with their American tobacco and cotton and sugar from the West Indies, and off it went to be milled or manufactured into goods that were shipped back to the colonies—and to Africa, to barter for more slaves to work the New World plantations. Round and round it went, with cargoes sold and resold even before they reached their destinations, making rich men of merchants and shipbuilders and making Liverpool the Empire's slave-trading capital. According to the historian Roger Antsey, one out of every four vessels that left Liverpool in the seventeenth century was a slave-trading ship.

Was that it? I wondered. Had one of the Crooks men of Lancashire been lured to the West Indies, to Jamaica, by the ships that docked so close to home? Even now, just south of Liverpool's city centre there's a road called Jamaica Street.

I spent long nights reading up on ye olde Crookses of Lancashire, rummaging through the links Mel sent and other sites I found, all of which confirmed that the northern England Crooks clan had lived and prospered in the region for some nine centuries. From the sixteenth to the early nineteenth century they had the largest manor in the township of Whittle-le-Woods (according to the digital library of British History Online, Crook Hall boasted nine hearths). There was a Thomas Crook of Hoole who founded numerous charities and left a will that mentioned more than a dozen different estates, at Bretherton, Much Hoole, Mawdesley, Walton-le-Dale, Billinge, Euxton . . . and on it went. His widow, Abigail Crooks, passed this and more on to her son. There was a Richard Crook in 1705, "a gentleman" who built a Nonconformist chapel in Hindley, and a Samuel Crooke who registered his house in 1749 as a meeting place for Protestant dissenters. There were Crookses all over the county, in Bolton-le-Moors, in Bury, in Abram.

Yet all the while I read, the futility of it nagged me. How could I guess if any of these people were my ancestors? What name was I looking for? I knew only the Captain's, and he was born centuries after the people in these accounts. I knew nothing of his parents, whether they had come from Europe or been Jamaica-born. DNA suggested that Lancashire was significant, but it was useless for suggesting a when or a how. I had known this limitation going in, but I imagine that knowing about quicksand and experiencing it are entirely different things. Finding a paper trail that might bridge the gap between continents seemed unlikely; Mel had been working at his genealogical puzzle for thirty years and he was still piecing it together. But if I could somehow get a DNA sample from a descendant of one of those Crooks men in Lancashire, and if it matched our Crooks Y, it would at least tell me if I was barking up the right family tree.

That line of thinking brought me right back to my original dilemma. I still had no confirmation that Dennis actually carried the Crooks Y. He had never matched anyone named Crooks. And I was still telling myself that the Meek match was a meaningless accident, a coincidence, but the possibility remained that it was not. Late one night I emailed the Meek contact on Dennis's list, and a Mrs. Meek in Virginia replied. She told me that the Y she had sent in for testing belonged to her husband and that he had a long ancestry in the United States and before that in Scotland. But at that point he had not been tested beyond twelve markers. That left open the possibility that Mr. Meek could still match my uncle if he were tested for more markers. A quick search of old English registers revealed that there were Meeks in Lancashire just as there were Crookses. That meant I couldn't rule out the idea that my uncle carried the Y of a Meek man. If I was going to start soliciting DNA from strangers named Crooks, I had better be damn sure I'd actually be comparing it to another Crooks sample.

My mother and I had hardly spoken of the matter since I'd first broached it the previous fall. I kept her up-to-date with the information flowing from Dennis's DNA results, my correspondence with Mel, the old Crooks manor I learned about in Whittle-le-Woods. My mother seemed content, as I was, to simply follow the trail blindly for a while. Still, she wasn't at all surprised when I told her that spring that at last I felt I had to ask Basil for his DNA. If his Y matched up with Dennis's, I told her, we'd be in the clear. "Let's pray to God it is the same," she said.

Uncle Basil was the perfect confirmation sample. He looks a lot like my grandfather. If appearances can be trusted, he carries the Crooks Y chromosome as surely as he does the Crooks curls. Also, his youngest daughter, Simone, has the best example of that celebrated head of hair in our family—long, kinky tendrils that would seem to stretch back to an elusive island past. Uncle Basil and my Aunty Norma live near my parents too. They were the first of the Crookses to emigrate from England in the late 1960s, raising four children and building a successful electronics business. It was their reports from Canada that made it a magnet for the rest of the family. So much space! Everything so new! Bitter winters, yes, but the promise of beautiful summers, and a bright future in a young country where immigrants were welcome.

Simone happened to be visiting when I dropped in on them, and she joined my uncle and me around the dining table, catching up. They asked how the research was going so far and I waffled my way through an explanation. I told Uncle Basil it looked as if Uncle Dennis's Y chromosome could be traced back to Europe but that I needed another sample to verify the results. My uncle said he was curious to see how the search would turn out. He was too young to recall any details about the Captain's story, but he hoped we could learn something at last about the family's connection to Jamaica. I drove his sample straight to the post office that afternoon, impatient for the result yet dreading it too.

On a morning in late spring when my parents were out, Aunty Merlyn dropped off a package for me in their mailbox. I drove out to pick it up as soon as my mother called, eager to see what Dennis had assembled. On the kitchen table sat a large white envelope containing four sheets of paper, all of them photocopies of old documents. One was a copy from Bombay's Public Health Department: my grandfather Freddie's birth record of January 31, 1905. Under the heading "caste" it said "Eurasian," and it noted his father's occupation as chief officer aboard SS *Ahmadi*. On the same page was a copy of my great-grandfather's certificate of death at the age of thirty-two, on September 29, 1906, listing the cause as beriberi. This time his occupation was recorded as captain of SS *Rahmani*; to my surprise, it listed his "caste" as "American." I wondered if the form had been filled out on the orders of his mysterious relatives in

New York, the ones said to be tight with the Freemasons and who had wanted to adopt my grandfather after the captain died.

There was a copy of my grandfather's 1906 baptismal certificate, from Emmanuel Church in Bombay, and a copy of the 1902 registration of marriage between my great-grandparents, Bridget Jane Meek and Frederick William Crooks. Under the heading for parents of the groom, it included the name of the Captain's father, my great-great-grandfather, George Atkinson Crooks. But by far the most significant document—the one I would study hard in the weeks ahead—was a legal-sized paper stamped "Certified Copy of an Entry in the Register of Baptisms." It was from the General Register Office, Spanish Town, Jamaica, and handwritten with the lavish elegance of a bygone era.

Register of Baptisms kept by E.A. Stewart, Minister to the Parish of Trelawny in the County of Cornwall in the year 1874.

When and where born: 17 July, 1873, Falmouth

Name: Frederick William Crooks

Sex: Male

Complexion: Col'd

Legitimate: Legit

When Baptized: 30 June 1874

Name of Father: George A. Crooks

Name and Maiden Name of Mother: Cath. Storks, Cath. Crooks

Rank or Profession of Father: Accountant

Abode: Falmouth

I called my parents to come take a look and we dissected the document for the new details it contained: the names of both the Captain's parents, that his father had been an accountant. And—unlike the charcoal sketch that had left open for debate the shade of my great-grandfather's skin—this form, under the heading "complexion," right there in black and white, described him as "coloured." *Coloured*, my father was quick to point out, was the most general term used by colonialists to describe anyone of mixed ancestry. To me the word was instant corroboration of the sub-Saharan African markers that had been tagged in my mother's DNA, of what we could see with our own eyes in the features of family members. Yet it brought with it so many more questions: Had the Captain's kinfolk been mostly black? The Captain had clearly been born free, and his father, an accountant, must have been a free man. But slavery was abolished in Jamaica only in 1838. Had the Captain's grandparents—my mother's ancestors, and mine—been born in bondage?

We were bewildered by the mention of Falmouth as their place of residence. "I thought they were from Kingston," I said. "Yes," my mother said, "I only ever heard they were from Kingston."

When I called Dennis to thank him for the documents, I asked him if he knew anything about George Atkinson Crooks or if he could shed any light on this unexpected mention of Falmouth. But he said, "No, my girl, I don't know anything about Falmouth. I always thought Papa's people were from Kingston."

It was entirely plausible that after two generations nobody would have a clue where the Captain had grown up, let alone where he had been born. It had taken some time before anyone recalled that Trichinopoly was the birthplace of Nana Gladys; certainly she never spoke much of it. And what did my siblings or I know about Jabalpur, the Indian city where my mother was born when her father was stationed at the railway colony there? My mother has always described it as an "up-country" posting, which I came to understand meant any place north of what was then Bombay. If I knew only that, it seemed certain my children would know even less, and what might their children ask?

I initially assumed Dennis had hunted down these documents himself, perhaps to prove his identity as a rightful beneficiary of the inheritance that New York Uncle Crooks had tried to leave him. But I noticed small print at the bottom of each document certifying they were true duplicates of original records requested between the fifteenth and twenty-third of May 1947—three months before India became an independent nation; less than three weeks before the British government accepted the Mountbatten Plan and carved up the subcontinent into states of chaos and slaughter. My grandfather must have scrambled to assemble these copies with a growing sense of urgency, requesting them all in a span of nine days, assuming they would paper his way to Jamaica. He must have passed them down to Dennis. I wondered if he had left any files to my grandmother or whether she had kept any of the papers from his old study back in England. My father had helped her apply for her British pension, filed her tax returns and acted as a co-executor of her will, and he once mentioned that he'd come across my grandmother's address book and wondered if it contained anything useful. It was time to find out.

A week later, Mum, Dad, Jade and I marched down to my parents' basement. Thirty years ago it was the heart of all our house parties: a sprawling hardwood floor for dancing, a stone fireplace, a Formica-topped bar. An old wicker-bottomed bottle of Madeira still dangles on the wall, obscuring a gift my father received from an Indonesian client: a painting on black velvet of a topless red-head with impossibly large eyes.

As Jade explored the adjoining crawl space, I sat on the bottom step, watching as my father searched through his filing cabinets.

"I think I may have put it in here," he was saying.

"It's the address book you're after?" Mum asked.

"Well, yes," I said, "but anything that might help, really."

Mum disappeared up the basement stairs. I didn't expect to see her back for a while. My mother is more of a hider than a filer, more likely to wrap an Important Thing in a handkerchief and tuck it between two cardigans than slip it into a labelled envelope. But she reappeared just a few minutes later, triumphantly waving a small gold address book.

I leafed through the pages alphabetically until I got to the

Cs. Most of the entries had been written in the large, even print of my mother's younger sister Doris. The first page of C entries included the addresses and numbers of all my uncles, complete with honorifics and initials and in descending birth order: Mr. O.T. Crooks, Kent, UK; Mr. T.A. Crooks, Surrey, UK; Mr. D.M. Crooks, Ontario, Canada . . . No one would guess from the formality of it that these were my grandmother's children.

I turned the page, expecting more familiar names, but the very first lines contained an entry for a Mrs. Clare Crooks, 492 Hancock Street, Brooklyn 33, New York, U.S.A. It was the address to which Dennis and my mother had once corresponded. I had looked it up through old New York property records kept online and found that a Frederick Augustus Crooks had once owned it. I assumed he was the mystery uncle, and from what I could tell he had run a successful real estate business in New York. I also found his death registration in 1969, the same year Dennis had been contacted about his will. It had listed his birthdate as 1893—twenty years younger than the Captain and so, perhaps, a nephew. Interestingly, it mentioned that he had died in Central America. When I phoned the number listed for 492 Hancock Street, an older woman with a thick Southern drawl answered and told me she recalled that Crookses had once lived there. But not for a very, very long time, she said, and that was all she knew.

Three entries below the Hancock address in my grandmother's book, the last one on the page, was yet another address for Mrs. Clare Crooks. Except this one was in Jamaica: 16 Sheriton Park Crescent in Kingston, no phone number. I was gobsmacked. Nana had an address for the Crooks family in Jamaica? She knew the family in Jamaica? Had she communicated with them? Why had she never mentioned it?

I pointed to the entry and passed the book to my mother. She looked at it quizzically and passed it to my father.

"Did you know Nana had this address?" Dad asked.

"No," Mum said.

"Well, she must have known the family in Jamaica," I said.

"She must have," my mother agreed, "but she never said a word."

"Well, it's all written in Aunty Doris's handwriting. Do you think Doris knows anything?" I asked.

"No, I think Doris only copied this for Nana from another book."

I'd been searching madly for a concrete lead in Jamaica and there it was in my grandmother's address book—no Q-tip required.

My father poured us all wine and we lazed around the living room that afternoon musing about the secrets my grandmother had kept, marvelling that she had never mentioned she knew the whereabouts of the Crooks family in Jamaica, and why that might have been so. Had their ties broken with Dennis's legal wrangling? Had my grandfather known them? You'd think Nana might have said *something* in all those years of Sundays.

At home later that night, with the rest of the house asleep, I flipped through my grandmother's book again. On the back pages Doris had written the birthdates and anniversaries of all her children and grandchildren. I found only two entries that my grandmother, in a shaky scrawl, had penned herself: a friend she'd met after moving to Canada and my grandfather's cousin Mervyn Meek, the son of one of Nana Bridget's brothers—but not Earnest. His name wasn't in my grandmother's book. Mum said the last time she had seen Earnest Meek he was standing alone on a pier in Bombay, waving goodbye as their ship sailed for England in 1958.

My father had filled a large manila envelope for me with a few of the other items Nana had left with my parents, including matching leather billfolds my grandfather had purchased for them both, their initials embossed in gold on the front. Inside one was a faded prayer card with a picture of Our Lady of Vailankanni on one side and an act of contrition on the other . . . *O my God, I am heartily sorry for having offended Thee.* . . . I returned it to the billfold, a mixture of emotions churning heavily in my chest—suspicion, mistrust, guilt. Why hadn't I asked her more questions?

Another pocket of the billfold held a peeling black-and-white photo of my grandparents standing in the back garden of their house in England. My grandmother is wearing a dark dress with a large floral print, and Papa, looking tall and lanky in a suit jacket and baggy slacks, has his arm around her shoulders. Mum always said people thought he looked like Jimmy Stewart with a good tan. What would Papa have said about all this fuss I was stirring up to find our Jamaican roots?

I turned on the computer and called up the website for telephone directories in Jamaica. Within moments I was scanning the Kingston white pages. There was nearly a full page of Crookses listed. Halfway down I found a Carol E. Crooks living at the address written in my grandmother's book, 16 Sheriton Park Crescent. After all these years, it was still the home of a Crooks.

The next morning I had a good breakfast and two cups of coffee before I called. I needed to think through the conversation, where I would start. . . . *Oh, hello. One hundred years ago a Captain named Crooks died in Bombay. You didn't by chance know him, did you?*

It is so much simpler to connect with perfect strangers when you share the same pattern of nucleotides. I tried the number several times that afternoon, but an electronic answering machine picked up with every attempt. I tried twice more in the evening. Finally, shortly after nine o'clock, a young woman answered. "Good night," she said.

This confused me for a moment. "Good night? . . . Hello?" I said.

"Yes, hello?"

"Hello," I said. "I'm looking for Carol E. Crooks."

"Yes, that is my mother."

"Well, I'm sorry to disturb you, but I'm calling from Toronto, Canada, and looking for some Crooks relatives there. My mother was a Crooks and I found your address in my grandmother's address book."

"I think you want to talk to my mother," the woman said. "Do you want to talk to my mother?"

"Yes, that would be great. I'm trying to find out some information about our Crooks family in Jamaica."

"I'll get my mother," she said.

The phone clunked down on a hard surface and I could hear the woman faintly in the background saying something about Crooks . . . family . . . Canada . . .

An older woman came to the phone. "Good night," she said.

"Good night," I replied, probably a bit too cheerfully. I apologized for the late hour and began my explanation again. "My mother's maiden name is Crooks and I found your address in my grandmother's address book. The listing is for a Clare Crooks."

"I'm sorry, I don't know Clare Crooks," the woman said.

Her Jamaican accent was as thick as molasses. I could barely make out her words until she said, "Gimme some nehms."

I started rhyming them off: the Captain's name, his father's, his mother's, the name of the New York Uncle, Frederick Augustus, and his wife, whom I assumed was Clare.

"Well, I know dere was a Frederick and Clare Crooks, I tink, dat used to live here. . . ." she said. Then she told me she had lived in the house for twenty-seven years, that she was a Crooks only by marriage, and that she was now estranged from her husband, James Crooks. If I wanted to know more about Frederick and Clare, who she thought might now be long dead too, I ought to ask these questions of James Crooks. She suggested that I leave her my number and she would get him to call me. I asked if I might have a number at which to reach him. She said she did not have one. "I see him from time to time," she said. "But I will tell him ya called."

"Well, I would be very grateful if you could pass it on to him. He could always call me here collect."

"Okay," she said, "I'll do dat."

I hung up, utterly deflated. The Kingston connection seemed

to have turned out to be like the address on Hancock Street and a Chinese haplotype—a dead end.

There may be no better remedy for the genealogy blues than the Internet and several uninterrupted watch-the-sun-come-up hours of clicking into the abyss. The sensation that you may be just a link away from pay dirt never leaves you. This must be why family-history hunting can be as addictive as gambling, why it rivals online gaming as one of North America's top pastimes. Keep plugging your ancestral particulars into the machine and some primitive region of the brain—perhaps a Pavlovian instinct conserved from a day when persistent spear throwing eventually led to dinner—suggests that your numbers will soon come up. One moment I'd be reading about the fancy-pants of Lancashire and the next I was trolling the Crooks discussion boards on Ancestry.com or GenForum.

At one point I shot off messages to Lanclist.com, where I'd found some present-day Crookses in the area, broaching the subject of DNA testing. One respondent asked for specific dates and places first, which, if I had them, would have made the DNA unnecessary. Another said she knew her ancestry back only two generations and thought it premature to consider such a drastic step as DNA testing. That sent me to Ysearch.org to see if anyone named Crooks had uploaded DNA results, and while I was there I checked in vain for matches for my father's Y chromosome as well. When this fell flat, I remembered that my mother-in-law had read a genealogy magazine that recommended Cyndi's List as the most comprehensive index of genealogy sites.

So off I clicked, only to discover TheShipsList, an astonishing online archive related to vessels, voyages and passenger lists. Two Canadian scholars run it, women by the names of Swiggum and Kohli. It was there I discovered the Bombay and Persia Steam Navigation Company, founded in 1877, which owned the ships my great-grandfather sailed. The ships were indeed active in the "pilgrim trade," and in 1939 the company was renamed the Mogul

Line, as my father had known it. But both ships, like the Captain, met tragic ends. SS *Ahmadi* was wrecked off the shore of Mombasa in 1909, where it still lies, and SS *Rahmani*, en route from Bombay to Genoa, sank in the Mediterranean Sea after a collision in 1917. Buoyed by information even tangentially relevant to our ancestry, I scoured (again) the Mormons' FamilySearch site, where I found a seemingly endless list of Crookses, from the West Indies to West Virginia. But none of them was named George Atkinson Crooks or Frederick William Crooks, and there was no way to distinguish my kin from the others.

I contacted the Jamaica Archives and Records Department and emailed a request for any records related to George Atkinson Crooks. A staff member replied, promising to take an initial peek at no charge, but within a week another message informed me that nothing had come up, either in Falmouth or in its entire parish of Trelawny. She could, she wrote, for US$30 an hour, continue to search elsewhere, but there were a full fourteen parishes in Jamaica's three counties. Beyond the birthdate of the Captain I had no other specifics for them to search. I envisioned taking out a second mortgage for what could be a completely pointless quest—my great-great-grandfather might not have been from Jamaica at all. Maybe George Atkinson Crooks was originally from England and had settled in Jamaica only later in life, marrying a coloured woman there. And so back I'd go to reading about the quasi-lords of Lancashire in Bolton-le-Moors and Whittle-le-Woods, finding myself humming "There's a Hole in My Bucket."

It was a book that saved me.

Some months before, the novel *Ancestors*, by the British author Paul Crooks, had arrived by mail. I'd put off reading it, too distracted by the questions about our DNA. But once I picked it up, it became my refuge that hot summer—an uncomfortable one but a refuge—my introduction to slavery in Jamaica. True, it was a work of fiction, but, as one reviewer put it, "fiction based on terrible fact," forcing me to look into the stony heart of the story I was chasing. It was impossible to read and not imagine that some version of it was our story as well, the backstory of our "coloured" Captain Crooks.

It begins with the Atlantic crossing, in 1789, in the dank bowels of a slave ship where a boy is shackled, a small link in a human chain of agony. Captured from his village on the Gold Coast of Africa, stolen from his parents, the boy finds comfort only in the words of a woman, Ami, a stranger who speaks to him of home. Her voice is a salve that sustains him through the hundred sunrises he counts through cracks and portholes, through miles of stench and death.

When they reach Jamaica, they lose each other, the boy and the woman, sold to different estates. At the slave market a white man brands the boy with a C, and he arrives in chains at Crooks Cove, a lush plantation on the coast. It becomes his new home and August is his new name, assigned to him by Big Belly Massa John, the white Crooks man, the *buckra*. Crooks lives in the grand house on the hill, watching over his cane and the slave village below, where August stays with an old woman who teaches him to survive a life of bondage. He becomes a field worker and a Christian with a Christian name—John Alexander Crooks—and he prays for freedom. It is a time of unrest, the eve of abolition. In the swirl of riots and rebellion he finds Sarah, a free mulatto woman, one of the "black-white" children of a neighbouring master—and, he discovers, the daughter of Ami, who nurtured him across the Atlantic so many years before. When freedom comes, John and Sarah Crooks leave with their babies and their loaded cart, heading deep into the hills of Jamaica, determined to put a "big mountain between us and this place. . . ."

I studied the author's notes, hoarding clues from his research, the true details that had inspired him to reconstruct the story of his ancestors. Paul Crooks wrote that he was an administrator with the National Health Service in England and about my age, from what I could tell. He'd also started asking questions about his ancestry when he was seven and realized the connection between Africa and black people. He wondered how they had got their family name, Crooks. It sounded odd to him. "Who was the first Crooks who ever lived?" he'd asked his father. "Was he a white man?"

Similar questions haunted him into adulthood, and eventually he became preoccupied with trying to find his slave ancestors. He spent long nights at the Mormons' Family History Centre and the British Library, and after more than a dozen years, his efforts paid off. He found his fourth-generation grandmother, Ami Djaba, born in Africa and the inspiration for the Ami character in his book. The boy whom Ami nurtures on the eighteenth-century slave ship was based on the life Paul Crooks imagined for his great-great-great-grandfather, John Alexander Crooks, who actually was kidnapped from Africa at the age of ten and put aboard a slave ship bound for Jamaica, and who eventually did lead his family to freedom.

Once liberated, they settled in the south-western Jamaican parish of Westmoreland, where many Crookses could be found. But what the author still did not know—the missing piece in his ancestral puzzle—was where they had all come from. Where had his Crooks ancestors been enslaved before abolition? At the Royal Geographic Society in London, he found his answer. A map of Jamaica from 1768 depicted a large plantation on the northwest shore of the island: Crooks Cove. I searched a modern-day map of Jamaica but found nothing in the region named Crooks Cove, only a Cousins Cove. If that was it, it wasn't far at all from where my great-grandfather had been born in Falmouth. I wondered if DNA would connect us to that place, whether my answer would lie on a genetic map.

12

MEN ABOUT TOWN

DNA first convicted a killer in 1986. It happened in Leicester, just a stone's throw from the English university where DNA fingerprinting was pioneered. Two local teenaged girls had been raped and murdered two years apart and the prime suspect was a seventeen-year-old local boy named Richard Buckland. A new DNA profiling test performed on semen taken from the crime scene, however, did not match Buckland. Instead, after police ran a DNA dragnet, testing five thousand area men, they found it matched a baker by the name of Colin Pitchfork. He was the first man ever convicted with DNA evidence, and Buckland the first man exonerated because of it. The double helix has grown in the public consciousness ever since, as a kind of weapon of truth wielded to prove guilt, innocence, paternity, history, health, identity.

But DNA can be a dull blade. A lab tech talks too much while processing a sample and her spit contaminates it. A prenatal scan points to a disability that isn't there in an unborn child. A Y-chromosome test suggests a family link between a Florida professor and Genghis Khan that doesn't exist. Like all human endeavours, genetics is a science subject to the fallibility of human reasoning, to errors and misinterpretations.

Never was this more evident to me than one Wednesday afternoon in August. I received a message from Family Tree DNA informing me that my Uncle Dennis had a Y-chromosome match with a man who shared his Crooks surname—my Uncle Basil, his brother. After a year of wretched hand-wringing, the ghost of anxiety lifted from my shoulders. Two men with the same surname and an exact twelve-marker match on their Y chromosomes have a 99 percent chance of sharing a common forefather in the recent past. In the case of Dennis and Basil, it couldn't be more recent. They were full brothers, fathered by the same man, my grandfather. I no longer had a secret to keep, a family skeleton to shove back in the closet. I had an urge to pull out my grandmother's prayer card and offer up an act of contrition. DNA had exonerated her. But then it was DNA that had misled me in the first place, wasn't it?

My maternal grandparents, Freddie and Gladys Crooks, enjoying cocktails on my father's ship docked in Bombay in 1951.

The circumstantial evidence had been striking: there was motive, opportunity. Earnest had been the live-in handyman, for crying out loud. And he liked to dance. What's more, the basic conclusion was not incorrect. At a dozen markers, Dennis's Y chromosome does match the Y of a man named Meek. But that is because the human population is so young and puny that the paternal lines of the Crooks and Meek sides of my family lead back to the same man, sometime between the last ice age and the emergence of surnames. The global family is just that tight.

Basil's test result made me as confident as I could be that I had the Crooks chromosome in hand, passed down from my grandfather and his father before him. It confirmed a branch of European heritage and made the connection to Lancashire more concrete. But most remarkable to me was what it said about the Captain. His christening record from Spanish Town described him as "coloured." But like a third of African-American men and many of the world's dark-skinned males, my great-grandfather carried the Y of a white man. And white men had been sailing to Jamaica ever since Christopher Columbus stepped ashore in 1494.

Columbus called Jamaica "the fairest island eyes have beheld," bigger than Sicily, full of valleys and fields and mountains that touch the sky. When his expedition arrived, it was home to the Taino people, a peaceful tribe of Arawak Indians who fished and farmed, drank cassava beer and slept in hammocks. They called their island paradise Xaymaca, meaning "land of wood and water." But it became their hell after the Europeans laid claim to it, bringing disease, enslavement, famine. The Arawak were wiped out—an estimated sixty thousand people in fifty years. The only trace left of the indigenous people Columbus encountered in the Caribbean may be genetic, the DNA passed down from Native women who bore the children of European men.

It was the Spanish who introduced slavery to the Americas. As the Arawak disappeared, the Spaniards began importing Africans to Jamaica. Columbus had originally claimed the island for Spain as a rich source of silver and gold. When it turned out not to be, the Spanish monarchy gave it to the Columbus family in 1540 as a personal estate. Not much was done to develop it.

Colonists established a few towns and farms, but the Spanish generally treated Jamaica like a drive-through, a port of call for its warships bound for South America. When the British Navy arrived in May 1655, the Spanish barely mustered a fight.

But for Britain too, Jamaica was initially the consolation prize of the Caribbean. Oliver Cromwell, who had recently defeated the royalists in England's Civil War and executed King Charles I, sent ships to attack Spain's trading power in the West Indies and stem the spread of Catholicism. Under the command of Admiral William Penn and General Robert Venables, they were to capture the Spanish-held island of Hispaniola (now Haiti and the Dominican Republic). But they were foiled by bad planning, bad drinking water and a motley crew. In the end, the British suffered a near massacre at Santo Domingo; only then, fearing Cromwell's reaction, did they sail for Jamaica.

Cromwell was not impressed: he locked up Penn and Venables in the Tower of London upon their return. But eventually he decided to make the most of his new island colony, offering free plots to the expedition crew and those willing to move there. Others he sent by force—criminals, unsavoury characters, Irish boys as indentured servants, Irish girls for the soldiers who stayed, and more than a thousand Scottish prisoners-of-war to serve wealthy English settlers. Thousands more Scots followed of their own accord: impoverished young men who signed on for years of servitude, and others keen to make a quick fortune in the white gold that was sugar. Europe had grown a sweet tooth and even men of modest means could become rich by the cane.

The Spanish were the first to bring sugar cane to Jamaica, importing it from Haiti in 1509. But it was the British who turned its cultivation into a behemoth industry, powered almost entirely by slave labour. After Cromwell's death and the return of the English monarchy, King Charles II made sugar the signature of his reign. He recruited investors and planters and chartered the Royal African Company to ensure that Britain would never have to buy its slaves from foreigners. By 1734 Britain was shipping in ten thou-sand Africans a year to toil on the island's 429 plantation estates, and at least one of them was owned by a man named Crooks.

It was hard not to picture him as the Massa John portrayed in Paul Crooks's novel—the fat, rum-swilling overlord having his way with his house slave, burning alive the black man who dared to rebel. In his afterword the author wrote that the Cove planta-tion actually did belong to a John Crooks for a time, but that a James Crooks owned it before him. I wondered if James Crooks had sailed there from Lancashire, whether he was a forefather of the Captain's—of ours—along with ancestors born in bondage on his land.

It sounded logical, the Crooks Y chromosome being of European origin, tying us to the European Crookses who settled the island. But the Meek match had taught me the dangers of assuming too much. Maybe there was more than one white Crooks settler in Jamaica, maybe an indentured servant from Scotland, for all I knew. But if I could find descendants of the Crooks planta-tion family—hopefully a male willing to donate his Y to my cause—I could theoretically learn whether we actually did have a connection to that slave estate by the sea, whether it was the cove our Captain had left and the place my grandfather had dreamed about.

I had no luck with the usual sources one uses to hunt for ancestors who crossed the pond. There was nothing about a Crooks sailing to Jamaica in *The Complete Book of Emigrants*, *The Complete Book of Emigrants in Bondage* or even the classic nineteenth-century tome *The Original Lists of Persons of Quality; Emigrants; Religious Exiles; Political Rebels; Serving Men Sold for a Term of Years; Children Stolen; Maidens Pressed; And Others who went from Great Britain to the American Plantations, 1600–1700*. That was compiled in 1874 by John Camden Hotten, the shady proprietor of a small London bookshop, distributor of pirated editions of Walt Whitman poetry and Mark Twain novels and a purveyor of his own eclectic body of work, which included biographies, erotic poems, picture books and *A Modern Dictionary of Slang, Cant and Vulgar Words* (which saw numerous reprints). He is rumoured to have died from eating too many pork chops. Hotten's text is a favourite of North American genealogists, but the only Crookses I found in his book ended up in Virginia.

I had more success tracking eighteenth- and nineteenth-century Crookses on twenty-first-century websites. One in particular, Jamaican Family Search, turned out to be an astounding trove of the island's history. The site was created and maintained by Patricia Jackson, a genealogist in California who grew up in Jamaica. All sorts of family historians have contributed to it over the years, making it a rich repository of directories; census records; birth and death registers; lists of early immigrants, landholders, and military personnel; wills; personal correspondence; newspaper clippings; and essays historical and contemporary.

I signed up, and on my first day trawling through it I found a reference to a George A. Crooks, whom I took to be the Captain's father and my great-great-grandfather. It was a brief item published in the *Falmouth Post* on Tuesday, July 24, 1877, under the headline EXTRAORDINARY BIRTH: "On Thursday night in this town, the wife of Mr. George A. Crooks gave birth to three Sons. The young fellows are strong and healthy, and along with the mother, are doing well." Triplets. We had triplets in the family. The notice did not spell out George's middle name as Atkinson, but the timing and the place fit perfectly—Falmouth, four years after the Captain was born.

The birth announcement was just one of 150 references to the Crooks surname on the site. In nineteenth-century directories for the north-western parishes of Trelawny—home to Falmouth and, apparently, the Captain's family—and Hanover, where the Crooks plantation had been, I found mention of a labourer named Crooks, a fisherman named Crooks, a schoolmaster, a schoolmistress, a merchant, a mariner, a carpenter, a tinsmith, a goldsmith, a deputy bailiff, a baker, a wharf operator and even a keeper of the town clock in Lucea. It seemed as if all the people who lived on this shoulder of the island were named Crooks. Then I came across a document that explained why. It was a slave register.

Written sixty years before the birth announcement of the Crooks triplets, twenty-one years before abolition, the register listed all the slaves owned at the Cousins Cove plantation. From the map of Jamaica I'd seen, Cousins Cove seemed to lie in the stretch of land where Crooks Cove had once been. Of the 179 men, women and children listed as slaves on the property in 1817, sixty-three were named Crooks.

Property owners in Jamaica had not been required to track slaves by name until Britain abolished the transatlantic slave trade in 1807. Only then did the Crown start demanding a regular accounting of slaves, to ensure that Africans were not being secretly imported to the island. The planters were apoplectic. They saw it as an attack on their right to govern their own affairs. Some even mused about following in the footsteps of American revolutionaries and breaking from Britain entirely. But for all their fomenting, the registration of slaves became law in 1815.

The tally I came across appeared to be the first one ever conducted at the Cove. It was titled "A Return of slaves in the parish of Hanover in the Possession of Richard Dickson as owner settled on Cousins Cove Sugar Plantation on the 28 day of June in the Year of Our Lord 1817." I wasn't sure who Dickson was, or how he had come to own the Crooks property and its slaves. The register listed their "old names," Christian name, colour, age and whether they were African-born. Two names were familiar to me: August, age thirty, the real-life grandfather, three generations back, of author Paul Crooks; and the African matriarch of his family, "Ammie Jabba," age forty, one of forty-eight slaves who had arrived in Jamaica from Africa. The rest had been born on the island and were designated as "creole," from the Spanish word *criollo*, meaning "to breed." The registration of creole slaves included information on their parentage. There was Pallas, a twenty-two-year-old

"Negro . . . Daughter of Fanny Frazer," renamed Fidelia Crooks. There was Richard, eighteen, a "Sambo . . . Son of Anny Dickson"; two-year-old John Stewart, a "Mulatto . . . Son of Margaret Stewart"; and wee Eliza, just four days old, the youngest slave at the Cove. Eliza was the daughter of Elinor Crooks, and Elinor was the daughter of "Blk Eliza Crooks."

The slave register was the only genealogical document I'd seen that included the identity of the mother—and only the mother. Of course it had nothing to do with recognition of women, quite the opposite. It simply confirmed them and their offspring as chattels. Any child born to a slave woman automatically became the property of the master, who essentially could breed his own assets. Identifying only the maternal line not only diminished the very existence of black fathers, it offered anonymity to the slave owners and their white associates who sired a substantial number of the slave children born on the estates. From what I could tell, that figure was more than 12 percent at the Cove.

Having the Crooks name did not necessarily mean the slave had a Crooks father, since slaves often ended up with the master's name one way or another. But the careful colour classifications of the slaves spoke volumes about paternal bloodlines. A negro was the child of two black parents. A mulatto had one black parent and one white. A sambo had one black parent and one mulatto parent. A "quadroon" was the offspring of a white parent and a mulatto parent, a "mustee" had a white and a quadroon parent, and a "mustafina" was the child of a white parent and a mustee; members of this last category were white by law and therefore free. India's ethnic designations paled next to such precision. But then, this colour code carried actual value in a slave economy. Those with less "black" blood were considered less rebellious and were therefore often more expensive.

Working from the assumption that the white parent was almost always male, it seemed that white men were the biological fathers of at least fifteen slaves at the Cove in 1817. Five of them, all bearing the Crooks name, were the mulatto children of Nancy Crooks, a forty-five-year-old creole woman. No wonder she appeared as the Massa's "housekeeper" in Paul's novel. But was she in fact the slave mistress of a Crooks patriarch? Could she have been a maternal ancestor of the Captain? Either of her two sons could have been his grandfather.

But my great-grandfather was born thirty-five years after slavery ended, and with it the official use of colour classifications. Knowing he was "coloured" told me only that he was a mixture of black and white, not whether his mother was black or a mulatto or a quadroon or whatever. By that vague descriptor, any one of the forty-one slave women at the Cove could have been a maternal ancestor of his, of mine. Or maybe none of them were. Maybe the Captain's line had originated with a Crooks man and a free coloured woman.

In his book *Between Black and White*, the historian Gad J. Heuman writes that by 1820 the free coloured population in Jamaica had tripled within a span of thirty years. By 1844 there were sixty-nine thousand free coloured people, outnumbering whites by more than four to one. Most of them had been set free by the white men who were their lovers or their fathers, a fact that brought me back from the slave register to the only solid lead I had: the Y chromosome of a European man.

He was a boy, the first white Crooks I came across—James Crooks, a minor, listed in the quit-rent book of 1754, a written record of annual fees paid to the Crown for land granted in Jamaica in the seventeenth century. It was a mysterious entry: the Crooks estate, all 763 acres in Hanover, was in the hands of a child. The second white Crooks I found was a "jobber" (someone I took to be a hired hand) by the name of Christopher Crooks who owned forty-one slaves in St. James, a parish near Hanover. The next mention of Crookses came in a 1776 list of Hanover property owners that identified the owners of Crooks Cove as the "Heirs of James Crooks."

One of these heirs must have been a Crooks named John, since it was his name that appeared as the author of this warm and fuzzy notice published in the *Cornwall Chronicle*:

> Cousins Cove, Hanover, Sept. 19, 1792
> WENT OFF in a Canoe, from Launce's Bay, on Monday the
>   17*th* instant, the following Negroes:
> GEORGE, a Moco, about 5 feet 8 inches high, very stout, and
>   of a yellow complexion.
> KENT, a Moco, 5 feet 11 inches high, very slim made, of a black
>   complexion, and stoops in walk.
> DONALD, a Moco, 5 feet 6 inches high, is well made, and has
>   a short round face.
> NELLY, a Moco, 4 feet 10 inches high, a yellow wench and
>   bow-legged.
> All of them, except Donald, (who was purchased about a month
>   ago) speak a little broken English, particularly Fox, they
>   have no brand mark. A suitable Reward will be paid to any
>   Person apprehending any of the above Negroes, and giving
>   information to GEORGE MALCOLM, Lucea, or the
>   Subscriber, or lodging them in any Workhouse.
> JOHN CROOKS.

They may well have been caught, those runaway slaves. Both a George and a Nelly appear on the 1817 slave register of the Cove property, and once again the fictional portrayal of Massa John Crooks had a ring of truth to it. But how, in real life, were these Crookses related to one another, the boy, the jobber, the slave-owner? It was a remarkable document from 1740 that first allowed me to piece some of it together: the last will and testament of James Crooks, the earliest known proprietor at the Cove.

> *I James Crooks of the parish of Hanover and Island of Jamaica . . .*
> *being sick and weak in Body but of a disposesing [sic] mind*

and memory thanks be given to the Almighty God . . .

Give and bequeath unto my brother Christopher Crooks one
    Negro wench named Betty with her three children named
    Sisley Jenny and Easthere to him and his heirs forever . . .

Unto my brother Rice Crooks six Negroes to be bought out of the
    produce arising from my Estate . . .

Unto Thomas George son of my sister Elizabeth George £100 at
    the age of twenty one years

Unto my daughter Ann Crooks £600 pounds at the age of
    twenty one years or six months after marriage and also one
    Negro girl to be chosen by her out of the Negroes belonging
    to my estate

Provided the child which my wife Anna Petronella now goes
    with be a Boy and live but in case it be a Girl I bequeath
    unto the said girl the Pimento walk with all the land
    thereunto belonging . . . and Ann Crooks shall have all the
    residue and remainder of my Estate both real and personal
    . . . and her heirs . . .

But in case a Boy be born alive then he shall have all the
    before mentioned remainder and residue of my estate . . .
    and his heirs . . .

I can't say how many times I read it. Enough that certain phrases lodged in my memory: *unto my brother . . . a Negro wench named Betty and her three children; unto my daughter . . . one Negro girl to be chosen by her.* How comfortably tenderness curled up with inhumanity. A man on his deathbed bequeaths black people, children, to his loved ones like silverware. The 1817 slave register was a cold inventory, but the will of James Crooks, with all its good intentions, seemed colder still.

The will contained enough details to sketch the beginnings of the Crooks family tree at the Cove. James Crooks had at least two brothers, Christopher and Rice, and a sister, Elizabeth. Christopher may have been the white jobber I'd read about who had forty-one slaves of his own in a nearby parish in 1774, but the timing—thirty years after James died—seemed off. Certainly James was the planter; dying young, he left behind his young daughter, Ann, and a pregnant wife. His widow, Anna Petronella, eventually did give birth to a boy and named him after his dead father. The younger James Crooks was the minor in possession of the Crooks plantation in 1754, the thirteen-year-old master of the Cove.

Nothing I found revealed how or when the Crookses had first come to Jamaica or whether they had set sail from Lancashire, only that England was their likely point of origin. They had to be among the island's earliest settlers, judging by the fees listed in the quit-rent book. But however James Crooks Senior came to be at the Cove, being a literate white landowner placed him among the island's gentry, and one in need of a wife. But women were in short supply in Jamaica, white women rarer still, and as one soldier hinted in a letter home, "comely white women" were as scarce as snow. Planters married cousins or neighbours if they married at all. When James Crooks married Anna Petronella, her father, William Launce, owned the estate next to the Cove.

I tracked the Crookses and their descendants through wills, registers, directories and personal letters. It was a story with all the trappings of a Jane Austen novel: A handful of wealthy plantation families establish themselves in the island's western parishes. Within a century they're all related by marriage, business and blood, by fortune and misfortune—of which the Crookses had their fair share.

Ann Crooks, who lost her father as a child, married John Dickson, a millwright from Scotland, had a daughter and seven sons and died at thirty-one. James Crooks Junior, who had inherited the Cove estate as a boy, was away on business in New York when he died at the age of thirty-three. He left his widow with five children under the age of ten and an estate struggling to survive in a time of falling sugar prices, successive hurricanes, debts and growing calls to abolish slavery.

Details of what happened to the Crooks family next were laid out in the letters of one Duncan Campbell, a London shipping merchant and a major figure in British penal history: he oversaw the notorious prison hulks anchored in the Thames and sent the first British convicts to Australia. The Campbells owned several estates in Jamaica, and one Campbell married the sister of Anna Petronella, making the family cousins to the Crookses. So it was that Duncan Campbell came to be the money man for his Jamaican relatives, selling their sugar and advancing them cash. After the death of James Crooks Junior, he also seems to have become guardian of the five Crooks children—three boys, two girls—who were sent to school in England after their father died.

Only one of the Crooks daughters returned to the island; the youngest girl died in England of a "violent putrid sore throat and fever" at the age of eleven. But from what I could tell, all three boys—James, Richard and John—made their way back to Jamaica. Richard became an army doctor or surgeon and disappeared from the records. James Crooks III may have become a merchant in Falmouth, the birthplace of my great-grandfather. It was John Crooks who took over the plantation. He kept it afloat for a while with borrowed money, most of it from his cousin Richard Dickson. One of the seven sons of John's late aunt Ann Crooks, Richard Dickson was a merchant and real estate mogul who eventually ousted John, merged the Crooks plantation with a neighbouring estate and called it Cousins Cove, as it appears on the 1817 slave register and as it is still known.

Duncan Campbell's letters stopped in the 1790s, and with them, my trail. I couldn't tell what had become of John Crooks after he lost the farm, whether he married and had sons, or whether his brothers had sons, leaving chromosomes for me to chase. But I thought there was a good chance that some of their descendants might still be living in Jamaica. Maybe a few of them were even scattered around the Cove.

I was sure that my family was somehow connected to that plantation. But I realized I might be confusing the familiar with family. I'd spent days poring over their correspondence, reading their old-fashioned English, envisioning ruddy complexions and riding boots, pale ladies hiding from the sun under silk parasols. Their own words had landed me in their big, sad house on the hill in the same way that reading Paul Crooks's *Ancestors* had drawn me into the tortured lives of the slave village below. I tried to reach the author in the fall of 2007, hoping he might provide his Crooks chromosome for comparison. It was worth a shot, even if it was a long shot, since I knew he'd already traced his father's line back to Africa. I also thought he might have come across my "coloured" branch of Crookses in his research. I sent an email, introducing myself and our mutual island roots, and raised the possibility of testing his Y. I didn't fully expect a reply.

My sister phoned on Halloween night. I could hardly hear her between the trick-or-treaters and the two four-year-olds, Jade and her friend, bouncing through the living room with their bags of candy.

"I know this probably isn't the best time to talk," Christine said. "But I just had the most incredible call from Aunty Doreen. She wanted to call you but she didn't have your number. She told me this amazing story about a patient of hers who knows a lot about the Crooks family in Jamaica."

Aunty Doreen is a retired nurse and the wife of my father's younger brother Howard. She was one of the few keepers of the Abraham family history and had a thick collection of birth and marriage certificates. I couldn't fathom why she would have information about my mother's side of the family.

"I know," Christine said. "It's almost unbelievable, but Doreen happens to know a man who knows about the Crookses. She heard you were going to Jamaica and so she wanted to pass on this information. So let me read you my notes."

She took notes?

I scrambled for a pen and a quiet corner and wrote the

highlights on a pizza box—*Doreen's old patient . . . a man from Jamaica . . . knows the Crookses . . . was adopted by the Captain's sister . . .*

It was uncanny. I'd just found out myself that the Captain had a sister. I'd spent time that fall at one of the Mormons' family history centres, trying to trace the ancestry of the Captain's father, George Atkinson Crooks, the old-fashioned way, reading records on microfilm—celluloid over cells. The centre I visited in Toronto's west end is one of more than 4,500 around the world. Each houses microfilm copies of documents held at the Family History Library in Salt Lake City, the Mecca of genealogy. That their documents are freely available to the public is a gift—but not an entirely altruistic one. Since Mormons believe that dead people can be baptized by proxy, hunting for ancestors holds posthumous potential for swelling the ranks of Mormons eligible for entrance to the Kingdom of God. Latter-day Saints adherents gather and organize documents from all over the world. I had tucked into the Jamaica microfilms, copying any mention of a Crooks in the island's western parishes—where the Captain was born, where the Crooks estate had been. I found a Sarah Crooks, an Edward Crooks, a May Crooks and a Rebecca Crooks, and at some point I'd come across the birth registration of a Margaret Isabella Crooks. She was described as "colored and legitimate," born July 1875 to George A. Crooks, a Falmouth accountant, and C.A. Storks. I assumed that Margaret Isabella had to be the Captain's sister. At the time I thought it was the only relevant note I had taken that day.

I called Doreen the morning after Halloween. She told me that the story she was about to share, she had first heard twenty years ago. She was working at a hospital in the Cambridge area, an hour west of the city, where she and Howard live. One of the patients in her charge was a gentleman from Jamaica. She grew fond of him, she said. He was good fun, and feisty for his age, which she guessed was about seventy then.

She and Uncle Howard bumped into him over the years at shops and malls around town, and they always had a pleasant chat.

During one conversation it came up that Doreen and Howard were Anglo-Indians from Bombay. That's when the man told her he'd had an uncle Crooks in Bombay, where he worked as a railway stationmaster. Doreen guessed immediately that he was referring to my mother's family. Then she'd run into him recently, she said, at a department store and delved deeper into his Crooks connection. The man told her he had been adopted as a boy by a Sarah Crooks, whose family owned a sugarcane estate somewhere on the island. He also said he had lived with Sarah Crooks in Kingston and that the uncle Crooks in Bombay had once written to them asking for financial help to immigrate to Jamaica.

I was speechless.

"Apparently they didn't have money to give away and Sarah got rid of the letter," Doreen said. "She was apparently very Victorian and firm in her ways." She added that she had never thought enough of the conversation to mention it. But when she had seen my parents recently and they'd told her I was heading off to do research in Jamaica, she thought this man would be worth a conversation.

I agreed. I reached him by phone the afternoon before we flew out. His name was Clive Harris. He was about eighty-eight, completely lucid and lived in a seniors' apartment. He had a wonderful voice, deep and warm, with a rich island accent that made a mischievous grin of every pause. I liked him instantly.

"I'm glad you called," Mr. Harris said. "I understand you're a young lady looking for answers. It will be my pleasure to help any way I can." This man could charm the headphones off an operator. Harris told me he had immigrated to Canada from Jamaica in 1987. He was an accountant, he said, and, not surprisingly, a public speaker.

"My aunt told me you happened to know my mother's family in Jamaica—the Crookses."

"Yes, I do. I do indeed." Harris told me that his biological mother was from Cuba and his father was a public works employee in Jamaica. They died when he was a boy and Sarah Louise Crooks adopted him.

Sarah came from a large family in the Falmouth area, he said. She had a sister, Maggie, who married a man from Panama in the horse-racing business. Maggie, I presumed, was Margaret Isabella Crooks, whom I'd discovered at the research centre. Maggie eventually moved to Panama, Harris continued. I thought of the New York uncle who had written to my mother and Dennis, and his death registration noting that he had died in Central America—perhaps while visiting his aunt Maggie.

Sarah also had brothers, Harris said—three or four, and one of them was a ship's captain. The captain had a son in India, and that son once wrote a letter to his mother from Bombay. "I was there when the letter came," Harris told me. "He said he wanted to come to Jamaica, that he was a stationmaster, but that he had a large family, several children, and needed assistance. She was quite peeved that this relative suddenly wanted to maintain ties. The Crookses were very snobbish people."

"Yes, I know my grandfather wrote letters looking for his father's family in Jamaica. I think he received only one reply, and it was harsh. It accused my grandfather of being an impostor and warned him against any future contact. Did Sarah write it?"

"No," Harris said quickly. "Sarah would not have written such a letter. She might have told him she had no funds—the boys had the money on the estate. Sarah did social work. She developed the Stoneyhill Reformatory for girls in Kingston—" Then he stopped himself.

"But now, wait," Harris said. "It could be that her husband wrote it. Sarah was married to a fellow named Braine, the son of a bishop, a nice-looking man who turned out to be a drunkard. He eventually got involved with voodoo. Sarah met him in Kingston, but the Crooks family did not approve of their union and they eventually did divorce."

Had it been just the scribbles of an occultist drunk trying to scare off his wife's nephew? Is that why my grandfather had crumpled that letter so quickly, why it had changed his mind so completely that, after all his efforts, he abandoned the notion of even visiting his father's birth land?

Harris wouldn't put it past Sarah's husband to send a poison-pen letter, and to my mind that's what it had been. Braine was a white man, or at least close to it, Harris said. Yet the reply sent to my grandfather warned him against coming to Jamaica if his wife was white, as if they were a black family that wanted nothing to do with whites. Harris had nothing good to say about Braine, but it was obvious his affection ran deep for the woman who had raised him.

"They called her Sally for short," he said. "She worked in a law firm and died in the 1960s at the age of eighty. She was quite a happy woman. She loved dancing; she used to attend dances at the town hall. She was short, only about five foot two, and slim. She was pretty fair in complexion."

"I know the Captain's baptism record says he was coloured," I offered.

"Well, there was some understanding that she had a touch of Ibo in her."

His revelation reminded me of a verse Paul Crooks had included in his novel that mentioned the Ibo, one of Nigeria's largest ethnic groups. It was a song that slave women sang as they worked in the fields with babies strapped to their backs:

> *If me want for go in a Ebo*
> *Me can't go there*
> *Since them tief me from Guinea*
> *Me can't go there . . .*

Harris knew nothing else about Sarah's Ibo heritage. "But they called her a mustafina because she was about 98 percent white. She had long black hair—what you'd call a white Jamaican, a good-looking woman."

"They call you sambo, you know, if you are 25 percent white," he said with a zesty laugh. "This means you have a little milk in your coffee!"

Sarah's father, George, died in the Falmouth area, Harris told me. But her mother, Catherine, came to live with her in Kingston for a time. He said she's buried there, my great-great-grandmother, in the Maypen Cemetery. He went there once with Sarah to visit her mother's tomb. "But you don't want to be walking through there without a police escort," Harris warned me. "You've got to get to Falmouth. The Crooks family was a big deal there, and that was when Falmouth was more developed than Montego Bay."

Did he know where exactly the family had an estate? He didn't, only that it was out towards Falmouth.

Did he know anything about their being members of the Masonic lodge?

"They might have been part of the Masonic lodge, the brotherhood helping each other. But you'll find something about them there. The Crookses also owned a wharf, and the Crooks boys seemed to be . . . men about town, if you get my meaning."

"Men about town?"

"I think they made lots of women happy—and there's nothing wrong with that!" He gave another big laugh.

I wanted to tell him that the Crookses had apparently been men about town since the last ice age, but I couldn't imagine where a conversation on the Y chromosome might lead, given the spry mind of Mr. Harris.

I sat at the kitchen table for a while after we hung up, trying to process the scale of the coincidence—that this honey-voiced old man from Jamaica, the adopted son of the Captain's sister and witness to the desperate letter my grandfather had sent from India sixty years ago, lived just up the highway. I didn't need DNA to tell me how interconnected humans can be.

13

AN ISLAND PLACE

"Oh, really?" people said when they heard. "You're going to do *research*—in *Jamaica*?" I understood their skepticism. I have the same reaction when I scan a list of upcoming medical conferences and see a winter meeting in Hawaii to discuss catheter techniques. But when the people you tell are family, they believe you. They say, "Well, if it's *family* research, the family should go along . . . to help."

So there we were that November on our roots tour—Stephen, Jade, my father, my mother, my sister and I—having lunch at the airport while we waited for a plane to Montego Bay. We ate club sandwiches and drank beer and bloody Caesars. We pulled out an island map and laid fingers on our destination. None of us had been to Jamaica before.

The country's annual homicide rate hovers around 1,500. On an island with fewer than three million people, that's nearly fifty murders for every 100,000 residents, twenty-five times higher than the Canadian rate and one of the highest in the world. Most of the bloodshed flows from the gang-infested slums of Kingston, where stories of drug wars and gunfights clog the press. It can leave the impression that there are safer places to get a tan. But the bulk of Jamaica's billion-dollar-a-year tourist industry revolves around the resorts of the north shore, far from the crime-plagued capital. That's where we were headed, to the north coast, partway between the archives of Spanish Town and the hometown of the Captain.

My father pointed out that Jamaica had a dramatically different reputation when my grandfather was hoping to sail there. In the 1940s, he said, *violence* was a word used only to describe the island's hurricanes. Jamaica had been like an exclusive country club for the rich and famous: Noel Coward, the Kennedys, Elizabeth Taylor, Princess Margaret, Errol Flynn, Clark Gable, Charlie Chaplin. Author Ian Fleming built a cliffside home on the north coast he called Goldeneye, where he brought James Bond to life in a booze-fuelled haze of five weeks. To Fleming, Jamaica was "a refreshment for all the senses."

"In Papa's time, when you said you were going to Jamaica, it sounded exotic," my father said as we ate. "That was all—an exotic place, still a British colony, as India had been, but a paradise of sunshine, farms and sand."

We touched down in the dark at Sangster International Airport and trudged blurry-eyed into the hot night air, herded onto resort-bound coaches headed east. We had more than an hour to ride, and the hum of the diesel engine lulled us. Jade stretched out across our laps and slept. My eyes slid over the black shapes of distant hills, where lights twinkled like stars. The requisite reggae played soft and low over the speaker system, Marley singing about how no one can forget their past.

"This is a nice track," my mother said. "Who is this?"

"Bob Marley, Mum."

"I must get this one."

Our first full day inched along as a good Sunday should in Jamaica, at the beach. My father was there first, stretched out with a newsmagazine under a thatch-roofed gazebo. Stephen joined him and I headed for the half-moon of the shoreline with Jade and my mother. It was hurricane season, and nearly empty. Jade busied herself gouging ditches against the tide. My mother and I wandered neck-deep into the sea.

"How does it feel," I asked her, "to be here?"

What could she say . . . warm saltwater lifting our limbs, the sun on our cheeks.

"It's beautiful," Mum said. "I wish my father could have been here. Who would have imagined that now, after all these years, I would be here, at this age, looking for his people."

His people. Our people. Mine. I floated along on my back. A few grey clouds drifted into the blue. The old Crooks Cove was probably just a few hours away by car. I'd seen slave quarters once, at an old plantation in Louisiana: small clapboard squares where whole families had lived. I wondered if my mother was prepared for what we might find here, or who we might find. When *Roots* first aired on television, she hid—not just her eyes but her whole self. You should see this, my father had said to her. But episode after episode, my mother would bury her face in her hands and then finally leave the TV room and stand out in the hall. My father narrated for her from the far end of the sofa. "Come on, Tweet! It's all right now; that scene is finished. Come back. You're missing it."

My mother's thoughts must have been gliding over similar waves. "We never knew anything about black people growing up in India," she said suddenly. "We never saw them. And oh, when they came, everyone was frightened."

"When who came?"

"During the war, must have been '43 or '44. Papa was posted at the railway station in Daund." It was a small town southeast of Bombay but a major railway hub. The Allies established bases in India to fight the Japanese on the Burmese front, and the Americans had stationed a "negroes only" regiment in Daund. "Everyone said, 'You better be indoors by six o'clock,'" my mother said. "No one knew what to think. Everyone was scared of blacks. No one had seen blacks before—can you imagine?"

My mother remembered returning from midnight Mass on Christmas Eve with Nana Gladys, her siblings and Nana's father, Grandpa Thompson. "We walked home from the church through a cornfield, and the corn was quite tall. One of the boys up ahead—Shepherd, I think it was—started shouting like mad. 'There's a drunken man down here, lying down. Be careful, don't step on him. He's black!' We were terrified; everyone started running. But Grandpa couldn't run, and we were so scared, shouting, 'Run, Grandpa, run!' But we all took off and left him behind."

"That's crazy," I said.

"It was, but we didn't know any better. I don't think those men were treated very well. The black soldiers rarely left the barracks."

Jade had wandered into the water at the shoreline and was rolling back and forth with the waves. Stephen splashed by with his snorkel gear but I was reluctant to join him. My mother was paddling quietly in circles, distracted.

"What is it?" I asked.

"I'm hesitating," Mum said. "I don't even like to think about this, and I do, because it comes back to my mind whenever I take a shower. Certain things stain your mind."

"Well, you can't say that and not tell me."

"During that time, during the war, I went away as a boarder to school. I remember coming back on one of the holidays and Papa's friend, Albert Hales, took us to the barracks in Daund and I saw a punishment they were giving to those black soldiers."

"Who were 'they'? White officers? To the black soldiers?"

My mother nodded. "They had them outside on the ground," she said. "Three or four of them, with a big kerosene vessel suspended over them, and water was dripping on them—*drip, drip*. And my father said, 'Come. Come quickly,' and he pulled me away."

"Water . . . It was water dripping on them?"

"I put it together later that it must have been some form of torture—maybe water torture, isn't it, when there's the *drip, drip*? I hate to think of it. I think of it in the shower, always, when the water is dripping down my back."

I wasn't sure if I was more surprised by my mother's having witnessed the torture of American soldiers by their own officers when she was a child, or by the fact that she had never told me the story. "That's a traumatic scene for a child to see. Obviously, if you still think about it in the shower."

She paused again. "I know, but you know, I never really *knew* what I saw. . . . I don't remember how they were held down to the ground, if they were lying on their backs, if there were three or four. . . . But I hate to think of it—*hate* to—and hate to talk about it."

I had always wondered if a certain prejudice had diluted my mother's interest in whatever African heritage she might have. But as we swam that day, I saw my mother's ambivalence about her Jamaican roots as something else: fear. It was the fear of discovering a family history she did not have the stomach to contemplate. I had told her about Paul Crooks's novel of his slave ancestors, but my mother never asked to read the book, or even to see it. But if we found out that we actually had slaves in our family, we'd all be pushed to consider their existence in one way or another—not in the abstract, as characters in a book or a miniseries, but as *our people*, our not-so-long-ago grandfathers and grandmothers, stolen from their homes, condemned to bondage and fates far worse than water torture.

Everton Esmie was waiting for us outside the hotel the next morning with his brand-new minibus and a smile like a wilted corsage. I couldn't blame him. Groups like ours are hard to move quickly. Trim, young and tidy, outfitted in a starched baby-blue shirt and navy slacks, Mr. Esmie gave the impression of a serious, all-business sort. Everything about our driver, except for that drooping smile, seemed permanently pressed.

"You must be Everton," I said, extending my hand.

"Please," he said, "call me Troy."

We took off westward along the north coast highway,

drinking in our first daylight views of the island beyond the resort. Like all West Indian islands, Jamaica is essentially the top of a submarine mountain range, prehistoric peaks that managed to keep their heads above water. They run like a spine from east to west, crisscrossed by ridges branching off north and south, making a rumpled mass of most of the island. With their limestone cliffs, their slopes clad in malachite coats of Jamaican pine and blue mahoe, the hills had been a temptress, once upon a time, to runaway slaves. If they didn't break out by canoe, they often disappeared into the hills, finding refuge and freedom with the famous mountain-dwelling Maroons.

Originally the Maroons were a band of African slaves the Spanish had armed and left behind to torment the British. But over time their numbers grew, and these rebels managed to wage two wars against the British before six hundred of them were shipped to Nova Scotia. In *Ancestors*, Paul Crooks writes that he longed to find that he had a Maroon ancestor, the more rebellious the better. I had brought his book along with me, tucked in my backpack with my notebook and maps. The author had finally replied to the email I'd sent him that fall. He was intrigued by my request to test his Y chromosome and said he would be happy to talk further. But I'd only managed to connect with his answering machine before we left.

Troy's minibus slowed to a crawl when we reached Falmouth. Its narrow eighteenth-century roadways teemed with life: school girls in kilts, old men, young men, women waiting for a bus, motorbikes, taxis, goats. Rastafarians in bright berets hung around tin-roofed shacks selling coconuts and pop, and we lurched to a halt in front of them. A Jamaican traffic jam.

Back when the island was the world's sugar bowl, when being "rich as a West Indian planter" meant wealth on par with monarchs, Falmouth was its heart. It had more sugar estates around it than any other part of the country. Local planters, in need of a port, founded the town in 1769, and like the cane, it grew fast and wild.

A giant cage once stood in the town square to hold the nightly batch of drunks, and money flowed like the rum. There were factories and foundries, shops, hotels and planters' town homes. Falmouth was said to be the wealthiest New World port south of Charleston; it had piped-in water before New York City. According to the historian Daniel Ogilvie, on any given day at least twenty tall ships could be counted in Falmouth's harbour, loading rum and sugar, unloading goods and slaves. But the steamship killed Falmouth. Its harbour was too shallow to accommodate the hulking bellies of the new ships, and with the abolition of slavery and sugar prices falling, plantations began to fail. Falmouth must have been dwindling by the time my great-grandfather was born, on its way to becoming a weekly market town, blighted by time and the salt air.

Ambitious efforts were underway to restore the port and its fine Georgian architecture, mostly coordinated by Falmouth Heritage Renewal, a non-profit group devoted to saving the city's history. I hoped to find leads to the Crookses of Falmouth at their offices, which were in a handsome moss-covered two-storey building with a portico and Palladian windows—and empty. The interior was stripped to its studs. The only people inside appeared to be carpenters and contractors. I asked if anyone could tell me where I could find the Falmouth Renewal offices. A voice called back from the darkness inside, saying they would fetch "Peter, the supervisor."

Peter appeared a few moments later, covered in a fine layer of dust. He was a young black man in a football jersey and jeans. "I'm sorry to interrupt your work," I said, and explained what we were after.

"Crooks?" he said. "Don't they own a nightclub in Montego Bay?"

"Oh. Well, could be," I said, thinking that would be an entirely predictable vocation for my kin. "Which club is it?"

"No, wait a minute," Peter said, pulling a cellphone from his back pocket. "Let me see if I can get Dr. Parrent."

Dr. James Parrent, the executive director of Falmouth Heritage Renewal, was away in Kingston. Peter got him on the line and passed me the phone. I told him briefly that I was looking for information on the Crooks family that I understood had lived in the area, owning land and possibly a wharf sometime back.

"Crooks . . . that's not ringing any bells," Dr. Parrent said. He added that he had just received a list of those buried in the local cemetery, and as far as he remembered, he was sure no one named Crooks was on it. He promised to check through his files and call back if he found anything.

I returned the phone to Peter just as my sister wandered over to tell me that the sign in front of the old building now under renovation said it had once been the local Masonic lodge. "How's that for a coincidence?" she said.

It had been the lodge, but more important, where was the lodge now? I asked Peter, and he said it was located further into town, above Brown's Supermarket. We passed small homes on our way there, some behind white picket fences, tarted up like Easter eggs, others ready to lie down in their yards. Brown's market sat on one of the main streets, its entrance half hidden by the scaffolding of another revitalization project. The smell of cinnamon and cloves greeted us at the door. It was a cool refuge from the midday sun.

Troy asked in patois where we could find Mr. Brown, and the cashier directed us to the back of the store. We were waiting there, Troy, my sister and me, beside shelves of instant oatmeal when a worker popped out of the storeroom and said something to Troy that made them both laugh.

"He says Mr. Brown is in the back talking, and that he can chat."

"You mean chat with us?"

"No," Troy said, "as in he can *really* chat."

Finally, after several minutes, Mr. Brown appeared. He looked to be in his late fifties. He had a thick afro with grey at the temples, gold wire-framed glasses and several pens in the breast pocket of his floral print shirt.

"Sorry to trouble you, but I understand that the Masonic lodge is located above your shop," I said.

"No, no," he replied. "It's not the Masonic lodge, it's the Mechanics' lodge."

"Oh . . . the Mechanics lodge? Do you know where we can find the Masonic lodge?"

No, he said, he didn't.

I told him we were looking for information about my great-grandfather's family, that they were Crookses who lived in town.

"Oh, hold on," he said. "There's someone could help."

Mr. Brown motioned for us to follow him through the back storeroom, past large burlap sacks of sugar and flour, to a small rear loading dock, where an old man was perched outside on a crate of dry goods, smoking and talking with two workers. Mr. Brown told the old man we were visiting Jamaica to look for Crookses. The old man studied us and I studied him—his face, cracked and hollow like a riverbed run dry, missing teeth and most of his hair. He turned back to Mr. Brown, said something, and the two of them erupted into rapid-fire patois.

Finally Mr. Brown translated. "This man knows a Crooks. He thinks he is your family," he said. And then, looking directly at me, "He has eyes like yours."

Eyes like mine?

"He lives in a big house that used to belong to an MP, outside of Wakefield. He used to be in sugar or something."

Brown gave Troy directions and we thanked him and the old man, who offered us a wide, toothless grin.

As the skies clouded over we sped south into the interior, rattling over gravel and rutted pavement. The further inland we drove, the steeper the roads became, until we were once again winding and climbing as we had been in the Nilgiri Hills. In Coonoor we could look out over the tea crops, marvelling at their brilliant green and compact geometry. Here the sugar cane dwarfed us. Gangly and wild, it flanked both sides of the narrow roadway, obscuring everything but the asphalt ahead, its leaves brushing against the minibus as we rumbled past. Our ancestors had probably toiled in both fields, sweating on opposite sides of the world for the British, who were our forebears as well. My family seemed to owe its existence to England's love of sweet tea. "So true," my mother replied when I said so out loud. "But who doesn't like a nice cup of tea?"

With the exception of salt, few condiments have inspired as much ink as sugar. There are books on sugar and slavery, sugar and power, sugar and ships, sugar and railroads, even a nineteenth-century manual written by an Englishman to encourage his fellow planters to stay in the sugar business after the slaves had been freed: *The Practical Sugar Planter; A Complete Account of the Cultivation and Manufacture of the Sugar-Cane According to the Latest and Most Improved Processes*. The oldest known variety of sugar cane dates back eight thousand years in New Guinea. A thinner version grew up around the riverbanks of India, where the sultan of Mandu fed it to his cows to sweeten their milk.

Indians were the first to find a way to convert the sweet sap of the tropical grass into crystals, naming it *sharkara* after the ancient Sanskrit word for gravel or sand. Once foreigners discovered "the reed that produced honey without bees," they showed it off to the rest of the world. Arabs carried the cane to northern Africa and the Mediterranean during their conquests; the Crusaders took the "sweet salt" back to Europe. The Portuguese introduced it to Madeira, the Azores, West Africa and the Canary Islands. From there, in 1493, Columbus transported it to Hispaniola, where it eventually evolved into the thicker "noble reed" of the West Indies, destined to transform kitchens, medicine cabinets and entire kingdoms.

But producing sugar was a brutal business. Sugar cane grows four metres tall, its long leaves sharp enough to slice flesh. Before a harvest, cane fields were often set alight to burn off the razor-like leaves and smoke out poisonous snakes hiding among them. The stalks were then cut from the root, requiring a bend-and-whack manoeuvre that taxed even the strongest backs. From there the canes had to be dragged to the mill, crushed, boiled and re-boiled. The extracted juices would finally cool into crystals around a hard core of molasses. Some say sugar cane is the most labour-intensive crop the world has ever grown. Of the twelve million Africans who survived the voyage to the New World—out of the some thirty million men, women and children who were kid-napped—an estimated 70 percent became slaves to the cane.

On the outskirts of Wakefield, Troy parked in front of a bungalow larger than any we'd seen in the area. It was set far back from the road, surrounded by a chest-high fence and an even taller hedge. From inside the minibus we could see over it and into the yard, which had the look of a bright, sprawling putting green. Troy and I climbed out. We walked around to the front gate, which was iron, and locked, but low enough to afford a full view of the rambling pale peach–coloured house. It was shaded by a striped metal awning, below which another iron barricade ran the length of the porch. Another set of bars covered the windows and doorway. It was a fortress—or a pretty pastel prison.

"The front door is slightly open," I said, and called out a hello.

"Hello?" Troy called as well. "Hello? Mr. Crooks?"

Beyond the bars I could make out a figure moving through shadows in the front hall. The figure seemed to be looking out. We called again. This time the figure opened the barred entrance-way wide and stepped out onto his gated porch.

I caught my breath. His face, his features, his colour . . . . He looked like my grandfather. He stepped out of the house, unlocked the porch gate and came down the front steps and up the walkway towards us. Then he stopped, three feet from where we stood on the other side of the gate. He didn't look like anyone else we'd met that morning. He wasn't black—he had a caramel complexion. He wasn't young or tall but was disarmingly handsome for his apparent years. He wore a golf shirt with thick vertical stripes in grey and burgundy, a ball cap emblazoned with a red New York

logo, and a chunky gold watch that suggested wealth. In one hand
he carried a cellphone and in the other, not surprisingly, an enormous bunch of keys.

The closer he came, the more he looked like my grandfather.
I turned back to see if my mother had seen him as well. She had.
Her face was pressed against the bus window with an expression
of delight and disbelief. She rose quickly out of her seat.

"How can I help you?" the key man said in a clipped Jamaican
accent.

"Hello. Are you Mr. Crooks?"

"Yes, that's right."

I introduced myself and told him I was from Canada, researching my mother's side of the family. "You see, my mother is a Crooks
and my great-grandfather was born in Falmouth," I said. "Some
people there mentioned there was a Crooks living out here, so—"

My mother was suddenly beside me, nudging in front of me,
my father too. We were all of us sandwiched between the idling
bus and the gate's metal bars, captivated by the familiarity in a
stranger's face.

"I'm a Crooks," my mother said.

"I know," he said, looking at her intensely from the other side
of the gate, grinning now. "I can see it."

For a few moments we just stared.

"What is your name?" my mother asked.

Everett Lance Crooks, he said, and then he volunteered that
he was seventy-four years old and that there were Crookses all over
Jamaica.

"Where did they come from?" my mother asked.

"All of them descend from three Crooks brothers who came
from Scotland to settle the island, a long ways back, maybe late in
the seventeenth century."

My mind leapt instantly to the Cove and the will of James
Crooks. I was sure those brothers had been named James,
Christopher and Rice.

One of the Crooks boys settled in Kingston, Everett Crooks continued, another in Westmoreland, the parish south of Trelawny, and a third in Hanover parish, which I knew had once been the home of Crooks Cove.

The heat of the idling minibus began to roast our legs and the diesel fumes billowed, but Everett Crooks seemed not to notice our discomfort. Even as an afternoon rain began to fall, he never found it in himself to pluck the front gate key from his jangling bunch and invite us under the awning of his verandah. But then, how bizarre our posse must have seemed to him—Stephen, a six-foot Scandinavian-looking fellow rambling around his perimeter with a long-range lens at the ready; Christine hovering too, with Jade in tow; me scribbling his words into my notepad; my parents in their matching Tilley hats, stuck to his gate like clematis. Yet Everett Crooks kept talking. He told us his father's name was Egbert and his grandfather was Simeon, that they had land in the interior, that he used to be in cattle, that he had bought this house from the former MP several years ago.

"You live alone?" my mother asked.

He said his wife and children all lived in New York now, but he was an island man.

"But to live alone?" my mother said. "At this age?"

"I know, I know, I'm getting on. I may have to reconsider."

All through the chit-chat I found my attention divided, wondering how I would ask Everett for his DNA. We'd only just learned his name. Of course, this was a scenario I had envisioned when I first began this project—finding a possible relative in a faraway place, proving or disproving it with a swab. But it was one thing to imagine it and another to have the patties to actually pull it off, particularly when the beguiling subject in question deliberately stands on the other side of an iron gate, beyond the reach of even a handshake. If he didn't feel comfortable enough to open his gate, to offer us shelter from the rain, what were the chances he would open his mouth to give his DNA to a stranger?

I didn't have much time to deliberate. The rain picked up speed and the ink in my notepad began to run. Everett finally seemed to notice the downpour and said he was sorry he couldn't be of more help. It was our cue to leave. If not his DNA, I did manage to ask him for his phone number (he obliged) and whether he knew anyone who could tell us more about the Crooks families. He suggested that a local relative of his, Curniff Crooks, might be helpful. As I jotted down the cell number he provided, Everett suddenly startled us all. He took two steps forward, shook our hands over his tall gate and wished us well. Then he was gone.

Bouncing down the road towards the coast again, we were all atwitter about our first Crooks encounter, dissecting his features, his coy grin (yes, he was a Crooks, all right), his iron-clad security and his insecurity. Even Troy chimed in. "That man had something to hide."

"He must have been frightened," Mum said, defending her father's lookalike. "It was his age, and he lives alone."

"No, no, he thought we were after something, all right," Dad said. "An inheritance, his property."

"Yes. Meanwhile, it was just a bit of his tissue."

"No, he's all alone there," Mum said again, "and there are so many of us." Meeting Everett had touched my mother—flesh-and-blood evidence of a Jamaican family perhaps, and a large one, apparently. Crookses all over the island, Everett had said.

As we neared the coastal highway again I dialled the number for Curniff Crooks. He answered on the first ring. "It's good to hear from some fellow Crookses!" he said immediately. Everett had clearly called ahead.

Curniff's accent was thicker than Everett's, his tone warmer. Like Troy, he was a driver with the Jamaican Tourist Board. He told me he was at a bank in Falmouth just then, and if we drove straight there we could meet in the parking lot.

A short while later, Troy pulled up beside the bank on Market Street and shut off the engine. We kept our eyes trained on the entrance, waiting for Curniff.

"This feels like a stakeout," Stephen said.

"I wonder who he's going to look like," Christine said.

"What's a stakeout?" Jade asked.

One of the town's retro new builds, the bank sits across the road from a house built in 1799 that once belonged to the family of Elizabeth Barrett Browning. The Barretts had owned great swaths of Falmouth once, and Edward Barrett, the poet's father, was born in Jamaica. But like so many in the island's early planter families, he left to be schooled in England and never returned. I had read that Edward Barrett forbade his eleven children to marry. He apparently knew that his Jamaican roots included an African bloodline, a secret he feared would be revealed in the complexion of a grandchild. But Elizabeth Barrett married Robert Browning all the same. Shortly after her elopement she wrote "Runaway Slave at Pilgrim's Point," telling the tragic story of a slave woman raped by a white master, bearing a white child she was compelled to suffocate with a handkerchief.

The poet was too frail for most of her life to endure the voyage to Jamaica, but in 1838 she wrote about her yearning: "My dream is of an island place, / Which distant seas keep lonely,—/ A little island on whose face / The stars are watchers only . . . ." I thought of my grandfather whenever I read it.

14

STICKS AND STONES

A heavyset man in his fifties stepped out of the bank. He had salt-and-pepper hair cropped short, a beard, jeans, a linen shirt and a cellphone clipped to his breast pocket. "Curniff?" I called out.

Where Everett had seemed wary and aloof, Curniff was warm and enthusiastic, greeting us with a broad smile and a vigorous handshake. "Yes, yes, you are Crookses, I can see it," he said.

It was inevitable that we would search each other's faces for traces of ourselves. He looked more African than Everett, but he too had that milk-in-his-coffee complexion, light brown eyes and something—in the slope of his jaw, the set of his mouth and nose—that somehow looked familiar. He didn't hesitate when we invited him to lunch.

"You like patties?" he asked, and climbed straight into our minibus.

On the way, he told us that he and Everett were related—second cousins or some such, he didn't know for sure. We told him we were looking into our grandfather's heritage and he told us the same story we had heard from Everett: that the Crooks name came to Jamaica with three brothers. He had heard they were Scottish.

At a fast-food restaurant in the newer part of Falmouth, my parents and I sat with Curniff on opposite sides of a Formica table. "I feeeel it," Curniff said suddenly, looking intently at my mother and me. "I feeeel de connection. We are family—you look just like my daughter," he told me. "All the Crookses on the island are one family."

Recalling the slave list from the Cove and the way surnames were assigned to Africans in mass baptisms, I had my doubts about that. But Curniff maintained that in one way or another the three brothers had left a legacy of hundreds of Crookses. We told him what we knew of our Crooks ancestors: George Atkinson Crooks, an accountant in Falmouth; the Captain; triplet brothers; possibly a sugar estate. The names meant nothing to him.

"The Crookses have tended to be high-prestige, low-profile people on the island," he said, "into cattle, cane and cultivation. Property owners, businesspeople." Then he added, "You know, you are not the first Crooks group from Canada to speak with me about their family here."

We were bewildered.

A man and woman from Canada came to Jamaica in 1974, he said, and spoke with him about their Crooks ancestors. He remembered the year clearly because he was in hospital at the time, in traction after breaking his leg in a car accident.

"What were their names?" I asked, wondering if we had been following in the footsteps of my uncle and aunt, Dennis and Merlyn. "Oh, I don't recall their names, and I wished I could have told them more," he said, "but I was in too much pain to talk."

Whoever they were, I thought, they must have been on an urgent mission, so intent on finding their Jamaican relatives they would interrogate a man in traction.

"I told them what I am telling you," Curniff said. "All the Crookses are one family on the island."

It was my opening, my chance. "You know, Curniff, there's a way we could actually find out if that is true in our case."

"Really?" he said. "What do you mean?"

Over the crumbs of our lunch I told him about the Y-chromosome tests we could take to find out if we were descended from the same male line of Crookses. "All I would need would be a sample of your DNA," I said. "It doesn't hurt at all—just a swab of your inner cheek."

"But why do you need the test? Don't you know the answer already? We are family. I do feel it. Can you feeeel it?"

Could I? Was it the resemblance—mine to his daughter—that convinced him of our kinship, the way it had convinced us with the elusive Everett? We'd known Curniff less than two hours, shared a ride, a meal, no more, and he was ready to embrace us as family—one clan, one love. What was my benchmark for feeling the bond, a common chromosome? I had swapped pictures and family stories with men I had never met, men in Maine, Brisbane, Miami, with only a meagre strand of DNA binding us. Yet here I was at last in the homeland of Captain Crooks, sharing a table with a man named Crooks who, if I squinted, bore some likeness to one or more of my uncles.

"So what will the test tell you?" he asked.

"Well, if we know for sure that we *are* related, we might be able to find out *how* we are related." We knew so little about our Crooks heritage in Jamaica, I told him, that maybe by learning the details of his family history we could discover our common male ancestor.

"Sure, sure," he said, softening again. "That sounds interesting."

I let the DNA issue lie for the moment; I wasn't keen to swab at the Juici Patti. Curniff mentioned that he had a bit of time before his next appointment and said that if my mother was certain her ancestors were Protestant, perhaps he could help us find their tombs in Falmouth's old Anglican cemetery.

"Oh yes," my mother said. "That would be very good of you."

The skies cracked wide open as we left the restaurant, drenching us on the short run to the minibus. We drove Curniff back to his car at the bank and then followed him to the centre of town, to St. Peter's Anglican Church, which from the looks of it had weathered its share of storms. It was the oldest public building in

Falmouth, a single storey of brick and stone constructed on Barrett lands in 1795. We took it in while waiting for the rain to stop: black mould clinging to its exterior, windows broken, the clock on its steeple stopped at ten past two, and the steeple a spire of such grand dimensions that the little church seemed to sink beneath it.

When the rain slowed, Curniff led Stephen, Troy and me into the church cemetery. The tombs sat a few feet above the ground. Grass and weeds had grown over so many that I didn't see them until my shins banged against stone. Many bore inscriptions too worn to read. There may well have been a Crooks lying in this verdant patch of anonymous souls, but there seemed no way to be sure. I was rounding the church to head back to the minibus when I noticed the goats. They stood like sentinels on top of the graves, staring at us. "Eerie," Stephen said.

Goats on tombs at St. Peter's Anglican cemetery in Falmouth, Jamaica.

And they were. In island folklore a goat might well be a duppy, the patois term for a restless spirit or ghost, and usually a nasty one. Jamaica loves its ghost stories: tales of departed souls tormenting the living, haunting mansions, taking animal forms, terrorizing people at night. Most of the island's superstitions stem from a long history of African folk magic that once made white captors fearful of the sorcery slaves might wield against them. To this day the Jamaica Customs Service allows no books on black magic to cross its borders.

Back at the minibus, Curniff put his arms around us and posed for a group photo before bidding us farewell. We all thanked him for the time he had spent with us. Just as he was turning to leave, he turned back. "Call me later in the week," he said. "Before you go, for my DNA."

"Really?" I said.

"No problem," he replied. "Why not?"

I had pictured how it would go in Spanish Town. My parents and I would get to the archives early and work backwards in the record books from the date of my great-grandfather's birth until I found the marriage of his parents. I was sure the registration of George Atkinson Crooks's marriage to Catherine Storks would include the names of the bride's and groom's parents, and then I could trace their history, perhaps to the Cove.

Troy picked us up early and we made it to Jamaica's old capital shortly after nine o'clock. Only after numerous lineups to get into the Registrar General's office did a glum woman in a grey tunic tell us that the lights had burned out in the vault where the records are held. She wasn't sure when they would be replaced. The best she could offer was to retrieve nineteenth-century records at random. She disappeared into the vault and returned wheeling a trolley piled high with ledgers the size of paving stones, and nearly as heavy. We hauled a few at a time onto a long table under fluorescent lights and dug in. We found loads of Crookses, but none with familiar names.

I found references to mass baptisms at which several African slaves were renamed Crooks on the same day. I also came across wills written by Crookses making it clear that owning slaves in Jamaica was not a right exclusive to whites. Free coloured people—men and women who were part African themselves—bequeathed African slaves to their loved ones just as the white master of Crooks Cove had done. For the first time it occurred to me that drawing lines between slave and slave owner in our family might well be impossible. I remembered reading in the nineteenth-century chronicles of John Stewart that coloured people were considered the worst kind of slave owners, mimicking the ways of the white man to excess, as if by mistreating blacks they owned they could beat the colour right out of themselves. "The negroes," Stewart wrote, "are wont to say: 'If me, for have massa or misses, give me Buckra one—no give me mulatto, dem no use neega well.'"

But for all the hours I had in that archive to imagine who the Captain's ancestors had been, I couldn't find them. None of us could. We stayed until closing, with only a few photocopied wills to show for it. One was written in 1919 by a David Atkinson Crooks of Hanover. I suspected he might have had some connection to the Captain's father, George Atkinson Crooks. He described himself in his will as a mariner, "exposed to the dangers of the sea," just like my great-grandfather. He'd apparently had a home on the shore of Johnson Town, a large tract of land that ran off the main road to Lucea, a town I understood to be near the old cove. Maybe his Crooks descendants still lived there.

On our last day with Troy, we were again cruising westward along the north highway when I reached Curniff by phone. He was in a chipper mood and we chatted a while before I asked.

"So, Curniff, I was wondering if you had a chance to think about it, allowing me to have a sample of your DNA?"

"Yes, yes," he said, without hesitation. "You can have it. Whatevahhhh you want, my deaaah."

I told him we were on the road, nearing Falmouth, and he suggested meeting outside a hotel where he had business that afternoon. We hung up and I cheered. But then panic set in. I grabbed my daypack and rummaged through it. I felt ill. I had switched bags before setting out that morning.

"Troy, I have to buy Q-tips. I forgot the DNA kit, and we'll never meet Curniff in time if we turn back."

"That we can get. No problem, don't worry," he said in that quintessential island way.

We stopped at a convenience store a few moments later, where I bought Baby Buds cotton swabs and zipper-lock bags to store them for testing. It was crude but it would have to do. I comforted myself with an assortment of DNA retrieval stories: labs that had managed to extract it from hair and licked stamps for other family researchers; police who had swabbed it off cars, floors, underpants; private investigators who'd pulled it off dental floss.

Back in the minibus, I wrote up an impromptu consent form for Curniff to sign, acknowledging that he was giving over his DNA to Family Tree DNA to be used only for Y-chromosome testing in my Crooks family project. I finished just as we arrived at the Starfish, a tall hotel in a patch of jungle by the sea, paint peeling off its sides like sunburnt skin. Curniff was parked across the road and we pulled up behind him.

"Hello, hello!" he said as he walked over, poking his head inside my window, greeting everyone. Then he asked if we could speak alone for a moment.

I jumped out of the van and we walked only a short way along the shoulder when Curniff turned to me with a solemn expression—and I knew. He had changed his mind.

"I'm not really sure about this DNA thing," he said. "I feel I should consult my attorney."

"Your attorney?"

"At first I didn't think anything of it, but say if it falls into the hands of someone who wants to accuse me of something—an investigator or something. I don't know if it will be secure, or who could have access, or if it might be used against me."

I tried for a few moments to assure him that tens of thousands of people had submitted their DNA for this sort of ancestral testing. I told him I would mail his sample directly to Family Tree DNA, which had a privacy policy preventing any other person or company from having access to it. Nor could any test be performed on his sample without his direct consent, and he could also have it destroyed immediately after the test.

But Curniff returned to his original point, that he need take only one look at me to feel the family connection. Didn't that make a DNA test unnecessary? I explained again that if we could confirm that we shared a common line of male descent, then we had a good chance of finding out precisely *how* we were related. That's what was missing in our Jamaica story, the who and the how of us.

But then it occurred to me that Curniff likely had little desire to know the how. I thought of Adrian Williams running his massive Williams surname project out of Missouri, and his great lament that so few Europeans were willing to take genetic tests to prove kinship with Americans. By his reckoning, it was because they already had a sense of origin and history, place and identity. They were living it. He guessed they saw nothing to be gained from a genetic test except the knowledge of distant cousins in the colonies. "For them it would be growing their family tree, finding new members to add to their branches," he had told me, "not finding its roots."

Maybe the story was similar for Curniff. A Jamaican born and bred knows who he is, where he comes from. He was satisfied that all the island Crookses belonged to one clan. Would it be worth the risk of using DNA to prove it when he feared that doing so might somehow come back to bite him? Or perhaps his reluctance was simply a visceral resistance to the prospect of giving his DNA to a relative stranger, baring secrets of his genetic soul that not even he, the bearer, might know. And what did it make me, with swabs in my pocket, verbally strong-arming this kind fellow who had walked me through a graveyard in the rain? What would

I feel like afterwards, driving away with his cells in a sandwich bag, knowing he was probably behind the wheel of his own vehicle feeling regretful or, worse, violated?

"Oh, Curniff, I don't want you to do anything that makes you uncomfortable," I said. "This really has to be something you decide yourself, not something I talk you into."

It was as if I'd handed him an antacid. He reached for my hand and smiled gratefully. "You know, you really do look like my daughter," he said.

"Thank you, Curniff, really, for all your help," I said. "I hope we have a chance to meet again one day."

"I hope the same," he replied.

I climbed back into a quiet minibus. No one had to ask. Nor, it turned out, was anyone surprised.

Troy did his best to raise everyone's spirits as we passed through Montego Bay, playing tour guide in his hometown, pointing out its clubs, the shops, the Pope's vacation residence on the water. But I was distracted, and wallowing—two Crooks men from the island and no Crooks chromosome for comparison; coming up empty in the Falmouth graveyard; mistaking the Mechanics lodge for the Masonic lodge; and then there was the dark vault in Spanish Town. With my luck we'd never find Johnson Town, where the very late David Atkinson Crooks had apparently once lived. Troy was certain that if it was west of Montego Bay, en route to Lucea, we were bound to see it eventually.

And we did, but only after we'd whizzed right past the small, faded sign pointing to Johnson Town. It took us along a narrow and badly paved road bordered by tiny old houses in disrepair. An elderly man and two women were sauntering up the lane as we approached. Troy called out to them and the two of us got out. The younger woman, with a baby on her hip and dark nipples poking through holes cut in her T-shirt, answered Troy's questions in a thick patois. She told him there hadn't been Crooks people around there for a while. There was once an old Crooks man who lived up in the hills, the man said, but no one was sure what had become of him. Go on to Lucea, the woman said. There's Crookses there.

Lucea, the capital of Hanover. I recalled from my online searches that the keeper of the Lucea town clock had once been a man named Crooks. The clock was a grand one, originally bound for St. Lucia but mistakenly sent to the little seaside town instead, where the residents refused to part with it. In *Ancestors*, Lucea was the place where Africans were sold in the marketplace, where the young boy August was branded with a C, destined for Crooks Cove. The town struggles now, like a middle child between the tourist hot spots of Negril and Montego Bay, to establish itself as a destination in its own right. To that end we passed a massive construction project near Lucea Harbour. Troy explained that it was a Spanish development, slated to be the largest resort on the island.

"Just think," Dad said, as we passed it. "They're building all this on your grandfather's land, Tweet."

In the absence of any other leads, we stopped at the bank to change money. I asked the teller, a thin young man in a tie, if he happened to know if there were any people named Crooks around.

"Crooks?" he said, and howled with laughter. "Lotsa Crooks round here!"

I wasn't sure if he was having sport with my asking for crooks at a bank. He turned and relayed my query to a colleague, and she laughed as well. "Oh yeah, we got Crookses. Even our mayor was a Crooks."

I had a brief flash of setting up a DNA dragnet in the bank parking lot. Was there anyone in the bank at that moment named Crooks, I asked. There wasn't. "Well, I understand there was once a Crooks Cove nearby, owned by a Crooks family a long, long time ago. Do you know where it is?"

The teller said he didn't but suggested we follow the highway through Hanover and ask at the library we'd find along the way.

"You must think we're slightly crazy with this hunt for ancestors," I said to Troy as we lit out westward once again.

"I'm going to advertise myself as a family history guide after this," he joked. "So this Crooks Cove, it was a plantation?"

"Yes, it was. I don't know if it still is. The first Crooks family was white, but our great-grandfather, he was coloured."

"Ah, everybody here has a little milk in their coffee!" Troy said cheerfully.

"Yes, I've heard that."

"Milk in your coffee, or sometimes ants in your milk," he said. "But what you definitely don't want are rats in your cupboard. You can't get rid of the rats!"

From his laughter we took *rats* to mean philanderers of any colour.

"Once you find yourself shacked up with a rat, there's no easy way out," he continued. "A lot of men in Jamaica, they have lots of children with lots of women." His own father had nine children with different women, he estimated. But Troy said he was determined to lead a "more modern" life. He had two children with one woman to whom he was happily married, and that, he said, was enough for him.

The greenery enveloped us on the spanking new leg of highway that led to Negril. Flanked by limestone cliffs, we crossed into Hanover, a small coastal parish of rugged valleys and peaks known for its fine cattle, yams and sugar. The library sat just off a bend in the road, and inside I met a pleasant young woman who directed me to old maps of the area. She'd never heard of Crooks Cove, but as we studied the coast together, she pointed out that there was a Cousins Cove nearby. I recognized the name instantly as the same one that had appeared on the old Crooks plantation when the first slave registry was compiled. We couldn't be more than fifteen minutes away.

As I returned to the minibus, it suddenly felt hotter than it had all week. There wasn't even the whisper of a breeze, and the salt was so thick in the air I could taste it on my lips.

"The sea is close," Troy said.

We passed new-looking homes on the hill, more stretches of green, scanning for something, anything, that would signal we had finally reached our destination. Off to the right the land dipped low towards the shore, where we spotted a cemetery below the ridge—tall headstones, bone white, glinting in the afternoon sun. Troy turned around and followed the dirt path that led down to the sea. A shack painted green, advertising videos for sale or rent, sat across the road from the shore. In front of it, two men toiled under the generous shade of a majestic old tree, fashioning a lobster trap from netting and whittled branches.

Troy turned off the engine and he and I got out. By now we had our routine down pat. In patois he told the men we were looking for people named Crooks, and asked whether this land had once belonged to anyone by that name. They answered and Troy translated.

It did, the elder of the two men said, a long, long way back. There was still a Crooks around: an old woman the men knew as Nan. Follow the road past the cemetery, they told us, past the store. Her cottage is on the right.

As we rounded the bend we saw a clapboard shack that served as a coffee shop and another, according to the spray painting on its side, that housed a farmer's market on Fridays. It suddenly dawned on me where we were . . . the road hardly wider than a footpath, the one- and two-room shacks and cottages of a tight and tiny community. This had once been a slave village. I pictured it as Paul Crooks described in *Ancestors*: the slave huts with their vegetable patches, loved ones buried before their time in their gardens, night gatherings by candlelight, the beating of drums, whispered plans to strike and rebel. I doubted that any of the original slave homes had survived this close to the shore; they would have been battered by the centuries and by hurricanes.

The first dwelling we saw looked modern and well kept. It was painted a deep Indian red and had a white iron gate across its front porch. Troy stopped. "This must be it," he said.

"I'll knock," I said. As I followed the walkway through a fragrant riot of palms and bougainvillea, I caught sight of a burgundy sun hat alongside the house. An elderly black woman peered around the corner.

"Hello," I said. "Sorry to disturb you." I explained that I was doing some family research, that my mother was a Crooks. "And we think there might be some connection to the Crookses here."

"Lucky you caught me. I was going round the back, herding my goats," she said. "I'm a Crooks."

I introduced myself and she told me her name was Henrietta Crooks.

"Have you lived here a long time?" I asked.

She sighed and chuckled. "Oh yes, a long time. My mother was born here, and her father and her grandfather. They were in cane and bananas," she said. "Going back, they were slaves."

She was born there, she said, in 1929, grew up there, left for a while and then came back to live again at the cove. She didn't look seventy-eight; her frame was straight and strong, her face full and unlined. She wore short denim slacks and a cream blouse embroidered with bright orange flowers.

Before long my mother was out of the van and at my side. "This is Henrietta Crooks, Mum. She has lived here all her life, and her parents and her grandparents."

"How lovely to meet you," my mother said warmly. "You have a lovely place, a lovely garden."

My father, Stephen and Troy joined us. All the visitors in Henrietta's front garden attracted a curious elderly man in a ball cap and red tank top. I couldn't understand him, but I guessed that he was asking Henrietta if everything was all right. She nodded and, it seemed, told him why we were there. Then she introduced him as Thomas.

We began sharing with her the little we knew of my great-grandfather, that he was a ship's captain born in Falmouth, apparently came from a plantation and was coloured. Henrietta told us that in Jamaica there were dark Crookses and fairer Crookses; some of them lived much further inland, at a place called Ginger Hill. I recognized the name from one of the wills we had copied and asked if she was related to them. No, she said, she didn't think so.

I told her I understood that a man named James Crooks was the original owner of the land.

"Yes," she said. "He buried up dere."

"Up where?"

"Up near de big houses."

But Thomas shook his head. "No, all de graves gone now," he said.

"No," Henrietta told him. "Some of dem still dere." She used to work up there, she told us, and remembered seeing the grave.

"No, no, dey gone," Thomas insisted. "When dey built de new road and de big houses, development pushed dem under."

"The big houses?" I asked.

"Yes. English people live up dere," Henrietta said.

I recalled the large new homes we had passed before we veered off the highway. Apparently it was still white folks up in the big house on the hill.

"Do you think you could find the grave?" I asked Henrietta. "Do you think you could help us find it?" I cannot explain why it felt important to actually set eyes upon the tomb. I suspect that I needed something concrete—hard evidence, finally, that there actually was a Crooks plantation, that it was a real place, not just an idea planted by a novel or a family rumour from long ago.

"Yes," Henrietta said without pause. "I could show you where it might be."

I imagined our convoy of seniors—my elderly parents, sep-tuagenarian Henrietta, doubting Thomas—trekking back up the dirt road in the heat, crossing the highway, then climbing the hill.

"We could drive up there, couldn't we, Troy?"

"Sure," he said.

"Would you come with us, Henrietta?"

"I can do dat. Lucky you caught me," she said again as we all piled into the van. "I was after my goats."

Troy pulled up on the shoulder of the north highway, just west of the big house. "It's somewhere up there," Henrietta said, pointing to the hills.

We stepped out to find ourselves on the edge of a ditch—a deep one—lying between us and the slope, a fifteen-foot drop down to a mattress of gravel and weeds. My mother took one look and waited by the minibus. My father, eighty-two years and three months that fall, hurtled headlong into it, testing the limits of gravity and his knee replacements.

"Dad, wait!" I shouted, scrambling after him, wishing that just this once he would act his age. It wasn't even his side of the family. Meanwhile, Henrietta had already climbed down and up the other side, and the seventy-eight-year-old was hiking, unruffled, onward and upward. I was travelling with a pack of bionic seniors.

Reaching the hilltop put us level with the big house. It was a custard-coloured two-storey, a handsome retreat with white trim, columns and a wide second-floor balcony that must have offered a spectacular view of the sea. A chain-link fence topped with barbed wire surrounded its yard, separating a manicured garden from the stubborn jungle of the hillside.

Henrietta and Thomas were still debating. "It *is* around here," Henrietta was saying.

"No, no, dere gone," said Thomas, still shaking his head.

Troy had wandered over to what looked like a knoll near the fence. Only when I drew up beside him did I see it was the grass-covered ruins of an old stone wall. "This must have been a building on the plantation once," he said, crouching down on his haunches to take a closer look.

It was then that I noticed the goats—a brown one with a white patch between its eyes, and another, black and skinny—atop another mound of rubble, still as statues, watching us. It froze me on the hillside for a moment. I stared at them and they stared back, acting as if they owned the place, just as they had on the tombs in Falmouth. I wished I'd never read that duppy lore.

"Henrietta," I asked, "the grave you remember seeing, was it from the seventeen hundreds?"

"Yes, yes," she said. "My mother, she was born in 1906. She used to talk about the Crooks tombs up here. Later, I remember when I worked up here for the Fowler family, I saw the graves behind a brick wall, and there was the Crooks name. I always remembered that."

Suddenly Troy began shouting. "I see two tombs here! Right here, two tombs!" He was balancing precariously on a bit of old stone, craning to see over the barbed wire of the fence.

"In the front garden?" I asked.

"Yes, yes," he said, leaping off the stone. He scampered along the fence, pressing his face against its links. "It's a Crooks! It's a Crooks! James Crooks!" he hollered, as though he were cheering for an underdog team that had finally scored.

My father, who had disappeared further up the hill, came striding back down towards us, waving his arms for us to follow him.

"Dad, Troy found tombs," I called out. "There's two in the front garden of this house."

"I know," he called back. "I've spoken to the gentleman who owns the house. He's in the back. He's a relation to the Crookses buried there. Come on, he'll talk with us."

A relation of the Crookses? A male? Thank God I'd stopped for Q-tips.

We paraded up the hill, Henrietta, Thomas, Stephen, my father and me, the two goats now bleating steadily behind us. Troy went back to pick up my mother and drive her around.

John Rosser awaited our arrival in his backyard. He was a pale and towering Brit with a crop of white hair and glasses. In blue satin sports shorts and a pink bush shirt, he had the rumpled look of a man who'd been loafing around the house. Yet for someone not expecting company, for someone suddenly ambushed by a seven-member search party creeping around his property, he was amazingly friendly.

Rosser told us that he and his wife had retired to Jamaica and built their haven on this hill by the sea. In recent times it had been a coconut and banana farm, until a yellowing fever hit the crops. The land was an overgrown cow pasture when they arrived, he said, but back in the eighteenth century it had indeed been the Crooks sugar plantation.

"I understand you are related to the Crooks family," I said.

"No, it's not me," he said. "It's my wife." But she was out with their son for the day, he said, and he wasn't quite sure precisely how they were related.

"Did you know the graves were on your property?" I asked.

"No, it wasn't until after the house was built. The landscapers were working in front and they hit upon the graves. They asked us if they should just plough them under. We said no, we didn't think that was right—and we didn't even know then that my wife was related to them."

We all gaped at that. It was one thing to discover graves in your front yard, but to learn they belonged to a long-dead relative was a coincidence beyond bizarre. I told John Rosser that I couldn't be sure our family was related to James Crooks but suspected that was the case. I explained that I was using genetic testing to trace our Crooks line, and that while our great-grandfather had come from Jamaica, the DNA test results suggested paternal roots in the northwest of England, in Lancashire.

Given the region's shipbuilding history, its swift trade with the West Indies, through Liverpool in particular, it sounded plausible, he said. The original Crooks immigrants might have sailed there from Lancashire in colonial times.

My mother and Troy had caught up by then, and Mum wanted to hear it for herself. "Is it true that James Crooks is buried here?" she asked.

"Yes, it's true," he said, grinning. "Come on, see for yourself."
He led us around to the front of the house, to the garden's west
side, where two headstones lay nestled in the grass at the foot of
an oval flower bed. I can't say whether it was respect for the dead
or simply—finally—the awe of discovery, but we all slipped into
silence for a few moments. Stephen and my father photographed
the headstones as Henrietta whispered an I-told-you-so to
Thomas. My mother marvelled quietly.

It was Troy who read the epitaphs aloud:

In Memory of
James Crooks
Of Hanover Parish
Who died the
16th of October 1740
Aged 32 *years*
8 *months and* 9 *days*

So there he was, James Crooks of the Cove, author of the will
I'd pored over for clues. Dead in his prime, leaving behind a young
daughter, a pregnant wife, an unborn son. Early death stalked his
heirs like a curse: his daughter, and James Crooks Junior, the son
he never saw, leaving thirteen children fatherless in all. The Captain
had died at the same age. All of them buried before reaching thirty-
five. Was it the sins of the father?

My mother didn't miss the coincidence. "Just like my grandfather," she told Rosser. "He died so young; my father was only
eighteen months old. That's why we never knew anything about
his people here."

Only a few inches away lay the tomb of James Crooks's
daughter (the surname had mysteriously gained a vowel).

In Memory of
Ann Dickson,

Daughter of James Crookes,
Who departed this life
January 7 1769
In the 31 year of her age
Leaving one daughter and seven sons
To mourn the irreparable lofs of a tender mother
And the Best of wives

I thought of the will, and the inheritance James Crooks had left the young Ann as a child: *six hundred pounds and one Negro girl of her choosing. . . .* It was one of Ann's seven sons who took over the land, saving it from bankruptcy and becoming master when the first slave register was compiled.

We peppered Rosser with more questions about his wife and her links to Jamaica. She'd grown up in a place called Maryland, he said, further inland. It was his wife's mother, a Campbell, who had told them they were cousins to the Crookses.

I recalled that the sister of James Crooks's widow had married one of the Campbells, a Scottish family with several island plantations. It was the famed Duncan Campbell of London, who sold his relatives' sugar in England, whose letters had told me nearly everything I knew about the white Crookses of Jamaica.

I asked if I could talk to his mother-in-law, but Rosser told me she would be too shy to speak to strangers about such things. Instead he described how easy it was to stumble over the past on this island, not just in the museums or by way of ruins. You could walk through fields not far from there and find bottles in the grass, hand-blown, from the eighteenth century.

As the chat continued I was again distracted, judging the distance of the grave from the sea, wondering about coffin materials and the moisture and acidity of the soil, whether 267 years beneath it would devour a cadaver, whether even a cheeseparing of bone might be left. For the second time that day I felt like a character from a horror film. *I wanted to dig him up.* After all the wild goose chases and dead ends and the prospect of going home empty-handed, I longed for a shovel. I wanted to pry that cracked head-stone from its dirt bed and scrape up whatever remained of the first master of Crooks Cove, extract DNA from his long-dead cells and bury more than a century of rumour and myth. I wanted to find out once and for all if he was our forefather, if it was his chromosome that crossed the Atlantic to Bombay, rooting us to this storied sugar plantation, a stronghold of slavery, a site of bondage, rebellion and death. Was that our story too? Were we fugitives in one hemisphere and captors in another?

I thought of Roberta Estes down in Michigan and the estimate she'd received of twenty thousand dollars to dig up her dad. How outrageous the prospect had seemed to me at the time; yet how entirely reasonable, even logical, it seemed at that instant, with mere barrows of earth between question and answer. Maybe the setting—the front garden of retirees—was obscuring the notion that I was contemplating desecration of sacred ground. After all, given the nod, the landscapers had been prepared to plough it under. And how many tombs were now buried beneath the new highway? How sacred was it to Henrietta to stand over the grave of the man who had brought her ancestors to this cove in chains? If we were next of kin, would we have a right to exhume him? Was it an *if* that only exhumation could resolve?

My head ached under the hot sun as I hovered over the two graves, wondering what to do next. I looked out to the sea and back to the hillside we'd climbed to bring us there. On the other side of the fence, the goats had drifted closer to the yard, still watching.

15

BONES OF CONTENTION

There have always been grounds for exhumation—grave-yards oversubscribed or reconfigured, post-mortem attempts to determine identity or cause of death. The Catholic Church has a long tradition of the practice. For centuries it has exhumed the bodies of saints to see if, by some divine inter-vention, their corpses have been spared decomposition. The Church puts the bodies of those deemed "incorruptible" on display in glass coffins, like precious jewels. That winter, in fact, the Vatican was poised to announce the exhumation of Saint Padre Pio, an Italian monk who died in 1968 (despite the protests of his relatives and devotees, it went ahead in March 2008, and a Church official declared him well preserved).

History has given exhumation a very bad name, rife as it is with tales of corpses ransacked and relocated or, as in the case of Oliver Cromwell, dug up and decapitated as a royal warning to dissidents. The head of the man who began the British peopling of Jamaica stood on a pole outside Westminster Hall for some twenty-four years. Disinterment was once so common that Shakespeare's last words to the world did not take the form of a sonnet or a farewell verse, but rather a threat, inscribed on his tombstone in 1616 (here, with spelling modernized):

GOOD FREND FOR JESVS SAKE FORBEARE,
TO DIGG THE DVST ENCLOASED HEARE.
BLESE BE YE MAN THAT SPARES THES STONES,
AND CVRST BE HE THAT MOVES MY BONES.

The Bard still has good reason to worry. Digging up dead people for DNA testing has become as fashionable as reality TV. Occasionally it's by court order or initiated by relatives hoping to prove the guilt or innocence of a long-dead loved one. But researchers, historians and the fanatically curious have propelled what many—scholars, ethicists, critics—refer to as the "exhumation movement." The desire to solve old mysteries, to rewrite history or to confirm final resting places of the famous and the infamous has led to a long list of the disinterred.

Genetic tests have been run on remains said to belong to the Romanovs, Josef Mengele, Christopher Columbus, Butch Cassidy and, yes, the Sundance Kid, the soldier beneath Arlington Cemetery's Tomb of the Unknowns, and Jesse James—repeatedly (since few agree on how, when or where the legendary outlaw finally met his end, the posthumous manhunt has so far led to the exhumation of three bodies). Not that every request to exhume is granted. It has been a no-go for Billy the Kid, the Kelly Gang and, so far, Galileo, disappointing scientists eager to find out if the Renaissance icon had a genetic eye condition that clouded some of his observations (he first mistook Saturn's rings for moons).

The efforts seem to reflect an unspoken mantra of modern science: if we have the know-how, we have the right to know. *Can we make a tomato frost resistant using the gene of a coldwater fish? Can we engineer flowers to bloom on your birthday? Can we find out if the father of astronomy had buggered-up eyesight?* On the altar of science, human remains are not sacrosanct; they're reference materials. And since certain rituals of science have found their way to the masses, maybe it was inevitable that the masses—that I— would consider them. People claiming to be descendants of Italian composer Giacomo Puccini, of Salvador Dali, of Benito Mussolini, plus Canadians and Americans who believe they're related to War of 1812 general Zebulon Pike, have all called for bodies to be exhumed to prove blood ties. No wonder Josephine Johnston reminded the genetic genealogists gathered in Houston not to do anything at night they wouldn't do in the light of day. Anyone who uses DNA to investigate family history will, at some point, likely be tempted to reach for a shovel.

After returning from Jamaica, I found myself flipping to the page in my notebook where John Rosser had written his phone number, wondering how on earth I could broach the possibility of unearthing James Crooks from his flowerbed. Would any excavator in duppy-fearing Jamaica even take on the job, and how much would it cost? It was a crazy idea, and I put the notepad away. But I would muse about it often enough that Jade drew a picture of James Crooks, a bird's-eye view of his skeleton lying in a grave and wearing a pirate's hat. "Here, Mom," she said. "This is to decorate your office." Wonderful.

My father saw exhumation as an entirely logical next step, which surprised me. My father is not a fan of open caskets, feeling they invite a certain disrespect towards the dead at crowded wakes. But on the phone one afternoon he told me, "Go on, make the call. You must exhume him. You have to do it. You never know, John Rosser might agree. . . . They might even have a bit of bone, something they came across during the landscaping."

"You mean something they kept? A bottled shard on the mantel or something?"

"Could be," Dad said.

It could be that the elusive story of my father's grandfather made him all the more determined to get to the bottom of my mother's, however radical the route. But I suspect the prospect of exhumation also appealed to my father's inner engineer: a cool, clinical approach—problem: solution—and one that involved tools. Exhumation offered the chance not only to run a DNA test but to test DNA itself. Was it truly possible to discover if there was a biological link between my Mississauga uncle and an eighteenth-century planter buried on a Jamaican hillside, just by using a bit of spit and a few centuries-old cells? Was I prepared to dig up a dead man to find out?

Roberta Estes told me the idea still kept her up nights. I had called her at her home in Michigan. From the talk she gave in Houston, I knew her to be one of the most experienced genetic genealogists around, and certainly the only one I knew who had gone as far as getting a quote to dig up her dad. But she hadn't gone through with it. Why? I wondered.

Roberta told me her story from the beginning: how her father had died when she was seven and how as a child she had always badgered her mother with questions about her ancestry. Then, after she grew up and had her own child, she began investigating her father's family. Her project eventually grew to involve Y-chromosome tests, tracing descendants of one Abraham Estes, who came from England to America in the seventeenth century. Finding a Y to represent her father's line was a struggle that eventually led her to a second cousin, a great-grandson of her paternal grandfather. His Y chromosome proved to be an odd mismatch with the Abraham Estes line, off by five markers on twenty-five tested. Strangely, the mismatches were not on markers prone to mutating but on those considered fairly stable. She thought work in the Kentucky coal mines might have messed with the Y of her Estes forefathers, or, if the mismatch was not the result of genetic damage, perhaps her father's family was indeed from a different Estes bloodline.

With no other Y sample available from her father's line to test, she thought it an unanswerable question. But then she came across a letter her aunt had written that revealed her father had led a double life. While he was married to her mother, Roberta's father had another wife in another city, and another child—a son;

in fact, she and her half-brother were born just five months apart. In 2004, Roberta found him in Ohio. His name was David and he lived just two and a half hours away. She wrote him a letter that included a picture of her father, and two weeks later he called. "This is David Estes," he said. "Are you my sister?"

That first contact was a "breathtaking experience," Roberta told me. They spoke for three hours. He, like her, had known nothing about his father's other life. They traded childhood tales, marvelling at the parallels, how good old Dad used to take them both fishing, tell them the same jokes, photograph them in the same poses. Roberta said she and her new-found brother made an odd pair, she a conservatively attired professional consultant who managed technology projects for the government, and he a tattooed, long-haired long-haul trucker. But there was no question about the fast bond they forged. "I had found my family," Roberta said.

Except the genetic tests said differently. David's Y did not match the Y-chromosome sample from her father's line. Roberta commissioned two other tests to compare her DNA with David's and the results showed they were definitely not siblings. "It was clear that my dad thought David was his son," she said, "but I finally had to accept that we weren't siblings." With the relationship that she and David had built, Roberta discovered that the test results meant nothing to her, that DNA is not the glue that binds families. Their emotional attachment proved to be the stronger adhesive: "I know there are better tests now that could tell me if he is my brother, but it doesn't matter. In my heart, he is my brother."

David's Y-chromosome result eventually raised new questions about her dad. Perhaps he was David's biological father; it could be that her father was not actually an Estes. Did that mean she was not an Estes? If she wasn't, who was she? It was that line of inquiry that led her to the brink of exhumation. She knew some relatives might object, and she knew too that there were no guarantees she could harvest enough DNA from her father's remains to conduct a reliable Y-chromosome test. But aside from all that, it was something else that stopped her—the lesson she had learned from her brother's DNA test. If she exhumed her father and ran the test, would the results change her life or make her think differently about her father, or herself? Were the questions, as she put it, "a good enough reason to dig up the dead"?

"There is still a part of me on long and lonely nights that still wants to go dig Daddy up," she told me. "But no matter what the DNA would show, I'm an Estes. It will be on my tombstone. The DNA really doesn't matter."

My mother had said hardly a word about the prospect of exhuming James Crooks. Considering that he was possibly a great-grandfather of hers, it seemed odd. One Sunday afternoon as we made an enormous batch of Christmas *kulkuls*, we talked it over. There is always time to talk while making *kulkuls*. I think of them as an Indian version of the Timbit, hardly bigger than a doughnut hole. They're made from a firm dough that's rolled into little balls, flattened against the back of a fork, then curled off it to form a ridged tube that's fried or baked and dipped in sugar. As far as opportunities for weighty conversation go, *kulkul*-making offers the indoor equivalent of fishing.

"You've never said what you think about exhumation, Mum. Are you for or against?"

"We'll need another cookie sheet," my mother said, leaving the table to hunt for one.

"Mum," I said, "what do you think?"

"Carolyn, it doesn't matter what I think. It's your decision. It's your project."

"Come on, it's your family too," I said.

My mother sighed. A long sigh.

"To tell you the truth, I'm not keen," she said, "not at all. I'm not worried about spirits or ghosts, nothing like that. But if someone is laid to rest somewhere, that's where they should rest. It's not for us to disturb it."

My father was rolling dough at the table, lining up perfect rows of bite-sized spheres. "It's only *bones*," he said. "I don't think he would mind you trying to find out if you're family."

"Who?" I asked. "John Rosser?"

"No, James Crooks," Dad said with a wink.

"But there must be some other way," Mum insisted. "I think there must be other means to find out rather than to do *that*."

At the end of the day that's what haunted me. Was I really willing to jump from confirmation of having a white man's Y chromosome in our family straight into a grave? It was like finding out you carry a few Native American genetic markers and then applying for tribal status—a hell of a reach. And when I did a logical accounting of the facts, I fell short, far shorter than the case Roberta Estes could make: I had a coloured Great-Grandpa Crooks born in Jamaica who carried a western European Y haplotype. That didn't seem quite enough to claim a blood connection to the European Crooks plantation family in Hanover. If I knew the Captain's family had come from Hanover, that would at least give me stronger grounds for considering exhumation to prove the link.

Yet a powerful gut feeling picked up where the facts left off. When we were there at the old plantation, I felt a connection to the Cove that reminded me of my feelings at the yellow church in Kochi. After we left the Rossers' yard that day, we had driven back down to Henrietta's cottage, triumphant in the afterglow of finding the tomb. We ate ackee, cut fresh from one of Henrietta's trees, and bought mango ice cream from an old man who sold it from a cooler strapped to the back of his bicycle. It was late, the sun dipping low in the sky, but we felt compelled to stop at the Cove itself, a tiny curve of beach bathed in the half-light, framed by rust-coloured cliffs that opened to the endless sea beyond. I thought of the many eyes before mine that had gazed out over those waters, the desperate souls who had lived in shacks by this shimmering sea, longing for a homeland that lay on its other side. Paul Crooks had imagined that too. In the afterword of his book he describes stopping in Lucea at a point overlooking the Cove: "Looking out over the horizon, I imagined a slave ship coming into port," he wrote, "the port where my ancestors entered the New World and a life of bondage."

Looking out to sea from the shoreline of Crooks Cove.

We all wandered down to the shore, even Troy, lost in thought. I took off my shoes and let the water wash over my toes. My father and I collected shells and bits of coral and Stephen filmed that final walkabout. Later, back home, I watched myself turn towards the camera after he'd asked, "So, what are you thinking?"

"I'm thinking we came from someplace," I said. "We didn't just come from the airport in 1972." I sounded so sure, as if I'd unravelled the final inches of an umbilical cord. Maybe it was just the moment's romance, finding myself in a scene I had envisioned while reading Paul Crooks's novel. Was that it? If I had never read the book, if I had never read up on the history of the Cove, would I have felt such a link to this former plantation? Would I feel as tempted to dig up the man who owned it nearly three hundred years ago? If we had come across the tomb of some other old Crooks in a graveyard, I wouldn't be mulling over the costs of a backhoe. But the story of James Crooks was one I knew, one that explained at least half the mystery of my great-grandfather, the coloured captain from a well-to-do plantation-owning family with his white man's Y chromosome. I wondered, had I found the first James Crooks buried in one of those overgrown Jamaican cemeteries, if his tomb were in a row of the forgotten, tended only by goats, would I have fewer qualms about exhuming him?

As it was, the Rossers were, however distantly, related to the James Crooks we'd found in their yard. Their inclination to honour his final resting place had shown itself—even before they knew he was kin—in their decision not to plough it under. Rather than disturb the dead, they had made a mini-cemetery of their front garden, adorned it with a rockery and shrubs. My mother was right. Before taking the extreme step of exhumation and horrifying that nice retired couple on the hill, I had to exhaust other means of confirming whether we had a connection to the Cove.

Besides, after looking into various cases of exhumation, I had serious doubts, just as Roberta Estes did, about the quality of DNA we could recover. One geneticist told me that if conditions are ideal, DNA has a shelf life of some twelve thousand years. But if conditions are less so—a wooden coffin immersed in warm, wet soil, for instance—the chances of extracting a Y chromosome are dodgy. Scientists working with the alleged remains of Christopher Columbus exhumed in Seville had no luck harvesting his Y chromosome. They have had to rely on the Y they managed to extract from the remains of his son, Hernando. The elusive Y has also been one of the obstacles to confirming the whereabouts of Jesse James's remains. In fact, in most cases involving ancient remains, or even those just a few hundred years old, scientists base their findings on mitochondrial DNA, the genetic material people inherit from their mothers. A cell can contain thousands of copies of the mitochondrial DNA women pass down, but only one copy of a

Y chromosome, and it's the tiniest one. That's why the genetic history of the world has traditionally been constructed from maternal lines. So even if I did receive permission to exhume James Crooks, there were no guarantees I would get the chromosome I needed.

So back I went to reading about the white Crookses of Jamaica, hunting for male descendants of James Crooks, potential proxies for his Y. By now I knew the generations by heart: James Crooks the first had one son; James Crooks the second had three—James the third, Richard and John. All three brothers went to England for an education after their father's death, but all three apparently returned. John ran the plantation before he went bankrupt and disappeared, Richard apparently was a surgeon in the military, and James Crooks the third became a Falmouth merchant. The only reference I found to a male descendant of any of them was a death notice in the *Columbian Magazine* from October 1798: "In Trelawny, at Falmouth, Mr. Thomas Crooks, only son of Mr. James Crooks." It seemed to place James Crooks the third, or at least his son, in the Captain's birth town. I could find no mention of any children Thomas might have had, or whether he or his father had any illegitimate coloured children. Yet I knew from the Cove slave register that there were fifteen coloured Crookses, nine of them men, who might well have carried the Y of a Crooks forefather. It was hard not to imagine them as some had been depicted in Paul Crooks's novel—as the master's children.

Desperate as I was for a lead that didn't involve a truckload of dirt removal, reaching the author took on a new urgency. Paul Crooks was the only living, Y-toting male I knew with a direct tie to that old Crooks plantation. On a November evening in 2007 we finally connected by phone. It was late in London, near eleven o'clock, but we had a long chat, talking about our day jobs but more about the family history work and writing that consumed our nights. There was a similarity to the rhythm of our lives, and after a few minutes we began comparing some of the names and details we had come across in our research.

He told me that none of the family names I had included in my initial email were familiar to him, nor, he said, did they appear in his files. I told him that was just the sort of luck I was having, and why I hoped I would have a better chance of piecing our story together with DNA testing. My mother's paternal line was a Y chromosome of European heritage, I said, but African markers had also been identified in my mother's DNA. I told him too that some relatives had certain African features. Although Paul had traced his paternal line to Africa and it was likely a hell of a long shot, I asked if he would be willing to let me arrange a test on his Y and compare it with our own. He didn't need much persuading. "Sure," he said. "I'm curious too."

His quick agreement surprised me, and impressed me. Paul had invested thirteen years, closed the book (literally) and travelled to Ghana, and still he was ready to jump into the gene pool to learn more. His signed consent form and two vials of buccal-cell swabs came back to me just before Christmas. I added his name to the Crooks project and sent the samples down to Houston.

Paul's was one of three tests I arranged that fall. Eager to cling to whatever threads science had to offer, I reread the results from DNAPrint in Florida—the test that had given us the first glimpse of our genetic diversity, the first to provide biological evidence of our East Asian ancestry and the only one to suggest an African origin. It was also the test that introduced the red herring of Native American ancestry, and scanning the genome had come a long way in the few years since. A new microchip had made it possible and affordable to quickly scan not just hundreds but hundreds of thousands of spots on a genome, or even multiple genomes, at the same time. The possibility of improving on those initial results from Florida led me back to Mark Shriver at Pennsylvania State University.

Shriver was the scientist who had helped develop that test for DNAPrint (which ceased operations in 2009), and he'd continued his research into ancestrally informative genetic markers. For a couple of years we'd been speaking about his possibly running updated tests on my family. Like most population geneticists he was hard to get hold of, spending weeks in the field collecting DNA to identify distinct mutations linked to human diseases and, in his case, markers related to facial features, jaw shape, nose shape, the space between the eyes and so on. Tying genes to physical traits had so far proved to be a tricky business, but one of Shriver's aims was to be able to generate a portrait of someone with nothing more than a DNA sample, which had big potential for forensics. For Shriver it was also helpful in his work on ancestry. By the end of 2008 he had a chip able to scan ten thousand markers across the genome that offer insight into a person's geographic heritage, dwarfing the power of the 176-marker test we took in 2005. It made it possible, for instance, to distinguish the DNA of East Africans from West Africans, and northern Europeans from southern Europeans. It was still a work in progress, but in November Shriver and I made a plan to test both my parents and me.

With its focus squarely on heritage information, Shriver's test had caught the attention of celebrities, predominantly African Americans, whose ability to glean their past through surname searches or property records so often runs into the brick wall built by slavery. Many African Americans have vigorously embraced genetic genealogy, with whole church congregations swabbing together and specific companies catering to people eager to trace their African lineage through the Y chromosome or mitochondrial DNA. That fall, Shriver had just wrapped up his participation in the second installment of the PBS television series *African American Lives*. The two-part documentary had relied on Shriver's admixture tests for a big-picture look at the ancestry of a wide range of black luminaries, Maya Angelou, Morgan Freeman, Henry Louis Gates Jr., Whoopi Goldberg, Quincy Jones and Oprah Winfrey among them.

Like the DNAPrint test, Shriver's work has its critics: those concerned that laypeople will draw more than they should from this sort of DNA analysis, getting hung up on labels that they are 20 percent white or 30 percent black or half Asian. Some have said it elevates the concept of race from social invention to scientific fact. But Shriver and other scientists argue that the genome exposes race for the social illusion that it is. Shriver, after all, is the white man who discovered he has West African ancestry of 11 percent only after testing himself. This jibed with what the testing had already revealed to me: that even someone, like Jim List, who suspects he knows his heritage can suddenly find he has a genetic relative in south India. Any deep dive into DNA proves that race is a skin-deep farce. No distinct lines can be drawn between or around any one group.

When Shriver asked me what I hoped to achieve with the test, I told him my story: the mix of our background, the mystery of my paternal great-grandfathers. I said I hoped that some hiccup in our DNA might lead us to the Chinese village where John Abraham came from, or perhaps some other signature would tie us to the natives of South Asia—the Kurumbas, perhaps—or point us to the African tribe hidden away in my mother's heritage. I knew it would probably be several years until researchers had studied enough genomes around the world to offer that sort of precision, so I offered Shriver my diluted expectations—that he would tell us once and for all if our so-called Native American heritage was authentic, plus narrow my father's roots to a region in China and my mother's to a region in Africa. As I expected, Shriver was pessimistic about China; they still didn't have much genomic data from the country. But he anticipated better luck with the African component. Of the ten thousand markers from eleven different populations that he would survey, two thousand of those are SNPs that could indicate whether we had West African heritage.

I drove to my parents' in early December to collect their DNA again. For the first time, it required a jab. Shriver's lab had sent three blood-stain collection kits that included paper cards, each with a blank circle the size of a quarter on it and a push-pin to puncture a fingertip deeply enough to completely blot the circle with blood. I loved my parents for this, that I could show up in the middle of *Coronation Street* on a Tuesday night and ask to bleed them, and they never groaned or rolled their eyes or asked, "What happened to those fancy Q-tips?"

My mother's blood refused to come. She could barely draw two drops from her fingertip. She tried squeezing it, rolling it, holding it downwards to accelerate the flow. My father milked it. I pinched and palpitated. Finally, after nearly fifteen minutes and two bloodied fingers, she managed to fill the circle. My father, however, pricked his forefinger and watched his blood flow like an April creek. He could have stained half a dozen cards. "See how it runs, Tweet," he cheered. "That's Chinese blood streaming out."

The results from Shriver's lab at Penn State played out over a series of emails and conference calls that began in January 2008. His research team had amassed a mountain of raw data from our three genomes. By combining the numbers gleaned from the absence or presence of the ten thousand SNPs, they estimated the percentage of our ancestry from each of the population groups. Shriver put the margin of error at 1 to 2 percent and offered a few highlights off the top, namely that the dominant elements in my and my father's ancestry appeared to be European and East Asian. My West African component was, as the DNAPrint test had found, 8 percent. But my contentious Native American component, originally pegged at 22 percent, had shrunk to 6 percent, which, Shriver was certain, reflected ancestors from Central Asia, not First Nations people of the Americas.

But the drastic change in my tally was modest compared to my father's, whose so-called Native American ancestry fell from 25 percent—a full quarter of his heritage, according to the initial test—to nothing at all. The new research found that my father's

Central Asian markers could not be distinguished from those linked to East Asian ancestry, which was now estimated to be 43 percent, 7 percent higher than the DNAPrint result. It's a good thing tribal status requires more than a genetic test. My mother's so-called Native American reading rose from 1 to 8 percent, suggesting this time around that I had inherited those markers from her, and again Shriver predicted this reflected Central Asian heritage.

Central Asian ancestry wasn't unusual to find in people from South Asia, or people from Scandinavia or France, Shriver added. It implied a heritage that spanned a massive area and so included several diverse populations: ancestors of the first Natives to cross the land bridge into the Americas, but also early inhabitants of northwest India, Afghanistan, China, Mongolia and parts of the former Soviet Union. Random thoughts came to me as he spoke: Jin Li's unpopular finding that the DNA of the Chinese is not unique to China; my Uncle Horace telling me how often he is mistaken for Native; and my own girl, turning five that year, whose Mongolian birthmark on her lower back was beginning to fade.

After our wild musings upon hearing of our supposed Native ancestry back in 2005, Shriver's estimates and conclusions were instantly believable. It helped to explain why my father's East Asian ancestry was deemed to be 43 percent instead of the 36 percent the Florida test had found. The estimate of his European ancestry rose from 35 percent to 51 percent, and the percentage of African markers climbed from 4 to 6 percent.

Later I told Stephen that he need not be jealous any longer. I had essentially been kicked out of the tribe; my Native American roots had shrivelled. He put on a brave face and shrugged. "I don't think about it anymore," he said. "You know, that story about my swarthy aunt was in our family for two or three generations, and then *snap*, that was it. I did that test and it was just gone."

"Yes, but if one test tells me I'm 22 percent Native American and the next just a paltry 6 percent, there's more than a good chance that your reading was incomplete." He raised an eyebrow for a moment. But he'd lost faith. "Nah," he said. "I've tried to focus more on the idea that we were Vikings."

My mother too had a startling change in her ancestry predictions. The puzzling finding that she had significant East Asian ancestry—22 percent, according to DNAPrint—was reduced to just 7 percent by the measure of Shriver's lab, which cut off another vein of speculation. Mum's European ancestry, meanwhile, increased to 75 percent from 68; it was the dominant element of her heritage. Her proportion of ancestry from Africa rose slightly, from 7 to 10 percent, and Shriver found it was rooted specifically in West Africa, where most slaves began their torturous journey across the Middle Passage.

Shriver's test may have been more thorough than the Florida scan, but I knew that testing a different set of ten thousand mutations could well tell a different story. The truth was, at that point, the science just left me cold. There were no "ancestors" to be found in our code, no narrative in our nucleotides or tales to share over a cup of tea, only the limp arms of percentages, margins of error, confidence intervals. When the Florida test came back, I had been a blank slate, a genetic virgin, excited by whatever legible memory our DNA held. But now, after confirmation of our Chinese great-grandfather, after a chromosome had led me to the Crookses of Lancashire, after connecting with distant genetic cousins, the science felt suddenly . . . underwhelming.

The questions the results raise will, in all probability, never be answered. Why does my father carry 6 percent ancestry from West Africa? Is it a lingering artifact from the first modern humans that birthed us all? Or is there yet another story linking us to slavery? Or might it reflect the ancient population that gave rise to India's tribes, even the Kurumbas? And what are the details of my mother's apparent East Asian ancestry? Shriver acknowledged the shortcomings up front: "These tests give you more information with less precision, less a sense of time, or proportion." I had known it going in, even as I pricked my own finger at the bathroom sink (flow good to moderate). Still, I looked at the new numbers for a long time, lamenting all the stories DNA could not tell. I doubted I would ever make peace with the frustration. But then science surprised me.

Months passed. Snow melted. Spring arrived, and on a bright day in May 2008, the Y-chromosome test results for Paul Crooks appeared in my inbox. When I sent in Paul's kit, I had set the parameters to show only matches with the Crooks surname. Presuming he carried an African Y, I didn't expect to recognize any names, if indeed any were included with his results. I expected to click in, take a quick peek and scoot off to work.

But I had to sit down. There were matches—two—and both of them were my uncles. At a dozen markers, the Y chromosome of Paul Crooks the author and my uncles Dennis and Basil shared a perfect match. Exact matches between men with the same surname mean they have, it's estimated, a 99 percent chance of sharing a common male ancestor in the past three or four hundred years. I put the chances even higher. I could see in my mind where our bloodlines had converged: a curved beach, a former slave village hugging the shoreline, perhaps an overgrown hill where a plantation house had once stood.

Had the DNA really done what the records had so far failed to do? Had a common chromosome proved our connection to the Cove? I clicked on Paul's haplogroup designation. It confirmed that his Y belonged not to an African lineage but to a European forefather. He was, as he had to be to match my uncles, a member of the R1b1 group. This stranger, this young black man who had grown up in England, not far from where my own family once lived, whose novel had first pointed me to the Cove, whose book I had toted around Jamaica like a travel guide, was our relative—a not-so-distant cousin, probably from not more than six generations back.

Our DNA had suddenly tied us to him and revealed what no other source had. If Paul Crooks had paper evidence linking his roots to that Crooks plantation, and we had links to Jamaica and a biological link to him, surely, somehow, we shared those roots. Our common descent was likely from the patriarch of a slave-owning dynasty, since it was a white man's Y that united us. But what had been the marrow of that union? The resignation of a woman owned? Rape? Was it as Elizabeth Barrett Browning had described in her poem, "Wrong followed by a deeper wrong"?

I thought of my mother fighting off bad memories in the shower, hiding during *Roots*. How would she take the news? As soon as my uncles' Y chromosomes turned out to be European, the probability of slave ownership had been there, but this sudden kinship with Paul Crooks seemed to cement it. And what of Paul Crooks, whose open-minded curiosity had led him to send his DNA to a stranger across the sea?

I couldn't tell him, not yet. The twelve-marker match was significant, given our common surnames and history in Jamaica, but it was hardly irrefutable. That morning, excluding the author, 606 men from all over the world also matched my uncles' Y chromosomes at twelve spots; the haplotype of our Euro-Y is just that common. That meant Paul Crooks also matched those other men, and none of those others was named Crooks. It was possible—if unlikely—that, while Paul carried an R1b1 Y chromosome, it had come by way of some other European man. If Crooks was a name given to his ancestor through a Christian baptism, it could be that his Y had come down from some other white man who had passed through the Cove.

I had to confirm the match; I had to increase the number of markers tested. The more markers compared, the higher the resolution of the test, the more solid the data. And with all that was riding on it, the result had to be solid. As illuminating as it was to my family, it could be equally devastating to Paul Crooks and his. He had spent thirteen years tracing his Jamaican ancestry, interviewing his relatives, painstakingly combing through records, maps and slave registers to put together the story of his slave roots.

He had not only concluded that John Alexander Crooks, his third-generation grandfather, was African-born and sold into bondage in the Caribbean, he had imagined an entire fictionalized life for him. His novel was in a different league altogether than the world I had created as a child for the juggler, but the two were not entirely dissimilar. We had both of us fashioned an identity for a forefather when none could be known. Now here was I, after a bit of research and a quick swab, with this rank footnote to foul his efforts: *Turns out your male line likely hails from Britain, old chap, possibly Lancashire. Turns out we descend from both slave and slave owner.*

It was not a shovel I suddenly envisioned in my hands. It was a sledgehammer.

16

SHADOW FAMILY

A year before I mailed Paul's sample away for testing, geneticist Mark Jobling and his colleagues at the University of Leicester published a paper about the puzzling case of a white Yorkshire man who carried a distinctively African Y chromosome, a genetic signature so old and rare that only twenty-three men alive were known to carry it—and all of them were West African. Never before had this subtype of the A1 haplogroup been detected anywhere in western Europe, which compelled Jobling and his team to seek out other carriers. They tracked down eighteen other males who shared the Yorkshire man's unusual surname—Revis—and found that seven of those white men also harboured the surprising Y haplotype of a black man. None of them had any inkling of an African heritage, and despite tracing their family histories to common male ancestors living in Yorkshire in the eighteenth century, none could be found. Had they descended from an African troop the Romans posted at Hadrian's Wall nearly two thousand years ago, from a captured African whom ninth-century Vikings may have brought north, from a slave who served British nobility in the sixteenth century? No one knows.

In the end, researchers cast the Revis Y as the first genetic evidence of blacks living among "indigenous Britons" for centuries, and further proof that race must be a flawed concept if a bunch of white Yorkshire folk can have an African forefather. The English press eagerly picked up the story. Jobling told me that his group initially withheld the Yorkshire surname in question, "concerned that tabloids would get hold of the story and say that all people called Revis are Africans." They feared that boys named Revis would face schoolyard beatings from racist bullies.

But how did those Revis men feel? I wondered. Did they feel any less European, any less white to learn they were part black? Jobling told me that the original Yorkshire man, one John Revis, a seventy-five-year-old retired father of three and grandfather of six, found the test result "fascinating." Revis had been away on holiday when the news broke and returned to discover that his DNA had made him a minor celebrity.

"I had no idea that I was so culturally unique. But I am not going to start eating couscous and riding a camel," Revis said to the *Mail on Sunday* newspaper. "It was a shock to find out that, because I was so blond and blue-eyed when I was younger, people thought I was Nordic or German. But the researchers said that if my DNA were examined then people would assume they were looking at a North African man."

He noted that the "very white establishment" where he bowls could now boast an ethnic minority member, although, he added, "I doubt anyone would be able to pick me out." But Revis had already constructed a new narrative for himself. His Y, he felt, was the souvenir of a Berber warrior who came north and "spread his seed all over Yorkshire."

His wife, Marlene, was just as startled. "I can hardly believe it," she told the newspaper. "John has always seemed very English to me. He likes his roast beef and Yorkshire pudding on a Sunday. He has never asked me to cook anything unusual. My friends think our news is hilarious."

Blacks who suddenly discover white ancestry rarely marvel at the mystery. The story never plays out as it did in Yorkshire, with shades of the comic. More often, DNA tells the story of European men—conquerors, colonialists, captors—who spread their Y across continents like jam on toast. Article after article on the subject convinced me that I was to be the bearer of decidedly unhappy news for Paul Crooks. African Americans whose DNA reveals a European paternal origin describe sadness, disappointment and desperation for another test to prove the finding wrong. It's like learning they've been branded by biology, the master's mark seared into their DNA by the hot iron of inheritance. Even Henry Louis Gates Jr., Harvard professor of African studies, one of the most prominent black scholars in the United States and host of *African American Lives* on PBS, admitted suffering "the blues" when genetic testing revealed he was half European. Would Paul suffer the same?

In the afterword of his novel, Paul mentions that he had once sent away for information about the Crookses from a family research agency, and the first thing to fall from the package that arrived was a picture of a white family. "What a shock!" he wrote. "The only members of the Crooks family that I knew were black—us."

I couldn't shake the guilt. The testing had been my idea, and while I had not expected his Y to match my uncles', given the depth of his research, I had hoped for it. I wanted it to be true. I wanted his story to fill the hole in our narrative, and I got my wish. Quickly and conveniently, Paul Crooks had provided a string of code to tie up one of our very loose ends. The author's Y proved to be an exact match with our Crooks Y chromosome not only at twelve markers but at twenty-five markers as well. At thirty-seven markers we were off by only one, and that one difference was slight. Where Paul Crooks has a particular bit of genetic code— G-A-T-A—repeated ten times at a certain point on his Y chromosome, my uncles have it repeated eleven times—a tiny change, to be expected after a few hundred years. (A later test determined that this was the only mismatch, even after sixty-seven markers were compared).

Experts estimate that the Y mutates an average of at least once every five hundred times it is transmitted to the next generation.

So even without taking into account our common history in Jamaica, the raw DNA match alone suggests the probability of Paul Crooks and my Crooks uncles sharing a common male ancestor within the last eight generations is about 95 percent. I tried telling myself I was merely the messenger and that Paul was himself keen to have the answer. He had swabbed and sent his DNA back to me in a matter of weeks. It would be paternalistic for me to assume he was better off never knowing who, at this genetic level, he is.

And really, what *is* this level? Just one tiny chromosome out of his forty-six, a twig on his ancestral tree, one line of descent out of the 1,024 a human has after ten generations. It should give him no cause to abandon the bond he felt with the man he considered his third-generation grandfather. By his telling, John Alexander Crooks had raised four children, showed them what it meant to be free, and shared the stories of their people's struggle, stories they would share with their own children. The author's great-great-great-grandfather was their patriarch in all the ways that matter. Whichever white Crooks it was who gave them life, he gave nothing more than a bit of biology.

But no matter how I looked at it, the result was a hell of a thing. I had set out to solve the mystery of our great-grandfather and inadvertently unearthed a secret about someone else's. It was vivid proof that no one takes a DNA test in a vacuum. The results have an impact on everyone who shares your DNA: your parents, your siblings, your children, uncles, aunts, cousins—and strangers you had no idea were relatives until genetic testing shook them out of the family tree. Your results are their results, your secrets become their secrets, and they learn them, as you do, whether they want to or not.

On a spring afternoon a week after Paul's first result came back, I marched through my parents' front door and pulled his book out of my bag. "Remember this? I had it in Jamaica? Remember I told you the author sent me his DNA?"

My mother took the book from my hands and studied the painting on its cover, called "Slaves on the West Coast of Africa," a tableau of men with whips and branding irons raised, black men and women pinned beneath them, a ship in the distance.

"What does it mean?" my mother asked. "This match."

"There's more testing going on, but I'd say this pretty much confirms it. The man who wrote this book knows that he descends from slaves on the Crooks plantation at the cove we visited, and his Y chromosome is the same as your Crooks family chromosome, so that tells us the Crooks family who owned that plantation were almost certainly your ancestors."

"You mean that plantation where we were? All that land? That belonged to the Crookses—*our* Crookses?"

"It seems so."

"Look at that," my mother said. She quickly put the book back in my hands. "What land they had. . . . Dud, are you listening?"

My father was going through mail at the kitchen table.

"See there, Papa was right—the Crookses had a big plantation," Mum said. "How much my father wanted to go there." She lamented that the Captain had died too young to take him to that beautiful property—the rolling hills, the inlet, the beach. Mum wondered if any Crooks would have a claim to that land now.

"I wouldn't think so. The Crookses lost the land two hundred years ago. It ended up with a cousin, a Dickson, one of the sons of Anne Crooks, the daughter buried in the yard beside James."

"Look at that! We were standing at the grave of, what, Papa's great-grandfather?"

"Well, we don't really know which of the Crooks men was our forefather," I said.

"That means you still have to dig up James Crooks," my father said to me.

"Again with the digging," my mother said. "We know through this other fellow, this Paul Crooks, that James Crooks was related to my father, that he was a grandfather of mine. Would you dig up your grandfather?"

"Maybe," Dad said. "If I knew where he was."

"Actually, Dad's right. It doesn't prove that James Crooks was our great-great-grandfather or whatever, but I'm hoping that once I talk to Paul Crooks we may be able to figure out the connection."

"How wonderful," my mother said. "We already know so much. It's amazing."

That's how it went the first time I shared the news. We were joyous just to have the knowledge. We said nothing of slavery or how it was our Captain had got his colour. We talked about real estate. We spoke of the place, not the people. Within that tight frame we could simply love the land as the fount of my grand-father's line. We could even covet that seaside acreage, wistful for a homestead lost, so long as we didn't mention the bleak history that must have played out upon it. But the conversation stretched over the seasons to come, and with time, as further tests confirmed the match with Paul Crooks, the blinkers fell away. Eventually we got around to speaking about the slave owners in our family.

In the aftermath of one of my sister's elaborate family feasts, bellies full and heads swimming with wine, we started in on Jamaica: how the Spanish lost it to the British; how Cromwell set it up as a colony to spite Spain and the Catholics; how, some time after that, in the late sixteen hundreds, our forefathers had arrived. My brothers chimed in with their English school history of Cromwell, his battle with the Crown, the prisoners-of-war he shipped to the Caribbean, his vicious treatment of the Irish and Scots—and the merits of *Braveheart*.

I told them I had to assume our Crookses came from England, but there was also a chance it was Scotland. Scots made up a third of Jamaica's white population in the seventeen hundreds, and Jamaica's patois was in part a mixture of African dialect and Scottish accent that evolved among the slaves. Someone asked how many slaves the Crookses had owned. More than 150, I said, maybe as many as 200 at some points. Conrad scowled as if something rotten had hit his tongue. "A hundred and fifty?" he said. "That's disgusting. Isn't that disgusting?"

"It is," Mum said. "It is terrible to think of it."

There was a pause then, and I would remember it—a moment when all of us perhaps did think of it, and none of us said a word.

The three-thousand-year-old Babylonian Code of Hammurabi, the oldest set of laws known to exist, prescribes death to the son of a carpenter who builds a shoddy house and cutting off the arm of a surgeon who loses a patient, and the breasts of a nursemaid too free with her milk. In it appears the earliest known written record of slavery. But even by then it was a system already well established. As soon as the hunter-gatherers threw down their spears in favour of ploughs, people enslaved other people—to hoe the land and pick out their lice, to build pyramids, fetch water, mine salt, row ships, scratch their backs. There was hardly a corner or culture in the world where slavery didn't spread: ancient Greece, ancient Egypt, India, China, the Roman Empire, Africa, the Middle East. In Europe, serfs replaced slaves only after the Roman Catholic Church decided it was a rather un-Christian thing for Christians to own other Christians; certainly Christians shouldn't be exported as slaves to non-Christian lands. For the Vikings (as I pointed out to Stephen more than once), slavery was a primary source of income; *thralldom* they called it, and slaves were *thralls*. The word *enthralled* comes from the Norse term for "captured." If we all descend from royalty in one way or another, we all descend from cruelty as well.

But what on earth, with the exception of our DNA, did we have to do with the lives and times of those ancestors? If we bore responsibility for those Crooks slave owners, did we carry a debt for the British, who subjugated an entire subcontinent; for the Portuguese, who pressed Indian women to convert; for a Chinese grandfather who left his children, or any of China's warring dynasties, or the last to rule in Vietnam? Where would our culpability begin? Where would it end? DNA can magically link us with ancestors from millennia past, but we can no more take blame or credit for their exploits than we can for the randomness of our own DNA. It just *is*.

Not everyone feels that way. In the summer of 2006, a thirty-seven-year-old white man named Andrew Hawkins, from Cornwall, England, flew to West Africa to apologize to black people for a sixteenth-century slave-trading forebear. Sir John Hawkins, who is considered a national hero in England for his victory over the Spanish Armada, was also the country's first slave trader. He made a fortune in the export of Africans and celebrated it with an image of a bound black man woven into the family crest. So it was that Andrew Hawkins, who had once admired his knighted ancestor, put on a T-shirt that said "So Sorry" and chained himself to twenty-six others at a football stadium in the Gambia, where thousands of blacks had gathered from around the world for the annual International Roots Festival.

The pundits weren't kind. One called it "absurd"; another described it as "nauseating." David Robson, a columnist with the *Daily Express*, wrote that it was "fatuous" to apologize "for misdeeds committed centuries ago," and that apologizing for the misdeeds of long-ago ancestors was "more fatuous still," and "when it is tricked-up into a tableau mimicking chained slavery, it is beyond fatuous." But the blacks at the festival were gracious. They applauded and accepted Hawkins's apology and those of his shackled peers (some were blacks apologizing for the blacks who had sold Africans to the Europeans). They offered their forgiveness and even said "Sorry" themselves, for thinking ill of Hawkins's family.

When I told my parents about Hawkins's apology, my father said he found it a worthy symbolic gesture. "The blacks were gathered for a roots conference, were they not, to commemorate their ancestry and what their ancestors had suffered?" he said. "This fellow was there to apologize for the role his ancestors played in it. I think it's excellent."

My mother sided with the critics. She thought it pointless and useless to be "saying sorry for something for which the whole world would have to be forgiven." If Hawkins felt the need to make amends, he should have done something more constructive, Mum said. Good works in the black community, for example.

I tended to side with my mother, largely because the apology seemed to have less to do with blacks than it did with making Hawkins feel better. But then, having never known the identity of our Crooks forbears, we, unlike Hawkins, had never held them up as champions of any kind. If we had, maybe there would be some instinctive need to say "Sorry" for our ancestors' slave ownership, though I can't imagine to whom. We had ancestors at both ends of the whip.

It was nine thirty, London time, on a Monday night in September when I reached Paul Crooks.

"Just watching telly," he said. "MTV . . . mindless stuff."

"Sorry it's taken so long to get back to you, but I was waiting for all the test results to make sure they were accurate." I thanked him again for sending his sample and told him it was so very good of him to cooperate, given that it was probably the longest of shots, since my Crooks line hailed from Europe and his African fore-father had been given the name Crooks through baptism.

I wondered if he could hear the deep breath I drew next. "Well, the first test, which came back in the spring, looked at twelve markers on your Y chromosome, and the results showed you had two matches with men named Crooks—and both of them are my uncles," I said. "We match. We're definitely related."

"Oh, really," he said.

I read nothing from his tone but genuine wonderment. "Yes, it was a surprise," I said, given that his hard-won paper trail had told him his paternal line led to Africa. "I wanted to be certain there was no mistake, so I increased the number of markers tested from twelve to twenty-five, then to thirty-seven. The match seems solid."

He said nothing, so I continued.

"The results are convincing enough. We share the same Y-chromosome signature and the same surname and we have Jamaica in common. All of it suggests we share a common male ancestor in a genealogical time frame."

"How long ago would that be?" he asked.

"All of these numbers are based on estimates, but roughly at some point in the past three to four hundred years."

"Oh," he replied.

"The thing is, Paul," I said, "because we match, your result also confirms that your Y chromosome belongs to the same haplogroup as my uncles'—the most common in Europe."

More silence.

I hated using the word *haplogroup*, hated that it sounded like a ten-dollar scientific term that would push the layperson to the sidelines of comprehension. But I saw no way around it, no other way to explain how a quick swab had revealed a secret his code had harboured for centuries. And so on I went, deconstructing the technical jargon, telling him that a Y-DNA haplogroup refers to a group of males whose Y chromosomes carry the same set of mutations, making the men related by way of a common male ancestor who passed them down thousands of years earlier. I described how scientists classify the major haplogroups by letters, and that each one is associated with a particular part of the world—A, B and E in Africa, O in China, J in the Middle East and southern Europe. And in western Europe it's R1. I told him that he and my uncles belong to one of the subgroups of R1 known as R1b1b2, the most common Y chromosome haplogroup in western Europe.

"What's its frequency in western Europe?" Paul asked.

In southern England, I answered, research suggests that it's 70 percent, but in parts of western and northern England and Scotland it's as high as 90 percent.

It seemed the implications were sinking in. He mentioned relatives in Birmingham who once told him their family had a Scottish ancestor, but Paul said he had never taken it seriously. Now, out loud, he began a mental accounting of his own research, trying to explain the unexpected. "Sarah Brown, who married John Alexander Crooks [his third-generation grandfather], may have been of mixed blood. She came from the Brown estate, and Brown is a Scottish name. A lot of Scottish owned plantations in Jamaica," he said, "particularly in Hanover Parish."

"That may be," I said, "but this is a Y-chromosome lineage, so it only reflects your paternal line—John Alexander Crooks and his male descendants—since the Y chromosome is passed down only from fathers to sons and doesn't alter much between generations."

"Oh," he said. Then, after a long pause, he added, "This is quite a turnout. . . . I'm sitting here thinking how this happened. I'm trying to picture the documentation. I might have to go back now and take a look." One moment he'd been sacked out watching mindless television, and the next he was pitched into a re-accounting of his family history.

"John and Sarah had three children," he was saying, "two boys and a girl. They did have three boys, but one died. . . . John Crooks was in charge of the estate at the time, and I wonder if he had some relationship with Sarah Brown. I had always assumed Sarah Brown was of mixed blood because there was no record of her in the 1817 register." He took her to be free, he said, but living among slaves at the Cove. Perhaps John Alexander Crooks had adopted Sarah Brown's children, perhaps they were not his own. "It was common for African men at the time to adopt the children of the women they were marrying," he said. "The three children were classified as sambo, meaning that they were mixed as well."

I described what I knew of the Crooks family that owned that estate: the three brothers, Christopher, Rice and James; James Crooks Junior, who at birth inherited it from his late father; and his son, John Crooks, who eventually took it over. I told him I had seen the notice John Crooks had posted for his runaway slaves in the *Cornwall Chronicle*. "I suppose it's a bit gruesome to think that this man might be our common link."

To my surprise, Paul didn't dwell on the idea. Instead he mentioned that someone at the Hanover Museum had told him that John Crooks had sold off much of the property and gone to Australia. My fears that our conversation would end once Paul heard his test results were proving groundless. Over the next hour I told him there were other men who shared our Y-chromosome signature and that the matches suggested a link to Lancashire, which has a long history of Crookses. Interesting, he said, since he had learned that John Crooks and Richard Dickson were sailing ships to Africa out of Liverpool, which was then in the county of Lancashire.

"I know these results must be a surprise, and I'm sorry to have to share them."

"Don't be," Paul said. "That's why we're here. If these sorts of things didn't happen, we wouldn't be. It's how we have come to occupy this space and time. But I am sort of confused now; there's a lot to turn over. I thought the male line led very clearly back to West Africa, so it's kind of surprising. It makes me question what they wrote in those registers." He spoke of the financial incentive for white planters to have children with black slave women, and mentioned that he had not spent much time looking into the white Crooks family. And why would he have?

When our conversation wound down, I told Paul I would email him his Y-chromosome test results and keep in touch with anything else I learned. I admired his reaction, his philosophical outlook, his calm. Several weeks later I returned to his website and discovered he was about to have a second book published that fall, this one a non-fiction guide to tracing one's roots back to Africa. Presumably he had not expected that the results of a DNA test could also lead him somewhere else.

I had come to see the family search as a modern tango, a dance between DNA and documentary evidence, science and paper. The Y chromosome told us the Captain had European forefathers; his baptismal record told us he was coloured. Genetic testing had uncovered our African ancestral markers and Paul Crooks's novel had introduced me to the white Crookses of Jamaica. The author's DNA connected us to those plantation Crookses, and now I needed a written record to fill in the details of that connection. Somewhere, some document or archive housed something to reveal which Crooks man, and perhaps which slave woman, was behind the Captain's line.

But I wanted more than that. Having come this far, it wasn't enough just to know how our black-and-white great-grandfather came to be. I wanted to know how he came to be born into a coloured family of social standing just thirty-five years after Britain abolished slavery in Jamaica. Most freed slaves who left the master's land spent the nineteenth century struggling to make a living as labourers and farmers. But the Captain's father, George Atkinson Crooks, was an educated man, an accountant, and the Captain's family—as Clive Harris had told me—were "men about town" in Falmouth, men of means and property.

My grandfather had believed that, dreaming of leaving India for his father's land. That couldn't have been the Cove estate, it had been out of Crooks hands for more than a century by then. So what land was it? Whose was it, and whose had it been? For the most part, the only free coloured people who had a shot at economic success were those supported by their white fathers, who schooled them and provided for them. In their wills, Jamaica's white men left so much land and money to children born of their black and brown mistresses that it threatened the white establishment. According to Gad J. Heuman's *Between Black and White*, as whites "realized how much wealth was passing into coloured and black hands," they did their best to put a stop to it. In 1761 the Jamaican government passed a law barring whites from leaving assets in cash or property worth more than 1,200 pounds to anyone coloured or black. "The whites," Heuman wrote, "had decided that it was more important to keep the land in European hands than to follow parental instincts."

The law eventually changed in 1830, after the coloured population had grown larger and more politically powerful. I was sure it was a Crooks man from the Cove who had been the benefactor of the Captain's ancestors. But discovering the identity of that man and my great-grandfather's link to the Crookses of Hanover would best be done on the ground in Jamaica, in the archives of Spanish Town and Kingston. I'd found nothing when I was there myself, when the lights had died in the vault, but that didn't mean there wasn't something to be found.

A few scrolls through genealogy sites led me to Dianne T. Golding-Frankson on the Internet. She was based in Kingston and came highly recommended as a family-tracing expert in Jamaica. She knew her way around the national archives circuit, wrote reports for the island's heritage groups, specialized in its pre-Columbian history, consulted on archaeology projects and most recently had worked on the genealogies of celebrities featured in the BBC series *Who Do You Think You Are?*

She told me during our first conversation that she is a black woman but of mixed ancestry. Her father had blue eyes, she said, brown skin and loose curls in his hair. Family legend suggested that their ancestors included a white planter, and when she grew up she tracked him down. Her fifth-generation grandfather was a Captain William Stoddart. There's a Stoddart's Peak named after him in Jamaica's Blue Mountains, where in 1734 her captain made history helping to destroy Nanny Town, the famous Maroon stronghold and refuge of runaway slaves. Family lore also had it that this very same captain was in love with one of his own slaves. "That's what we heard," Dianne said, "that it was not a relationship of suppression." When she found his will in the late 1980s, she discovered it was true. "Stoddart spent three pages waxing poetic about his slave mistress," she said. "He never married her. Whites were forbidden by law from marrying slaves." But when he died, in his will Stoddart freed his slave mistress, Mimba, her mother and her brother. He also provided for the two children they had together. One of them was Dianne's fourth-generation grandmother.

I fantasized about tales of forbidden love after this first conversation. I wondered if our story was, like Dianne's, romantic. Maybe it wasn't the black-and-white tragedy Elizabeth Barrett Browning had described at Pilgrim's Point. Maybe it was something else, grey—like all our stories, something in between.

Winter came early in 2008, and I would have paid Dianne to ring me whether she'd found something or not. She had that fabulous Jamaican way of oozing sunshine over a telephone line. "Hullo, daahling. How are you, my deah? And how is dat bun in de oven? You keepin' it warm?"

"Dat bun" was our second child on the way, and Dianne asked for a progress report whenever she called with news—and she always had news. In late November it was the marriage record of the Captain's parents. George Atkinson Crooks had wed Catherine Ann Storks in February 1866, she told me, in the parish of Trelawny, where the Captain was born seven years later. The record indicated that both George and Catherine were coloured, Dianne said, which meant that the black and white blood that flowed through the family had mingled in an earlier generation. In mid-December, after a long search in the Registrar General's Department in Spanish Town, she uncovered a geographical link to the Crooks of Hanover. According to a baptismal record she had tracked down, the Captain's father, George Atkinson Crooks, was born in Hanover in 1833. That was five years before slavery ended in Jamaica, and Dianne told me he was listed as a quadroon.

"Meaning his mother was mulatto and his father was white?" I asked.

"Yes, it does mean that," Dianne said, "but in this case his parents were both quadroons. The child of two quadroons is also a quadroon." It was complicated, this colour business. "I know they were quadroon because the document also named the parents," she added. "They were William James Crooks and Sarah Atkinson of Lucea, in the parish of Hanover."

"Oh, you found the names of the Captain's grandparents!"

"Yes," she said, "I most certainly did. And this William James Crooks must have been of standing, because he's referred to as 'a gentleman' in the baptism record of George Atkinson Crooks—who, by the way, was one of twins."

I told her I'd read that George Atkinson Crooks eventually had triplets, three boys born a few years after the Captain. Their safe arrival had made the papers in Falmouth at the time.

"There are lots of multiple births in Jamaica," Dianne told me. "It has one of the highest rates in the world, I think." She told me she herself was a twin, but her twin brother had died as an infant.

I knew of no multiple births on my mother's side of the family. I had to ask, "Are these natural multiple births in Jamaica today, or the result of fertility treatments?"

"Oh, very natural," Dianne said, laughing her big laugh. "It's all dem yams!"

From what I could tell, no experts have been able to dispel the yam-and-multiple-baby theory, particularly in West Africa, the ancestral home of most Jamaicans. There the rates of natural non-identical twin births are four times higher than the rest of the world—forty-five twins for every thousand live births. Southwest Nigeria is the epicentre of the phenomenon. In the sleepy farming town of Igbo-Ora, a sign apparently welcomes people to "The Land of Twins." Most people who live there are Yoruba, one of Nigeria's largest ethnic groups, but it's also a home to Ibo people, and from what Clive Harris told me, we had "a touch of the Ibo."

Many believe the babies come in twos because of a diet heavy in tuber yams, which scientists have found contain high levels of phytoestrogen. In theory, this estrogen-like plant hormone could be triggering Nigerian women to release more than one egg at a time—most twin births in the region are non-identical, meaning the result of a multiple-egg conception. It could also be that genes make Nigerian women susceptible to the estrogen effects of yams. Either way, experts believe that genetics must play some role in the remarkable multiple-birth rates of West Africa, to which our quadroon Crooks parents of twins and triplets owed, apparently, at least a quarter of their heritage.

The Spanish were the first to call them *cuarterón*, meaning literally "a fourth": people who were one-quarter black and three-quarters white. Britain adopted the term as *quadroon* throughout its colonies, right down to Australia, where the quarter referred to Aboriginal, not African, parentage. But it was the quadroons of the Americas, particularly the women, whose honey skin and broken hearts inspired writers and poets. While Dianne searched and the snow fell that long winter, I read Henry Wadsworth Longfellow's "The Quadroon Girl," from 1842.

> *"The soil is barren,—the farm is old,"*
> *The thoughtful planter said;*
> *Then looked upon the Slaver's gold,*
> *And then upon the maid.*

> *His heart within him was at strife*
> *With such accursèd gains:*
> *For he knew whose passions gave her life,*
> *Whose blood ran in her veins.*

> *But the voice of nature was too weak;*
> *He took the glittering gold!*
> *Then pale as death grew the maiden's cheek,*
> *Her hands as icy cold.*

The Slaver led her from the door,
He led her by the hand,
To be his slave and paramour
In a strange and distant land!

Most writers painted quadroon women as Longfellow had, and Walt Whitman as well: tragic beauties "sold on the auction-stand." James Mursell Phillippo, a Baptist missionary who authored a book on Jamaica in 1843, wrote that parents of coloured daughters often raised them to be concubines—that this was "the general rule . . . rather than the exception"—to be given away in friendship or sold as slave mistresses. Quadroon women were regarded as prized mistresses at a time when mixed marriages were forbidden. In his 1928 book *Fabulous New Orleans*, Lyle Saxon describes the lavish nineteenth-century Quadroon Balls, weekly affairs attended by wealthy white men, free quadroon women and their mulatto mothers, anxious for a liaison that would give their coloured daughters economic security if nothing else. Heuman wrote that coloured women themselves sponsored the same type of dances for white men in Jamaica. So even if these *cuarterón* lovelies were freed, or born free, many remained trapped, like exotic birds in a cage.

Had the Captain's grandmother been a bird like that, my grandmothers going back two or three generations to a mulatto woman on the Crooks plantation? If the Captain's grandfather William James Crooks was a quadroon, and if he belonged at some point to Crooks Cove, only four adult slave women at the plantation in 1817 could have been his mother: Nancy, Peggy and Lucy, all listed as mulattos, and Bessy, whose Christian name was Elizabeth Smith, the only quadroon.

Dianne had yet to determine if William James Crooks had been born in bondage. But even if the Captain's grandfather was born free, freedom for coloured people before abolition came with strict limits. They couldn't vote; they were forbidden to testify in court; they were kept out of theatres, church pews and any public place designed for whites; they couldn't hold public office of any kind or become overseers or bookkeepers. They were not permitted to possess sugar or coffee estates, and unless they owned an estate they were barred from posessing so much as a cow or mule (though owning slaves was acceptable). Those without an estate to their name had to wear a blue cross on their right shoulder as proof of their freedom.

Richard Hill, one of Jamaica's most prominent coloured citizens of the time, once said that educated coloureds in Jamaica regarded themselves as "blasted trees—barkless, branchless, and blighted trunks upon a cursed root." Phillippo put it this way: "In whomsoever the least trace of an African origin could be discovered the curse of slavery pursued him, and no advantages, either of wealth, talent, virtue, education, or accomplishments were sufficient to relieve him from the infamous proscription." So how was it that the Captain's quadroon grandfather managed to become "a gentleman" by 1833, five years before slavery ended?

From what I could gather through the Jamaican Family Search site, my third-generation grandfather William James Crooks had been a bit of a mover. His wife, Sarah Atkinson, seems to have had ties to a prominent white island family. John Atkinson was an American Loyalist whom the British rewarded with a land grant in Jamaica in 1784. A decade later, George Atkinson became the island's secretary. I could only imagine what stories Sarah's bloodline might have to tell. Had she named her son, George Atkinson Crooks, the Captain's father, after the white man who freed her or freed her mother?

One of the oldest references to William James Crooks I found appeared in *Caribbeana*, a periodical of miscellaneous historical papers. It seemed that in 1822 he and five others had jointly signed a deed for a property known as the Lyesworthy estate. One of the co-signers was Utten Thomas Todd, whose father in England, Thomas Todd, had forged a partnership with William Crooks as a West Indian merchant. In his 1836 will, Thomas Todd left to

William Crooks a portion of various properties acquired under Thomas Todd and Company. By 1840 William James Crooks is listed as owning sixty acres in Hanover, in the same parish as Crooks Cove. By the time the Captain's father, George, was born, William James had become "a gentleman" with a wharf near Falmouth and slaves of his own. According to the Jamaica Almanacs for Hanover, in 1825 he kept a dozen slaves, and he owned them straight through to abolition thirteen years later. Dianne told me that wasn't unusual. In Jamaica, she said, as soon as a coloured man earned his freedom and a bit of money, "the first thing he did was set up house and buy himself some slaves."

The more she spoke and the more I read, the more convinced I became that I could just as easily have been reading about the history of Anglo-Indians and Eurasians in British India. Our captain must have felt right at home in Bombay in that in-between world of a hybrid people, dismissed by whites and disdainful of dark skin, emulating the ruling class and denying any tie to those being ruled. In Jamaica the coloured population adopted the Anglican religion of the white planters, sought a European education and the latest European fashions, developed European-styled cultural organizations with names such as the Society for the Diffusion of Useful Knowledge, and owned slaves. Still, the whites never accepted them. After all, as Heuman pointed out, "the privileged free men [of colour] upset the racial stereotype that was at the heart of the slave society." If people of half-black descent could be as smart and successful as whites and own land and slaves, then how could whites continue to lord over blacks?

As we cleared the dishes on the Sunday evening before Christmas 2008, Dianne called with her final report. "Hullo, dahhling!" she said. "I have news for you, my deah." I could tell by her tone it was big news. She had combed through all the eighteenth- and nineteenth-century birth and marriage records for black, white and coloured Crookses in the island's western parishes, plus the registers, and they told quite a racy story. "All three brothers from the Crookses seem to be pretty free-wheeling with the dark women that you have so many coloured Crookses around in two generations!" she said.

I wasn't surprised to hear it. I had lost count of the Crookses in the nineteenth-century directories I found online. At the same time, my uncles' twelve-marker matches were by then nearing eight hundred. Dianne promised she'd send a full report of her findings in writing, but in the meantime, she said, she wanted me to know that she had indeed found a connection between our captain and the Cove. The proof appeared to be in the registry for the western parish of St. James, which neighbours Hanover. It was there that the Captain's grandfather, William James Crooks, was baptized on June 18, 1789. He was fourteen months old at the time, she said, and the record described him as a quadroon with a white father and a mulatto mother. In that same register she had discovered that William had two quadroon siblings: Christopher Rice Crooks, christened that same day in 1789, at age five, and Elizabeth Crooks, baptized in 1797, when she was eight. "Unfortunately there is no mention of the parents," she told me. "It notes only that the father was a white man named Crooks."

I assumed it would have to be a Crooks from the Cove, I told her. These quadroon children carried the same first names as the white Crooks family: Christopher, Rice and Elizabeth, all mentioned in the will of James Crooks Senior. "That's a bit weird, isn't it?" I asked. "Naming your coloured children after your white family?"

"No," Dianne said. "White men often named their coloured children after members of their own family." It was usually a sign of their emotional attachment to them, she added, even if the law forbade them from marrying their mothers. What a thing, that you could tell by a name whether a child was loved.

Dianne said that even though the father's name was missing, she had a solid hunch that our white forefather was James Crooks the third, the one who had returned from England to become a merchant in Falmouth.

"What makes you think it was James Crooks?" I asked her.

James, she said, had a white wife, Sarah Green, and they had named their first-born son William James Crooks. They had him christened on the same June day in 1789 that our coloured William James Crooks was baptized. But the white William Crooks was an infant, Dianne said, and in those days infants were christened quickly only if they were expected to die, or even if they actually had died. By her reading, the white William had passed away, and that very same day, James Crooks the third had dashed out and baptized his coloured child with the name of his dead white son.

"The same day?"

"Yes, the same day."

What coils of sentiment might unwind in a man's head on a day like that? Did James the third then redirect all his affection and assets to his illegitimate heir? Is that how my grandfather's Jamaican family first acquired their wealth? I tried to remember what I'd read of James Crooks the third: one of the five children left fatherless at the Cove plantation; schooled in England; a Falmouth merchant with, according to Dianne, a wife and a mistress and children with both of them. "Do you think there might be any way of finding who the mistress was—the mother of his illegitimate children? I suppose she would be my fourth-generation great-grandmother." Dianne said she doubted it. Her name was not recorded at any of the baptisms. For whatever reason, she had remained in the background.

Whoever she was, her blood ran through us just like that of the Crooks man who kept her. But with no paper record of her existence and no genetic test available to reveal her identity the way the Y can point to a patriarch, she was out of reach. That was the aching truth of it. Using only the male chromosome to trace family history is like making your way into a smoky old boys' club: it's hard to see clearly and the women are always left out.

My son arrived in the spring of 2009, all eight pounds, nine ounces of him. Jackson came home two days after his birth, and we studied him as we had Jade during those long quarantined hours, to see what permutations of the past would show up in our new boy. He had the family cleft in his chin, a hint of a tan and the length of his father. Like his older sister, he carried a Mongolian birthmark on his tailbone, big, blue and shaped like Asia. A nurse at the hospital, utterly unprompted, said he looked Chinese. I couldn't wait to tell my father. But then she added that, in her opinion, most babies do.

The week he was born, Dianne sent an enormous electronic file of original Crooks wills she had managed to locate and photograph. So that spring, in those unpredictable hours when the baby slept, I read them. Despite the books and chronicles I'd read about Jamaica's "coloured society," the stories they told still came as a revelation. Every generation of Crooks men from the Cove, from James the first, buried in the Rossers' front yard, to James the third, had a shadow family—coloured sons and daughters born of black women, mulatto women, quadroon women. Sometimes they left them money, a bit of land and slaves. Sometimes they gave them their freedom and then gave them slaves. James Crooks the second, who had inherited the plantation upon his birth and then died young himself, left behind five legitimate children and four illegitimate mulatto slave children, whom he freed, promising each one a slave when they turned sixteen. In turn, the mulatto children grew up to leave land, money and slaves to their coloured children—one set born to their coloured wives and another to their coloured mistresses.

How flatly naive I had been to imagine I could distinguish whether we descended from slave or slave owner. In Jamaica those lines were as entangled as a double helix. Polygamy of a sort was as systemic as slavery itself. John Stewart wrote of it: "Every unmarried white man, and of every class, has his black or his brown mistress, with whom he lives openly; and of so little consequence is this thought, that his white female friends and relations think it no breach of decorum to visit his house, partake of his hospitality, fondle his children, and converse with his housekeeper [the island euphemism for mistress] . . . as if he had been guilty of no breach of decency or dereliction of moral duty! . . . a brown or sable favourite, and sometimes even a har[e]m of these ladies, was considered as an indispensable appendage to the establishment of a married man."

What nagged at me, as I read of all the provisions made for their illegitimate coloured children by the Crooks Cove men, was that nowhere did the name of William James Crooks appear. In the 1794 will on record by James Crooks the third—the man I assumed to be his father—he had set free "my mulatto woman Judy . . . and her child . . . a quadroon daughter Rebecca . . . and their issue and offspring." It went on to bequeath new Negro slaves to his mistress and child, but there was no mention of a William James Crooks or any of his siblings. How was it that a quadroon man who quickly acquired land, wealth and social status during slavery days could be born of a white father who never once mentioned him in his will? Had the law capping the inheritances of coloured heirs resulted in a secret codicil, a document never officially filed? Dianne thought it was possible; coloured people often kept their wills private, and perhaps it was a custom passed down from their white forefathers.

As summer faded into fall, I continued to scroll through the photographic copies of the wills Dianne had sent: Amee Crooks, Maudlin Crooks, a mulatto John Crooks, a coloured Richard Crooks. One afternoon a string of words suddenly leapt out at me from a grey sea of two-hundred-year-old text, as though by some optical illusion they had been penned in bold type: "Two Quateroon Boys named William James Crooks and Christopher Rice Crooks, sons of a Mulatto Woman named Lucy James . . . ."

I scrolled up to remind myself what I was reading. It wasn't the will of a James Crooks, or any Crooks of the Cove. It was the last will and testament of Christopher Crooks. *Christopher* Crooks? It felt as if someone had tipped my chair. I had been so sure, so convinced that we descended from the Crooks of the Cove, so trusting in my gut, the sway of a novel and a sandy beach, and what the Y-chromosome match with Paul seemed to confirm, that I never entertained the possibility of our descent from one of the other Crooks brothers. But there it was in black and white from 1793, in the words of my very own fourth-generation grandfather.

We descended from a Christopher Crooks: a relation to the James buried at the Cove, a nephew perhaps, the son of one of James's other brothers; possibly the "jobber" Christopher I had first come across in the 1774 Jamaica Almanac; or perhaps his brother Rice, a tavern keeper in the area. My God, what if I had dug him up, old James Crooks? His Y would have matched my uncles' Y all the way up to sixty-seven markers and beyond, but it would have strung us along the wrong branch of the family tree. As brothers, James, Christopher and Rice would have inherited their Y chromosomes from the same man, but only one of those brothers was our forefather—and it wasn't the man in the Rossers' front yard. That truth wasn't written in our cells after all; it was written in ink.

Deciphering the eighteenth-century script exhausted the brain. But it wasn't just the physical effort that drained me. The words themselves were hard on the stomach. When I'd started reading, there had been wonderment—our true descent confirmed, the identity of my great-great-great-great-grandmother revealed, a name, first and last—Lucy James, who had passed down to us stretches of her African code. Lucy James, apparently, was "his favourite sable." As soon as I read it, her name seemed somehow familiar. It sent me back to the notepad I'd filled at the Mormon family research centre two years earlier, when I wrote down all the Crooks references I could find.

And there it was, and had been all this time: Christopher Crooks, a white man, and Lucy James, a free mulatto woman, listed as the parents at the baptism of one Rebecca Crooks. Lucy James's designation as a free mulatto woman immediately told me two things about her mother: she was black, maybe even Ibo, as Clive Harris suspected, and in all likelihood a slave, owned by a master named James. I had read that a Montague James first sailed out to Jamaica with the fateful Penn and Venables expedition to the West Indies in 1654. His grandson was William Rhodes James, whom James Crooks Senior referred to in his will as a relative and co-executor. Perhaps that's how Christopher first met Lucy James—as the mulatto daughter of a cousin's slave.

The romantic in me wanted to embrace the will of Christopher Crooks as testimony to a taboo love, a story like Dianne's—a white man pledging his undying commitment to the coloured woman he could never marry, the coloured woman with whom, according to the will, he had five children in all, two boys and three girls. Christopher and his legitimate white wife apparently had no children at all; he mentioned his wife only once, in the will's opening passages: "I Give, devise and bequeath unto my beloved wife Ann Crooks an annuity of seventy pounds current money of Jamaica, that sum to be paid her Yearly and every year during her natural life."

Lucy James, on the other hand, cropped up repeatedly as Christopher set out his instructions to provide for both her and their "quateroon" children. To his mulatto mistress he left the annual sum of fifteen pounds a year for the rest of her life and the purchase of a new slave. He also set out a plan to use money owed to him by a neighbouring estate owner "to be laid out on purchase of Land or a House . . . in the name of Two Quateroon Boys named William James Crooks and Christopher Rice Crooks, sons of a Mulatto Woman named Lucy James, than deliver the premises so purchased to her the said Lucy James To hold for them the said William James Crooks and Christopher Rice Crooks until they shall attain to the age of Twenty One Years."

I wondered if Christopher Crooks was deliberately vague about the sum of money that was to be used to provide a future property for his "two Quateroon boys." If he didn't specify an amount, perhaps he could skirt the law that limited how much a coloured person could inherit in Jamaica before 1830. And it certainly wasn't the only purse he left his quadroon children. Instructions were drafted to ensure that each of his five children—William James, Christopher Rice, Elizabeth James, Sarah James and Rebecca James—should be paid fourteen pounds each on their birthdays until they turned sixteen, for their upkeep and maintenance.

Yet for all the provisions made, something troubled me as I read. When Christopher Crooks referred to his wife, who merited just a single mention in his will and then disappeared as though she had never existed, he called her "his beloved wife Ann." When he laid out plans to support an invalid brother with a slave named Jack, he referred to him as his "beloved brother William." He also mentioned a "beloved brother James," "a beloved sister Barbara" and his "well-beloved friends and relatives." Yet the woman with whom he had had five children had no such adjective preceding her name. Lucy James was simply "a mulatto woman," their sons and daughters "two Quateroon boys . . . three Quateroon girls." Never once did he use the word *beloved*, or any other term of endearment, to describe his coloured family members.

In Toni Morrison's masterpiece novel, dedicated to the millions of African lives lost to slavery, Beloved was the name of the baby girl murdered by her runaway slave mother to ensure she would never know a life in bondage. Beloved was the dead baby's wily ghost, a vivid symbol of the psychological torment of repressed memories, the sacrifice one makes to forget the past. In my fourth-generation grandfather's will, *beloved* was a sentiment reserved for whites. Was the omission to spare the feelings of his wife at the reading of his last testament? Or was it a stark reminder that his coloured mistress and their coloured children were but a whim away from slavery themselves?

Dianne said that her Captain Stoddart had waxed poetic in his will. But there was no poetry here. As I ploughed through to the will's final sections, I realized what a fractured heart this man must have cultivated. He had a white wife, a brown mistress, beige children and a lucrative business built on the trade and training of black slaves. By then I was well accustomed to reading of slaves left to loved ones, but it was the way he referred to the transactions that made it unlike any other will I had read. Of his eldest son, Christopher Rice Crooks, he wrote, "when he shall attain to sixteen years of age then seven prime young new negro slaves to be purchased by my Executors for him, and Have them apprenticed, of the slaves to be purchased five of them to be boys, the other two to be Girls, and the males To be apprenticed." For his three quadroon daughters he ordered that, upon turning sixteen, each girl should have "two new negro boys and two new negro Girls to be bought by my Executors out of Guinea Cargoes of Slaves that shall be imported into this island and delivered unto each of them."

He was so clearly at ease with the acquisition of "young new negroes," so savvy as to their worth, as if he bought them in bulk from "Guinea Cargoes"—those slaving ships that sailed directly from West Africa to Jamaican ports. Yet Christopher Crooks had no plantation of his own; neither did his will contain anything to suggest that he raised livestock or relied on the land for his living in any way. Why on earth would he have so many slaves? What work did they do on a cropless property? Did he train his own gang of slaves for renting out? Did his livelihood have something to do with turning newly imported Africans into compliant workers or skilled slave labour? Why else would he instruct his son Christopher Rice to send out the "seven prime young new negro slaves" bequeathed to him to be apprenticed? On the eve of abolition, slaves on the road to freedom became wage-earning apprentices, picking up a trade as a carpenter, say, or a blacksmith. But Christopher Crooks lived and died decades before abolition, when transforming an African into a willing "apprentice" suggested only one thing. Was my fourth-generation grandfather a slave-breaker, a jobber whose job was teaching Africans unconditional obedience?

Slave-breakers—that's what they called them in the Americas. In Jamaica, the British in their genteel way called it "seasoning," and the island was infamous for its so-called seasoning camps, where Africans fresh off the boats were broken like wild horses, then often shipped on to the Americas to fetch a good price. In 1770s Jamaica, a "new negro" was worth only half as much as one who had been "seasoned." Slave-breakers had elaborate instruments with which to ply their trade, but they failed so often at their job that about a third of their captives died during the first year. The seasoning process resulted in such a great need for doctors that it brought boatloads of Scottish medical school graduates to Jamaica. When I told Dianne about the will I'd found and my suspicions about Christopher Crooks, she said instantly, "Oh yes, he was a jobber all right."

"I'd assumed a jobber was someone who took various jobs, as an overseer or property manager."

No, she told me, jobbers made their money with blacks on hire, and that made the will historically significant. Her own ancestors, coloured though they were, had also been jobbers, she told me, renting out slaves to help around the house or to various estates through the summers. "They were all slave-breakers," she said. "They had to be; they had to season them. If they had just come off the boat, they had to make them realize this misery was now the reality of their lives. . . . They regarded slaves the same as they did cattle—intelligent cattle, but cattle."

I wondered if Christopher Crooks sent his "young new negroes" to seasoning camps or if he "broke" them himself. I wondered whether he sold his seasoned slaves to planters in America as well as those on the island. It would explain why he was owed money by the other island estate owners, why he was so familiar with the investment value a "new negro" carried. It also explained how an islander without a plantation had managed to set up his coloured children for life, so that William James Crooks had the means to establish his own business and own land and eventually a wharf, becoming in the process "a gentleman."

The discovery of our slave-breaking forefather overshadowed any satisfaction I had about finally learning the truth about the Captain's family. It took me weeks to tell my mother. When I did, I knew she was fighting the urge to run from the room. Instead, she stayed and listened and whispered, "My God almighty." Even my father could do little more than shake his head.

My mother said she was thankful now that her father had never gone to Jamaica, that Papa Freddie never learned the history of his father's side of the family or profited from the proceeds earned through the torture of human beings. "What wickedness, what viciousness," she said. "But the world was barbaric then, wasn't it."

Suddenly the Cove seemed a place of sunburnt ignorance, a plantation worked by slaves already broken. To be a breaker required an iron heart and stomach that not even many of the day possessed. It had to be as far down the chain of humanity as it was possible to slither. What kind of man does that for a living? Was he the inevitable by-product of an inhumane culture? Or was it an evil inherent in his character? Was it—I had to ask myself— in his DNA?

17

A TALE OF TWO CHROMOSOMES

My mother looked several times for the glass tumblers John Abraham had made before he disappeared, the ones Aunty Julie gave her after she first learned my great-grandfather had been a juggler. If Mum happened to be in the basement crawl space for paper towels or ginger ale, or for any item bought in bulk in the event of a natural disaster or a good sale, she'd poke around. I went with her one afternoon. We crawled along the concrete floor, keeping our heads low, opening old trunks, unpacking boxes. My parents had started culling the past that lived under their house, carting bags to Goodwill or the curb. I assumed the glasses had ended up in one of them.

Mum was reluctant to tell my father she couldn't find them, but when she finally spoke up, Dad said, "I moved them up from the crawl space long ago." He reached into the back of the living room cabinet and, just like that, pulled them out one at a time.

All four were identical: tall and lightweight, made of a thin, clear glass and unusual in shape, rounded at the bottom and squared at the top; their sides were flattened by a deep indentation about the size of a thumbprint, possibly *his* thumbprint. It gave the glass a slight wavy appearance. Whatever else he did or may have done, my great-grandfather had a remarkable talent for glassblowing. It was remarkable too that, more than a hundred years after he made them, they were still intact, having survived the trip down from the Nilgiri Hills to Bombay in 1958, the fretful sea voyages from India to England and across the Atlantic in 1972, and three house moves in Canada since then. His glass had endured, out of sight but preserved, like his Y chromosome. John Abraham had left us that much, if not his true name—four tumblers and a smattering of genes.

Further testing confirmed that my father's Y chromosome is a subtype known as O3a3c (formerly known as O3a5). It totes the hallmark SNP mutations that define the branch of haplogroup O3 so prevalent in China. But as an offshoot, it also carries a unique blip known as M-134—a certain spot where a G, the nucleotide guanine, is missing from its code. Most research has found that this mutation is closely linked to Sino-Tibetan–speaking peoples and the Han Chinese, China's largest ethnic group. But this sub-group of O3 also has a long reach, through East and Southeast Asia and all the way down to the South Pacific. Up to 3 percent of Aboriginal men in Australia carry it, perhaps a remnant of pre-colonial mingling between the Chinese and Australians. It can also be found in men from Nepal and northeast India, possibly a molec-ular memento of early Tibetan populations whose genes made a one-way trip south through the Himalayas. The O3a3c designation told a story about our ancient wandering ancestors, but once again it told me nothing about the wanderer my great-grandfather had been. The Abraham Y was still a lonely chromosome, with no apparent match to any man who could fill in the gaps of my great-grandfather's story.

In the spring of 2007 I'd begun exchanging emails with a young entrepreneur in Moscow by the name of Denis Grigoriev. Like my father, Denis had had his Y tested through Family Tree DNA, and like us he was one of its few customers to carry the O3a3c Y signature; we also had a few short tandem repeat markers in common. As small-world stories go, ours seems like a whopper. This young, white, muscular Russian shared the same branch of the human family tree as my octogenarian, brown, slight father in

Mississauga. But then the Y is a master of disguise; no gene in its code is known to influence a man's appearance, and nothing about a man's appearance can confirm which Y he carries.

At the time, not many Russian men were known to belong to the O3a3c haplogroup, but the test result came as no surprise to Denis. He told me that his paternal line descended from the Atagan tribe of Outer Mongolia, a nomadic group of herders who were exposed through the ages to both Tibetan and Chinese genes. Mongolian tribes had raided farms and wealthy kingdoms scattered along the northern border of modern-day China since prehistoric times. The pillaging became so frequent that by 221 BCE it prompted the Qin Dynasty, the first imperial government to rule over a unified China, to begin work on that famous 7,200-kilometre barrier to keep them out. More than two thousand years later, Denis and I could claim a common line of descent from a chromosome that took root on both sides of the Great Wall.

Denis felt he could see evidence of his ancestry in the mirror, in his eyes and cheekbones. But he'd lost his Mongolian surname somewhere during his forefathers' migration to Russia, and he hoped his Y chromosome would lead him back to it. He was also determined, he told me, to connect with his "Chinese brothers." He launched an online forum to discuss issues related to the O3 haplogroup and formed one of Russia's first genetic genealogy companies, and on the Family Tree DNA website he spearheaded a project page for those interested in the O3 Y chromosome. It included a dynamic world map where the current location of men who had uploaded their O3 Y-chromosome test results appeared as blinking yellow lights—places such as Lincoln, Rhode Island; Brighton, England; Brantford and Nepean, Ontario; Los Angeles, California; Kharkov, Ukraine; Seattle, Washington; Reston, Virginia; Izmir, Turkey; Prague, Czech Republic; Singapore . . . and on it went. But China, the country that should have lit up like a neon sign, produced but one flashing pixel. When more than one in seven people in the world is Chinese or of Chinese descent, the darkness told a story. In the Family Tree DNA database as of 2007 there were only forty-two samples from people of Chinese ancestry. And as Bennett Greenspan told me by email, "it is NOT legal to ship DNA out of China." When I phoned to ask more about this, he explained that his company had tried to start a branch in China and process DNA samples within the country, but even that effort led nowhere.

I wondered if it was the strict rules around genetic information that prevented Jin Li, one of China's leading population geneticists, from replying to the many messages I sent inquiring about the fate of my father's DNA. When I'd last spoken to Li— or Felix, as he preferred to be called—in 2006, he was doing fieldwork on Asian DNA, collecting for his research and the Genographic Project. He had since gone on to become vice-president of Fudan University in Shanghai. I could not be certain whether the sample had ever made it past Customs, despite its circuitous route through Cincinnati.

I wasn't the only one waiting for East Asian DNA to make its way into the gene pools of comparison. If the Internet had revolutionized genealogical research, adding genetics to the pursuit was heralding genealogy's next great shift. Comparing DNA test results online was turning genealogy into a hobby as concerned with the present as the past, allowing the addition of "genetic cousins" to social networks, recruiting potential relatives for testing, communing with fellow members of a haplogroup. In the case of East Asian groups, there were online discussions around the date of the Mongols' westward expansion and the genetic forces that had shaped Kazakh tribes. And there were debates, sometimes ugly, over how much influence "Chinese genes" had on the Japanese and the Vietnamese, and even whether kung fu legend Bruce Lee could be counted as an O3a3c member. Often participants lamented the dearth of Chinese DNA available for comparison.

I had to wonder too whether there was much interest from the Chinese within China to embrace DNA testing for ancestry.

As Felix had told me, the genetic record tends to challenge traditional notions of what it means to be Chinese, contradicting a cultural perspective that suggests Chinese DNA is distinct from that of other world populations. Yet with so many families having lost their ancestral records in the late 1960s, during the purges that accompanied the Cultural Revolution, he believed there could be wide interest in DNA ancestry testing. He had hoped that the descendants of Confucius might help to illustrate just how effective genetic testing could be in genealogy. But in 2008 the Confucius Genealogy Compilation Committee rejected the use of DNA tests to complete its fifth revision of the ancient family tree. It had finally made the move to include women and minorities, but DNA results were out. According to an article published in *Seed* magazine, the eighty-two-year-old head of the Confucius committee felt that traditional, and less expensive, sources of information were more appropriate. But some felt conservatism had trumped progress, and that fear had something to do with it, given the very real risk—which I knew well—that DNA tests might *disprove* many families' descent from the great philosopher, a pedigree that has long brought status and prestige.

I was tempted to give up, to leave the Abraham Y languishing in the database. The intrigue of the Crooks chromosome had begun to consume me, and my father had long ago stopped asking for updates about his side of the family. But as Confucius said, a man who stands on a hill with his mouth open will wait a long time for roast duck to drop in. So from time to time I plugged my father's test results into the Ysearch database, and on a hot afternoon in July 2007, a little duck fell from the sky.

His name was Longtang Lin. He was forty-eight then, an engineer living in Chicago but originally from Taiwan. He had been tested using the mail-away kits sold through the Genographic Project and had uploaded his test result to the Ysearch.org database to see if he could find relatives. His Y matched only ten of my father's twelve markers, but when there had been nothing for so long, it felt like something worth pursuing, even if a measly ten-marker match might be laughed out of the R1b crowds. Besides, I told myself, the two markers that differed between Longtang Lin and my father were off by only one allele. Where my father had the sequence GAAA repeated twenty times at a certain place on his Y chromosome, Lin had a repeat of nineteen. Where he carried the sequence TAT fourteen times in another Y location, my father had a repeat of fifteen. The two markers that weren't exact matches were as close as you could get. What would the picture look like if we compared chromosomes at twenty-five markers, or thirty-seven, or sixty-seven? Then there was the auspicious omen of his surname. Lin was the name I had given my great-grandfather back in my grade-school essay. If the Web had thrown up that karmic bone, I thought, why bury it?

```
Hello there
I realize this is a very long shot, but
I see that we share a 10/12 marker Y-DNA
match. My father's grandfather is believed
to have been Chinese and his last name
may have been Chu (it is difficult to
tell from the handwriting of a mission-
ary in 1886). Are you considering having
any more markers tested? And is there
anything you could tell me about your
family's history in Taiwan?
```

Longtang Lin responded that afternoon. He told me he goes by John Lin, and although English is not his first language, he composed a lengthy and enthusiastic response: "Thanks for your email to me," it began. "Since you are Chinese offspring, I think it is fair for me to provide you some information to share our common past. . . ."

John grew up in Taiwan but his ancestors were originally from China's southern Fujian province or possibly Guangdong—or Canton, as he sometimes referred to it—and only moved to Taiwan sometime between 1750 and 1850. The O3 haplogroup was the most common type in Fujian, he said. Some estimates put it as high as 97 percent, which John felt could be expected, since it was *the* haplogroup of the Han Chinese, "the biggest branch in the human tribe." The Han presided over the country's second imperial dynasty; when the Han army conquered central and southern China in the second century BCE, the invaders wiped out most of the men who carried the original O-haplogroup Y chromosomes in those regions. "Those O3 soldiers killed a huge portion of the native males who carried the Y chromosomes of the original O haplogroup," he wrote, and they took the local women as their wives.

John described himself as an avid student of Chinese and Taiwanese history, and from the research he had seen into how and where certain Y chromosomes spread in the region, DNA matched the written record. If he had to guess, he said, my great-grandfather likely came from a province in the southeast—Fujian, his own ancestral home—making us, as DNA suggested, "cousins!"—however distant.

John was game to test more markers and see how far our match extended. As I made arrangements to transfer his sample from the Genographic Project to Family Tree DNA and have it tested for twenty-five markers, we kept up our correspondence. He told me many things about China, its people and its history, and things that might be pieced together about my great-grandfather—his name in particular. He suggested that Chu might mean "small hill" or, possibly, "red." I told him I had been baffled by the various meanings and Chinese spellings when I looked it up, and only more so since I couldn't be sure that Chu was my great-grandfather's real name. After all, twice in the church registry in Coonoor it was written as Atchu or Atchoi.

That detail struck a chord with John. "Chu is more like a traditional Chinese last name than Atchoi, which sounds like a localized call-sign," John wrote. *Chu* in Fujian dialect is pronounced like *Choi*, and pronounced like Ah-Choi by his countrymen, John said. In the case of his own name, Longtang Lin, people from Fujian addressed him as Ah-Tang and people from Canton called him Ah-Lin. "The *At* or *Ah* is added with no real meaning," he wrote. "Again, this call-sign habit only exists in southern China, in [Fujian/Guangdong], the mother land of most out-going Chinese immigrants. So now, I am more sure that your great-grandfather is from the same area as my ancestors due to the 'AH.'" If Chu was the name my great-grandfather had spoken aloud to a French missionary, and if he had come from Fujian or Guangdong, then what John told me jibed perfectly with the names we'd seen in the record books. The *Ah* and the *At* were the best phonetic efforts of the priest to capture in his own language what he had heard.

My father was excited by the match with John Lin. The prospect of finally knowing his grandfather's home province set his mind on a new adventure. "Time to plan a trip to China, Tweet."

I knew he was only half serious. My father had grown skeptical about the concept of genetic matches. After all, there was the intriguing but inexplicable link between Gladwyn and the biologist in Maine, and the staggering list of international strangers with a chromosome closely matching the Crooks chromosome.

"How good is this match?" Dad asked.

I told him that I was making arrangements for more testing to find out. But without knowing more about how their Y chromosomes compared, all I could share were the things John had shared with me. When I described John's "Ah-Chu" observations, it triggered an old memory for both my parents. They recalled that Chinese people they encountered in India often had the *Ah* pronounced before their names, which jibed with its being a custom of southeast China. As coastal provinces, Guangdong and Fujian have always been prime departure points of Chinese emigration, to India included. And during the latter years of the nineteenth century, when my great-grandfather turned up in south India, the Chinese exodus was in large part born of desperation.

From 1850 to 1864, the Taiping Rebellion locked southern China in a civil war. Hong Xiuquan, a village tutor from Guangdong who experienced feverish visions that convinced him he was the brother of Jesus Christ, led a bloody revolt against the Manchus' Qing Dynasty. Even for those who doubted Hong's heavenly status, the temptation to oust the non-Han rulers, who were seen as cruel and corrupt, was enough to rally support behind him. The fighting killed an estimated twenty million people, making it one of the deadliest conflicts in human history, and one that left southern China impoverished and hungry. If the church records in Coonoor had listed my great-grandfather's age accurately, and if he was a native of southern China, John Abraham was born on the eve of rebellion and would have grown up with war. Murder may have been a necessity of the times. Perhaps he killed to survive, or to escape. And if he did hail from those mountainous southern provinces, the Nilgiri Hills must have felt a lot like home.

My great-grandfather would have been one of thousands of Chinese men who set sail from southern ports to find work and feed their families back home. Some went as indentured servants, some to North America to build railroads, to South America to mine gold, to Caribbean plantations where slavery had been abolished, to India to pick tea or lay railway tracks for the Raj, or any other job the British could offer in their sprawling empire. So many Chinese sold their labour to foreign powers in the late nineteenth century that colonialists called it the "pigtail trade."

I told John that we believed my great-grandfather wore his hair in that long braided pigtail, that it was one of the few personal details we knew about him. John guessed my great-grandfather must have arrived in India in the late 1800s directly from China, where under the Qing Dynasty the single-braid hairstyle was mandatory for all males. The Manchus, he said, being a mixture of Han and Altai tribes from the north, had permitted the Chinese majority to maintain most of their cultural traditions under their rule, but hair was an exception. As soon as they had fought their way to power, they decreed that all men, with the exception of monks, young boys and men in mourning, were to lose the long hair and topknots that had been the style under the Ming Dynasty. Instead they had to shave their scalps bald at the front and sides, leaving only enough hair in the rear to be braided into a single plait. The queue, they called it, and any man without it was put to death for his disrespect to the emperor. "The slogan was 'you keep your braid in order to keep your head,'" John said. "Even when Chinese travelled overseas, they still kept their braid for one generation."

The Manchu braid was completely abandoned after the fall of the Qing Dynasty. It had long been a cultural thorn inside China, yet ironically it was a leading symbol of Chinese-ness to the outside world. I always found it peculiar that my great-grandfather, who had apparently fled China and gave up his Chinese name and religion, had clung to its traditional clothes and hairstyle. "The Chinese are a rigid people," John said. "When they immigrate to Southeastern Asia or USA, they still [do] not mix with local people and they speak their old China local dialect, which was spoken by their thousand-year-old ancestor in China. They tend not to speak China's national language, Mandarin," he added. "The funny thing is that although Chinese immigrants might [be living in] Southeastern Asia for 400 years, they still consider themselves to be pure Chinese."

No matter what a comparison of chromosomes had to say about our familial link to John Lin, we'd made fast friends. His readiness to share and help reminded me of what Roberta Estes had said about the compassionate man she regarded as her brother, even when DNA said otherwise. And in the case of Dad and John, it did seem to say otherwise. In comparing twenty-five markers, they were off by seven, with a match of only eighteen alleles. But then I thought, eighteen—wasn't that a decent match? Wasn't seventeen the number researchers had used to conclude that an African-American man carried the Y chromosome of Thomas Jefferson's family? John and my father didn't share a surname, or maybe they did but didn't know it. Every Y marker mutates at a different rate, and those rates can be affected by all sorts of factors, including the age of the father who passes it down. So what could be said about my father's eighteen-marker match with John Lin? Was it meaningful? Did it put us in the genetic ballpark of a familial relationship?

I called Mark Jobling at the University of Leicester to ask him what he thought. As a leading expert on Y chromosomes, surnames and populations—and one of the scientists involved in the Jefferson discovery—Jobling agreed that not enough was known about Asian haplotypes to say. If those eighteen markers are very common in the region, then many other men might also match that number of markers, he said. If it is as ubiquitous as the R1b1b2 imprint is in western Europe, for example, then a great chunk of the male population in China will share eighteen markers, since they all share a common ancestor but not in the recent past. But if the eighteen-marker haplotype my father and John share is fairly unusual in the region, that would suggest a more recent common ancestor.

Mark explained that he and his colleagues had relied on seventeen markers to determine paternity in the Thomas Jefferson case in part because those markers represented a very rare genetic signature. When they compared the Jefferson Y to a large control group of Y chromosomes from other European men, they did not find another like it, making that one seventeen-marker match with the great-grandson of Sally Hemings all the more compelling. If Jefferson had carried an R1b, he estimated they would have had to test upwards of thirty or forty markers to be certain about paternity. Yet they didn't really know this starting out, Jobling said. At the time they tested only seventeen markers because back then they knew only a limited number of short tandem repeat sequences on the Y that could act as markers. The technology was also much less affordable in 1997. The bottom line, he told me, is that until there is more understanding of the diversity of Y chromosomes in China, it is hard to place the match between John Lin and my father in context.

"It could be that researchers eventually discover that O3a3c is as common . . . as R1b," he said. And despite the widespread studies on R1b, surprises were still cropping up. He and his colleagues had just concluded research that suggested western Europe's hallmark R1b haplogroup might have roots in the Fertile Crescent, and that it came north with Turkish farmers who spread both their agricultural know-how and their seeds. This migration likely occurred over thousands of years, he said, but in certain regions the move had a major impact on the population. In Ireland, for instance, more than 80 percent of men carry the R1b chromosome, which suggests that most Irishmen descend from Turkish farmers. Researchers speculated that the dark strangers from the south with their land-cultivating ways must have seemed tempting mates for native Irishwomen accustomed to their pale local hunting-gathering crowd. (*The Irish Independent* greeted the finding with good cheer: "It is time to roll out a magic carpet, don a fez, and sing Istanbul at great volume down in the pub.")

The Irish-Turkish connection is just one in a long list of identities that genetics recasts. There's a Korean sequence of mitochondrial DNA wound into the cells of Norwegian fishermen, Finnish men with a Chinese Y, Yorkshire families with a North African chromosome. Even the Jefferson Y—the chromosome that helped launch the age of genetic genealogy by proving a white president's bloodline connection to an African-American man—turns out to be a chromosome common in Africa. Jobling and his team never found a Y to match Jefferson's male chromosome in a European control group because they had been looking in the wrong population. Only years later did they discover that Jefferson's Y belongs to the K2 haplogroup, found most often in the Middle East and West Africa and rarely among Europeans.

I emailed Mark Jobling the values of my father's twenty-five markers to see how they compared to his own collection of Asian Y chromosomes. He replied that he had plugged my father's genetic signature into his database, which included 1,625 haplotypes from Nepal and Bhutan. "There is only one match for the fourteen markers that can be compared, in a Gurung male from Nepal," he said. "So, it's certainly a rare haplotype, and difficult to say where it originated without more East Asian data."

The Gurung are an indigenous people of the Nepalese mountain valleys who can trace their cultural traditions and language to Tibet. Mark could not give me the name of the Gurung man in question since once again his DNA had been collected as a research sample. But the exercise convinced me that if, as it seemed, my father's haplotype had an uncommon signature, there was merit in testing John Lin and my father all the way up to sixty-seven markers.

In the meantime John Lin had received a test result on his maternal line and wrote to tell me that his mitochondrial DNA belonged, like my father's, to haplogroup M. It seems that the ancient woman who founded most of India's population is also one of China's founding mothers—just as she is the matriarch of one of the Nilgiris' vanishing tribes, the honey-collecting, forest-dwelling Kurumbas.

I had tried several times to track down Marion Martin, Aunty Julie's granddaughter and the last woman known to carry the mitochondrial DNA of the juggler's wife, my great-grandmother. I wanted her cells, but I wanted her memories even more. Aunty Julie had raised Marion after her mother died in childbirth, just as she had Papa Albert. I suspected Marion might know more about John Abraham than anyone else alive, but the tales surrounding her fate seemed to have grown as tall as those surrounding the juggler himself. The last time anyone in my family saw her, both my brothers had hair, and they wore it down to their shoulders.

It was the early seventies, and my sister and I were away with my parents on that memorable first trip to India, when Marion phoned our house outside London to say she was popping in. My brothers and their friends had a party planned and expected an awkward encounter with a square Anglo-Indian relative, probably "gift-wrapped in a sari" and bound to cramp their style. But Marion, as Conrad told me with some relish, was nothing of the sort. He opened the door to a round-eyed beauty, hip and groovy, wearing bell-bottom jeans and a big smile. She spent the evening. Con heard she'd up and married a lord some years after that. My mother heard she'd married a British pop star, a Teddy boy, and gone off to live the hippie life in Goa. My father's cousin said she had appeared with her foreigner husband "out of God knows where" for a wedding in the Nilgiris in 1975 and then disappeared. I emailed anyone I could find named Marion Martin, including a woman in London who appeared to do public health work in the Nilgiris (what were the chances?), but I never received any reply.

Every lead that had something to do with those blue hills only lured me deeper into the mist. On a later trip my parents made back to south India, my mother met a nun in a shop in Chennai who was originally from the Nilgiris. She said her last name was Enos and that she was well acquainted with the Abraham family in the area. My parents eventually told her about my father's Chinese grandfather, and the nun thought there might be some connection between the Enos and Abraham clans. She had relatives, she said, with Chinese features.

I reached Sister Maria Fides by phone in Chennai and we spoke for an hour early one morning. She told me she knew my Great-Aunty Flo, the juggler's daughter who had lived into her hundreds in Coonoor. She knew her as Aunty Florrie, and recalled that she had been "very sad" when Marion Martin moved away to England. She assumed Aunty Florrie was related to her grandmother Mabel. Like Julie and Flo, Mabel had Chinese features, she said, and they were close, often spending time together at Christmas. At first I wondered if Mabel was Mary, the missing sister from the records and the one Aunty Flo had asked my father about the last time they met.

Mabel was married to a Joachim Enos, and she was a staunch Catholic who had fourteen children, including seven sons she named after popes. One of them was Leopold, or Leo, as everyone knew him. I remembered what my mother had heard—that Flo had been in love with Leo Enos her entire life and yet they had never married, because Aunty Julie had never permitted it. Perhaps it was a family connection that made the match unthinkable. If Mabel was one of the sisters, then Mabel's son Leo would have been Flo's nephew. Sister Maria thought that might be the case. But I could not confirm it, not by paper trail or by inquiries through other relatives.

Neither did I make any headway tracing the fate of Papa Albert's other surprise siblings, Arokiam, Annie and Mary. I did come across one early twentieth-century reference to an Arokiam Abraham in south India who joined the priesthood, with dates that seemed to fit the time frame of his birth. But all of it was speculation. In the end, I had nothing but the science to follow.

The sixty-seven-marker test I arranged for John Lin and my dad turned out to be off by twenty-one markers. The lab estimate concluded that we had zero chance of sharing a common male ancestor within the past four hundred years, and even at twenty-four generations back, or about five hundred years, the odds were 0.03 percent. Immediately, of course, I saw two ways of looking at this. The glass-half-full perspective was that it was an exact match of forty-four markers. A thirty-seven-marker match had drawn a concrete connection between the Crooks chromosome and men with ancestors in the north of England, Lancashire in particular. So wouldn't a forty-four-marker match between my father and John suggest a meaningful tie as well?

Sadly, the glass-half-empty view was the only one that mattered. Even if they had matched at more markers, or even shared a perfect score of sixty-seven out of sixty-seven, it would do little to lift the curtain on John Abraham's family history. In the case of the Crooks chromosome, my uncles' Ys matched the Y of a man who knew enough to write a book about his heritage, a book that led me, in part, to our Crooks story. But Longtang John Lin and my father cannot help each other much with their family history— neither one knows it.

John's knowledge reaches back only to his paternal grandfather, who left Fujian for Taiwan. It was one reason he had been drawn to the Genographic Project in the first place, to try to learn more about his ancestry in mainland China. He'd never had the chance to ask his paternal grandfather about the past. "He died before I was even born. All I saw was his grave." His grandfather, not unlike ours, was a lone male who travelled from place to place looking for jobs, "like nomadic Mexican farm labourers working the U.S. west coast nowadays."

When he was growing up in Taiwan, John's family raised chickens and ran a small grocery store near the Keelung River in Taipei. "We were a typical poor family in Taiwan at that time. Everyone is poor except a few elite." But his parents worked hard and devoted their efforts to saving enough money to send him to university in Taiwan. That set him on the path to his earning a master's degree in mechanical engineering from the University of Texas in El Paso.

"Now here I am, living in the USA, a naturalized U.S.A citizen from a small humble family on a far away island—amazing," he said. "And now I even get a chance to know I might have a distant cousin in Canada . . . more amazing. Life, fate is a twist."

Like the glassware John Abraham made, his chromosome distorts what I can see through it. There is China, but nothing more specific than the rough outline of a southern coast.

In the seven years since I began testing my family, new ways to explore the genome for clues to ancestry have evolved. There are tests for regions on the X chromosome, which only women carry in pairs and men inherit from their mothers. There are also tests that scan various regions across all the chromosomes that men and women carry, allowing people to find relatives who share the same segments of genetic code, indicating that they also share a recent common ancestor. But the databases still have few Asian samples.

There are also signs that personal DNA testing is slowly taking off in China. Demand is rising for DNA paternity tests, particularly among the nouveaux riches—men who want to confirm they are the biological fathers of children born to the mistresses they can now afford to keep. An online report from CNN in 2009 chronicled a new program in China to use DNA testing to try to identify a child's natural talents and predict which career—sports, music, or science, say—might suit him best and then train him for it, much like the life I once imagined for my acrobatic great-grandfather. China is also fast earning a reputation as the world leader in decoding human genomes. The coastal city of Shenzhen, a famous manufacturing hub for cheap clothes and electronics, has become the site of a massive DNA-sequencing centre poised to decode the world's human genomes. Under the auspices of the Beijing Genomics Institute, they've cracked the code of the first Arabs and made a sequencing deal with the Scots. Perhaps the Chinese population won't be far behind.

Online, the Chinese community is also slowly coming together to share and swap chromosomes. A small China DNA group has sprung up on Facebook. Many members are people who adopted children from China and hope to use DNA to learn more about their child's ancestry or find biological siblings. Others are interested in their own ancestry. I posted an invitation on the site to anyone interested in comparing Y chromosomes, but have had no takers so far. At Family Tree DNA, the number of samples from people with Chinese ancestry finally cracked one hundred by the summer of 2011. It includes DNA from those who know a great deal about their Chinese ancestry, as well as from those of us who know virtually nothing and hope to learn from those who do.

There are moments when the long wait for a Y to match my father's seems more like heartbreak than frustration. But there are other times when it seems fitting that a strand of DNA cannot so easily unravel our juggler's secrets. His enigmatic legacy has been mine since childhood, and my father's too. It's as much a part of our family as the Abraham name, and the very reason we have it. Even my father, who now uses Chu in his email address, has come to accept that his DNA may never pave the way back to an ancestral village in China. Still, at eighty-seven he is planning his first trip there. Then too there is the lesson learned from my mother's side and the captain's Y chromosome—that sometimes living with the mystery is better than the truth.

Jade was in kindergarten the first time she asked. I was upstairs in the room where I write and one afternoon she was there too, on the floor, drawing pictures on scrap paper. Without preamble or even putting down her pencil, she said, "Mom, what are we?"

"Do you mean where are we from?" I asked.

"Yes," she said. "Where?"

I wondered why she was asking, whether someone had asked her. No, she said, it's just that she had noticed she was a bit different from kids in her class, "a little more chocolate than vanilla."

I spun the globe we keep near the computer and asked if she remembered the wooden elephants we'd brought her from India. I pointed to it, a mustard-yellow teardrop hanging above the equator, and then to China, over to the right. I turned it again and waved my finger over Europe, pointing out England, Ireland and Sweden, where Stephen's family was from, and Germany too, then down to Portugal, trailing my finger to the west coast of Africa before spinning over the Atlantic to the small orange dot of

Jamaica. I was set to bring it all home with the multicoloured, multicultural land mass of Canada when I looked up to see that Jade had gone back to her drawing, probably long before I'd stopped spinning. I wondered if she would remember any of it.

I think sometimes about the questions my brother Kevin asked a few weeks before that first swab on my mother's birthday— whether the results of a DNA test would change how I felt about myself or the family. I believe it has. Questions I'd always had about our heritage are no longer questions. They're points of fact, elevated to that status by science, but not by science alone. Church records in Cochin and Coonoor, books at the Toronto library, the wills from Jamaica and people's memories had revealed our story as much as the genetic filaments of our cells had done. It has given me a confidence in the mix of our ancestry, a certain peace, not to wonder what is true about us but to know. Some answers remain elusive: what brought our Captain Crooks to India, and what drove our juggling John Abraham away. But a genetic journey can be as endless as it is unpredictable. Even now, somewhere, someone with the missing pieces of our puzzle may be swabbing.

Yet perhaps more surprising than how the quest changed me is how it changed the way I see others. I have not walked through a crowd the same way since; I wonder what common stretches of code might prove a family tie between unlikely strangers—the Asian boy with the neck tattoo, the black woman handing out copies of the *Watchtower* at the mall. The idea that humans belong to one family, that there is but one tree, was once an abstract notion to me, if slightly hokey—a Coke commercial with candles and a Christmas tree that tries to teach the world to sing. But our genes have made me feel otherwise. The threads of our DNA have woven us to a galaxy of strangers in faraway places with histories so different from our own. Jim in Maine, Mel down in Australia, Paul in London, Longtang John Lin in Chicago, even Ton That in Miami and Denis in Moscow: each one is living proof that no one is any one thing, regardless of what we think we are or how we look. In one way or another, we all have family in the hills. A mere chromosome, and a puny one at that, has linked my family to all these men and connected them—however tangentially—to ours.

"All the blinkers are off now," as my mother put it. Even my husband turns out to have a Y chromosome that belongs to the same haplogroup as my Crooks uncles (but happily not too many markers in common—just enough to convince him that I may be part Viking too). I have come to regard our juggler, or his art at least, as the metaphor for it all: millions of nucleotides in continuous motion, tossed up, generation after generation, and scattered by the wind and by warriors, by the kidnapped and the curious, the hungry, the greedy, the pious, the scared and the lovesick. The forebears of us all.

On an August night in 2008 we watched the opening ceremonies of the Beijing Olympics on television. Jade was watching too. She was just learning to read and write, and was enchanted by the Chinese dancers whose steps left a trail of black calligraphy across a giant white canvas. But it was the parade of athletes that charmed her, the exuberant procession of teams and flags from around the world. The commentator announced the countries as they passed, and Jade began to interject.

"Hey, we can clap for them. We're from there."

A few countries later, she said, "And we can clap for them too, right? . . . And them . . . and them . . ."

Until finally she jumped to her feet with realization and laughed. "Hey," she said, "we can cheer for everybody!"

She had remembered.

ACKNOWLEDGEMENTS

This was a long journey, and I was graced with the help and guidance of many people who kept me on course along the way. But it would have been stalled from the get-go without the boundless support of my parents. Dudley and Thelma Abraham answered years of questions, gave me their insights and their DNA (in more ways than one). For their open minds, and always, for their love, I cannot thank them enough.

Several scientists took the time to educate me for this book, generous with their time and their valuable insights. I owe a special thanks to Stephen Scherer at the University of Toronto, who has long schooled me on the latest in genetic science, and reviewed sections of this manuscript. Peter Underhill at Stanford University, along with his expertise, shared relevant papers and reviewed excerpts. Mark Shriver at Pennsylvania State University let me give his new test a whirl, and Mark Jobling at the University of Leicester offered terrific input and ran my father's DNA through his own database. Thanks go, as well, to Karl Skorecki at Israel's Rambam Medical Center and Jin Li at Fudan University in Shanghai.

It took a global village to raise this book. In India, I was fortunate to have the hospitality and help of the deCoutos, Gladwyn and Noella; their daughters, Angel and Trianna; their aunt Yolanda; our driver, Joseph; Dean and Liz deCouto; Hazel Banerjee and her daughter Isha. Father Francis Xavier, the speedy priest, Father

Vincent, Charles and George were our tireless tour guides deep in the hills and beyond.

In Jamaica, our driver, Everton (Troy) Esmie, was a true Sherpa. Curniff Crooks took the time to show us around and to share. Behind the scenes, Patricia Jackson, founder and curator of jamaicanfamilysearch.com, its prolific contributor Peter Dickson in England and artist David Arathoon in Toronto, helped me navigate the maze of social connections in colonial Jamaica. Dianne T. Golding Frankson, savvy researcher and genealogist, jumped into my journey with both feet, just when I needed her most.

Despite the demands of their own schedules, my sister and her husband, Christine and George Clutterbuck, looked after my daughter so I could travel in India and Jamaica. Christine has been my safety net throughout, incomparable sounding board and booster. My brother Conrad Abraham inspires me in more ways than he will ever know, and my brother Kevin Abraham has always supported my work, even as he asks the hard questions.

My nieces and nephews, Shayna, Katelyn, Kari and Jared, let me know that they were curious too, and Christopher Clutterbuck gave up a hunk of summer to transcribe miles of tape on my behalf. My niece, Candice Abraham, hooked me up with Troy, but I am most thankful for her big heart, her reading and our long talks about writing.

I owe special gratitude to my uncles and aunts, who gave when I asked, Dennis and Merlyn Crooks, Basil and Norma Crooks, and Charles Crooks, and all their families.

My newfound genetic relatives made this book better with their willingness to share. Thanks to Paul Crooks for saying yes and writing *Ancestors*, the novel that pointed the way to the cove. Thanks to Denis Grigoriev, Longtang John Lin, Jim List and Melvyn Lomax.

In the United States, I learned from the family quests of others, Roberta Estes, Bennett Greenspan, who always made time to answer my questions, and Adrian Williams.

Ron Forbes, president of the Anglo-Indian Association of Canada, treated me to his valuable perspectives and an afternoon in the sanctuary of his lovely garden.

Many friends and relatives offered encouragement in various forms over the years: Doreen Abraham, Sheri-Levy Abraham, Brigitte Audet-Martin, Shireen Bennett, Ellen Braganca, Clive Crooks, Simone Crooks, Erin Elder, Colin Embree, Clive Harris, Supriya James, Caroline Mallan, Karin McGeoch, Karen McNeil, Stephen Northfield, Ralph Pereira, Lisa Priest, Derek Raymaker and Christine Reymer.

Jeanette Rouse, my mother-in-law, who caught the genealogy bug long before the Internet debuted, provided helpful hints along with her well wishes.

Kim Honey, who has more than a bit of science in her soul, helped push me to the finish line, reading and listening for years— and often late into the night. To Darren Fryer, who read several drafts of this work, and provided important suggestions from start to finish, my gratitude runs deeper than a tea root.

Editors of the *Globe and Mail*, John Stackhouse and Sylvia Stead, afforded me the time to work on this project, and Edward Greenspon backed it in its earliest days.

My agent, Dean Cooke, along with Suzanne Brandreth, championed this project from its genesis and, with care, helped bring it home.

Strange things happened during the writing of this book. Tree roots erupted out of the basement floor. The house flooded—twice. There were a few rounds of pestilence, and then came a baby out of the bulrushes to shake up the hierarchy of demands. But Anne Collins, publisher of the Knopf Random Canada Publishing Group, who believed in this book from the outset, never gave up on it. I owe a great debt to her faith and near-biblical patience, her cheerful wit, even as she cracked the whip, and the keen eye she brought to this project.

Wrestling the first draft of this book down to a length that didn't compete with the Bible took the support of a brave editor.

The skill, thoughtfulness and good humour of Craig Pyette were gifts to me on every page. Copy editor Gillian Watts also brought an unwavering eye to each word.

As I worked away on this book about family, my own family had to do without me on many days and nights. They never let me dwell on that irony. Jade and Jackson are my very best teachers. Stephen Rouse lived this journey too, filmed, photographed, helped with research, read, re-read and still props me up in all the ways that matter. Words cannot express what their unconditional support, sacrifice and love have meant to me through these years.

SOURCE NOTES

All genetic tests conducted for inclusion in this book were provided by private companies at regular cost and were paid by me as a customer of both Family Tree DNA and the now defunct DNAPrint Genomics. This includes tests for those who agreed to be tested, or have further testing done, at my request. For tests performed on my parents and myself by Mark Shriver and his lab team at Penn State, I covered fees related to running the 10,000 marker chip test in development, and analysis of the results.

The following is a select bibliography of books, academic studies, articles and websites. In many cases, I have cited sources directly in the text, particularly as it relates to documents, and private correspondence accessed through the subscription-based archive found at Jamaicanfamilysearch.com.

I wrote this book as events unfolded over the years, and in some cases, the science has evolved. Where relevant, I have noted these advances below the particular journal reference.

BOOKS

Anstey, Roger. *The Atlantic Slave Trade and British Abolition, 1760-1810*. London: Macmillan, 1975.

Bayer, Jennifer Marie. *A Sociolinguistic Investigation of the English Spoken by the Anglo-Indians of Mysore City*. Mysore: Central Institute of Indian Languages, 1986.

Bristow, Sir Robert Charles. *Cochin Saga: a history of foreign government and business adventures in Kerala, South India by Arabs, Romans, Venetians, Dutch and British, together with a Personal Narrative of the Last Adventurer and an Epilogue*. London: Cassell, 1959.

Burton, Richard F. *Goa and the Blue Mountains; Or, Six Months of Sick Leave*. London: Samuel Bentley and Company, 1851.

Caplan, Lionel. *Children of Colonialism: Anglo-Indians in a Postcolonial World*. United Kingdom: Berg, 2001.

Collins, Larry and Dominique Lapierre. *Freedom at Midnight*. New Delhi: Vikas Publishing House, 1976.

Crooks, Paul. *Ancestors*. London: Arcadia Books, 2002.

Danvers, Frederick Charles. *The Portuguese in India*. New York: Octagon Books, 1966.

D'Cruz, Glenn. *Midnight's Orphans: Anglo-Indians in Post-colonial Literature*. Bern: Peter Lang A.G., International Academic Publishers, 2006. (It was D'Cruz who made the front page of the *Times of India* in 1998 when a reporter covering the Anglo-Indian gathering in Bangalore learned he did not know how to jive.)

Devine, T.M. *Scotland's Empire, 1600-1815*. London: Allen Lane, 2003.

Evolution: A Scientific American Reader. Chicago: University of Chicago Press, 2006.

Gaikwad, V.R. *The Anglo-Indians: a study in the problems and processes involved in emotional and cultural integration*. Bombay: Asia Publishing House, 1967.

Gupta, Shiva Kumar. *Marriage Among the Anglo-Indians*. Lucknow: Ethnographic and Folk Culture Society, 1968.

Hart, Henry H. *The Sea Road to the Indies*. New York: MacMillan Company, 1950.

Hawes, Christopher J. *Poor Relations: The Making of a Eurasian Community in British India 1773 – 1833*. England: Curzon Press, 1996.

Heuman, Gad J. *Between Black and White: Race Politics, and the Free Coloreds in Jamaica, 1792-1865*. Westport: Greenwood Press, 1981.

Hudson, J.B., J. Durairaj and N. Muraleedharam. *Guidelines on Tea Culture in South India*. New Delhi: Allied Publishers, 2002.

Humble, Richard. *The Explorers*. Virginia: Time-Life Books, 1978.

Jones, Steve. *Y: The Descent of Man*. London: Abacus, 2002.

Keay, John. *A History of India*. London: HarperCollins, 2000.

Kennedy, Dane. *The Magic Mountains: Hill Stations and the British Raj*. California: University of California Press, 1996.

Kennet, Debbie. *DNA and Social Networking: A Guide to Genealogy in the Twenty-first Century*. Gloucestershire: The History Press, 2011.

King, Liet. Colonel W. Ross. *The Aboriginal tribes of the Nilgiri Hills*. London: Longmans Green and Co., 1870.

Lach, Donald F. and Edwin J. Van Kley. *Asia in the Making of Europe*. Chicago: University of Chicago Press, 1993.

Metcalf, Thomas R. *Ideologies of the Raj*. Cambridge: University of Cambridge Press, 1995.

Ogilvie, Daniel. *The History of Trelawny*. Kingston: United Printers, 1954.

Pereira, Ralph. *ONE HOUSE – TWO WORLDS: The deCouto-Pereira Family History*. Ottawa: Gilmore Doculink International, 2002.

Ravenstein, E.G., ed. *A Journal of the First Voyage of Vasco da Gama, 1497–1499*. New York: Cambridge University Press, 2010. (Originally published 1898)

Ridley, Matt. *Genome: The Autobiography of a Species in 23 Chapters*. New York: Harper Collins, 2000.

Saxon, Lyle, *Fabulous New Orleans*. Louisiana: Pelican Publishing, 1988. (Originally published 1928)

Sherrow, Victoria. *Encyclopedia of Hair: A Cultural History*. Connecticut: Greenwood Press, 2006.

Singh, Khushwant. *India: An Introduction*. New Delhi: Vision Books, 1990.

Singh, Rama S., "The Indian Caste System, Human Diversity, and Genetic Determinism." In *Thinking About Evolution: Historical, Philosophical, and Political Perspectives*, Vol. 2. New York: Cambridge University Press, 2001.

Spear, Percival. *A History of India: Vol. II, From the sixteenth century to the twentieth century*. New Delhi: Penguin Books, 1990.

Thapar, Romila. *A History of India: Vol. I*. New Delhi: Penguin Books, 1990.

The Gleaner History of Books. Kingston: The Gleaner Company, 1995.

Wells, Spencer. *Deep Ancestry: Inside the Genographic Project*. Washington: National Geographic, 2006.

Younger, Coralie. *Anglo-Indians: Neglected Children of the Raj*. Delhi: B.R. Publishing Corporation, 1987.

STUDIES

Akinboro, A. et al, "Frequency of Twinning in Southwest Nigeria." *Indian Journal of Human Genetics*, Vol. 14, May 2008.

Balaresque, P. et al, "A predominantly neolithic origin for European paternal lineages." *PLoS biology*, Vol. 8, Jan. 19, 2010.

Bamshad, M.J. et al, "Female gene flow stratifies Hindu castes." *Nature*, Vol. 395, October 1998.

Chaix, Raphaëlle et al, "The Genetic or Mythical Ancestry of Descent Groups: Lessons from the Y Chromosome." *American Journal of Human Genetics*, Vol.75, December 2004.

Chakravarti, Aravinda, "Tracing India's invisible threads." *Nature*, Vol. 461, Sept. 24, 2009.

Foster, E.A., et al, "Jefferson fathered slave's last child." *Nature*, Vol. 396, Nov. 5, 1998.

Gresham, David et al, "Origins and Divergence of the Roma (Gypsies)." *American Journal of Human Genetics*, Vol. 69, December 2001.

Hammer, Michael F. et al, "Extended Y chromosome haplotypes resolve multiple and unique lineages of the Jewish priesthood." *Human Genetics*, Vol. 126, November 2009. (Further testing of Cohen Y chromosomes reveals *kohenim* men descend from several unrelated paternal lines, rather than one single paternal root. By testing more markers, the researchers found that not all, but roughly 30 per cent, of *Kohen* men carry a genetic Y-DNA signature indicative of a paternal origin in the Near East reaching back some 3,000 years to the time of Aaron.)

Hughes, J.F. et al, "Chimpanzee and human Y chromosome are remarkably divergent in structure and gene content." *Nature*, Vol. 463, Jan. 28, 2010.

Hughes, J.F. et al, "Strict evolutionary conservation followed rapid gene loss on human and rhesus Y chromosomes." *Nature*, Vol. 483, Feb. 22, 2012.
(Recent paper demonstrating that the Y chromosome's methods of preserving its code have held steady for the last 25 million years, when rhesus macaques are estimated to have diverged from humans.)

Jobling M.A., "In the name of the father: surnames and genetics." *Trends in Genetics*, Vol. 17, June 2001.

Kalaydijeva, L. et al, "A newly discovered founder population: the Roma/Gypsies." *Bioessays*, Vol. 27, October 2005.

King, T.E. et al, "Genetic signature of coancestry within surnames." *Current Biology*, Vol. 16, Feb. 21, 2006.

King, T.E. et al, "Africans in Yorkshire? The deepest-rooting clade of the Y phylogeny within an English genealogy." *European Journal of Human Genetics*, Vol. 15, March 2007.

King, T.E. et al, "Thomas Jefferson's Y chromosome belongs to a rare European lineage." *American Journal of Physical Anthropology*, Vol. 132, April 2007.

King, T. E, and Jobling M. A., "What's in a name? Y chromosomes, surnames and the genetic genealogy revolution." *Trends in Genetics*, Vol. 25, August 2009.

Moore, L.T. et al, "A Y-chromosome signature of hegemony in Gaelic Ireland." *American Journal of Human Genetics*, Vol. 78, February 2006.

Myres, Natalie M. et al, "A major Y chromosome haplogroup R1b Holocene era founder effect in Central and Western Europe." *European Journal of Human Genetics*, Vol. 19, January 2011.
(One of several recent studies presenting evidence that R1b, Western Europe's most common Y haplogroup, is much younger than previously estimated, emerging 10,000 years before present, or less, perhaps as farming spread to Europe from the Middle East.)

Reich, David et al, "Reconstructing Indian population history." *Nature*, Vol. 461, Sept. 24, 2009.

Rootsi, Siiri et al, "A counter-clockwise northern route of the Y-chromosome haplogroup N from Southeast Asia towards Europe." *European Journal of Human Genetics*, Vol. 15, December 2006.

Sharma, S. et al, "The Indian origin of paternal haplogroup R1a1 substantiates the autochthonous origin of Brahmins and the caste system." *Journal of Human Genetics*, Vol. 54, January 2009.

Shi, H. et al, "Y chromosome evidence of southern origin of the East Asian specific haplogroup O3 – M122." *American Journal of Human Genetics*, Vol. 77, September 2005.

Shriver, Mark D. and Rick A. Kittles, "Genetic ancestry and the search for personalized genetic histories." *Nature Reviews*, Vol. 5, August 2004.

Skaletsky, Helen et al, "The male-specific region of human Y chromosome is a mosaic of discrete sequence classes." *Nature*, Vol. 423, June 2003.

Skorecki, K. et al "Y Chromosomes of Jewish Priests." *Nature*, Vol. 385, Jan. 2, 1997.

Sykes B., and C. Irven, "Surnames and the Y Chromosome." *American Journal of Human Genetics*, Vol. 66, April 2000.

Thanseem, I. et al, "Genetic affinities among the lower castes and tribal groups of India: inference from Y chromosome and mitochondrial DNA." *BioMed Central Genetics*, Vol. 7, August 2006.

Tharakan, C. George, "The Mixed Economy of the South Indian Kurumbas." *Ethnology*, Vol. 42, Oct. 1, 2003.

Thomas, M.G. et al, "Y chromosomes traveling south: the cohen modal haplotype and the origins of the Lemba – the "Black Jews of Southern Africa." *American Journal of Human Genetics*, Vol. 66, February 2000.

Trumme, T. et al, "Genetics in genealogical research, reconstruction of a family tree by means of Y-haplotyping." *Journal of Biological and Clinical Anthropology* (Anthropologischer Anzeiger), Vol. 62, December 2004.

Underhill, P.A., "Y chromosome sequence variation and the history of human populations." *Nature Genetics*, Vol. 26, November 2000.

Wilder, J.A., et al, "Global patterns of human mitochondrial DNA and Y chromosome structure are not influenced by higher migration rates of females versus males." *Nature Genetics*, Vol. 36, October 2004.

Xue, Y. et al, "Recent spread of a Y-chromosomal lineage in northern China and Mongolia." *American Journal of Human Genetics*, Vol. 77, December 2008.

Zerjal, T. et al, "The genetic legacy of the Mongols." *American Journal of Human Genetics*, Vol. 72, March 2003.

ARTICLES and ESSAYS

Allan, David G. "Jamaica's Golden Age." *The New York Times*, Nov. 9, 2008.

Baumeister, Roy F. "Is There Anything Good About Men?" Full media transcript address to American Psychological Association, August 2007.

Bielenberg, Kim, "So, that's why we love kebabs." *Irish Independent*, Feb. 6, 2010.

Cyranoski, David, "China bioscience: The sequence factory." *Nature*, Vol. 464, March 3, 2010.

Frudakis, Tony N., "Powerful but Requiring Caution: Genetic Tests of Ancestral Origins." *National Genealogical Society Quarterly*, Vol. 93, 2005.

Gonzales, Juan, "Puerto Rican Gene Pool Runs Deep." *New York Daily News*, Nov. 4, 2003.

"Genetic ailments due to endogamy." *The Times of India*, Sept. 25, 2009.

Harris, Paul, "Society: The genes that build America." *The Observer*, July 15, 2007.

Hotz, Robert Lee, "DNA Study shows Jefferson Fathered His Slave's Child." *The Los Angeles Times*, Nov. 1, 1998.

McGowan, Kathleen, "DNA could help unlock origin of Melungeons." *Discover Magazine*, April 30, 2003.

McKie, Robin, "A Scientific Milestone: Meet the DNA genius who fears the dark side of his discovery: Twenty years on from his first DNA testing, Professor Alec Jeffreys says that, despite its real benefits, genetic technology can destroy our civil liberties." *The Observer*, Aug. 8, 2004.

"More women than men have kids, more female ancestors in the tree: Evolutionary Biology; Genes expose secrets of sex on the side." *Genomics and Genetics Weekly*, Oct. 15, 2004.

Nicol, Mark, and Ross Slater, "I've just been told I'm an African Warrior…and my friends at the Bowls Club are astonished." *The Mail on Sunday*, Jan. 28, 2007.

Olson, Steve, "The Royal We." *The Atlantic*, May 2002.

Ramachandran, R. "The genetics of caste." *Frontline* (India's National Magazine), Vol. 18, June 9, 2001.

Robson, David, "How do you apologise for your distant slave trading ancestor?" *Daily Express*, June 24, 2006.

Rutherford, Adam, "India's genes uncovered." *The Guardian*, Sept. 25, 2009.

"Study gives insight into ancestral population of India." *The Times of India*, Sept. 29, 2009.

Thomson, Ian, "Gangster's paradise." *The Independent On Sunday*, May, 10, 2009.

Wade, Nicholas, "In Caste System, Women Can Marry Up." *The New York Times*, Oct. 27, 1998.

Younge, Gary, "The desire for identity." *The Sun-Herald*, Feb. 26, 2006.

Trevor, B. and K. Morgan, "The Dynamics of the Slave Market and Slave Purchasing Patterns in Jamaica, 1655-1788." Featured in "New Perspectives on the Transatlantic Slave Trade" a special issue of *The William and Mary Quarterly*, Third Series, Vol. 58, January 2001.

WEBSITES

"Anglo-Indian of the G.I.P. Railway at Poona: application to Lord Clydesmuir for free passages for self and family to Jamaica, Feb. 1948–Apr. 1948," reference located at The National Archives online, File 7237/48.
http://www.nationalarchives.gov.uk/a2a/records.aspx?cat=059-lpj7_12027-15831&cid=1-1-551-1189#1-1-551-1189

British Library online: www.bl.uk/

Cacciottolo, Mario, "My ancestor traded in human misery," BBC News, June 23, 2006.
http://news.bbc.co.uk/2/hi/uk_news/5105328.stm

Chandler, Arthur, "On the Symbolism of Juggling: The Moral and Aesthetic Implications of the Mastery of Falling Objects." *The Journal of Popular Culture*, Vol. 25, Winter 1991. http://www.juggling.org/papers/symbolism/

Crooks wills, personal correspondence of Duncan Campbell, Cousins Cove Slave Register 1817, Directories, civil and military, lists of landowners, slave owners, periodicals, Quit Rent book records, essays and excerpts related to colonial Jamaica. www.jamaicanfamilysearch.com

Database to freely upload and compare Y-DNA test results with those who have tested through other companies or projects, operated by Family Tree DNA. http://www.ysearch.org/

East Asian haplogroups and forum discussions: http://www.familytreedna.com/public/O3 http://www.asiasfinest.com http://s6.zetaboards.com/man/topic/8571522/1/

"Falmouth Wharves," presented by the Jamaica National Heritage Trust. http://www.jnht.com/site_falmouth_wharves.php

Farrer, William and J. Brownbill, "Townships: Abram," *A History of the County of Lancaster: Volume 4,* Victoria County History, 1911. http://www.british-history.ac.uk/report.aspx?compid=41389

General Y-DNA haplogroup distributions, origins and general information on using DNA to investigate ancestry.

www.isogg.org
Free online resource operated by the International Society of Genetic Genealogy, a non-commercial, non-profit group designed to promote the use of genetic testing in genealogy.

http://www.eupedia.com/genetics/
An open resource covering subjects related to European Prehistory, Anthropology and Genetics, including articles, studies, and discussion forums.

https://genographic.nationalgeographic.com/
Home page of the Genographic Project, the multi-year, international effort to map the history of human migration through DNA, operated jointly by the National Geographic, IBM and headed by Dr. Spencer Wells.

Genealogical sites containing various vital and property records, discussion boards, census materials and related links:
http://www.ancestry.com
http://www.britishsurnames.co.uk/surnames
http://www.cyndislist.com/
https://familysearch.org
http://genforum.genealogy.com/
http://rootsweb.ancestry.com/
http://www.theshipslist.com/.

Harper, Robert Francis, ed., "Hammurabi, The Code of Hammurabi, 2250 BC." Chicago: University of Chicago Press, 1904. Translation posted at The Online Library of Liberty. http://oll.libertyfund.org/?option=com_staticxt&staticfile=show. php%3Ftitle=1276&chapter=79599&layout=html&Itemid=27

Ibagere, Eniwoke, "Nigeria boasts world's twin capital," BBC
    News World Edition, Sept. 13, 2002.
    http://news.bbc.co.uk/2/hi/africa/2253845.stm

Lei, Dr. Hsien-Hsien, "Genetic Genealogy and the Chinese."
    DNA and Genealogy, blog post of Nov. 7, 2007.
    www.eyeondna.com

Lewbel, Arthur, "Research in Juggling History," November 1995,
    revised March 2002, condensed version appearing in
    Jugglers World Magazine.
    https://www2.bc.edu/~lewbel/jugweb/history-1.html

"My diary or Route Book of P.T. Barnum's Greatest Show on
    Earth and The Great London Circus for the Season of 1884,"
    photocopy transcribed and posted at
    www.circushistory.org/History/PTB1884.htm

Phillipo, James Mursell. *Jamaica: Its Past and Present State.*
    London: W. Clowes and Sons, 1843, excerpts.
    www.jamaicanfamilysearch.com

Qifeng, Fu. *Chinese Acrobatics Through the Ages.* Beijing: Foreign
    Languages Press, 1985, excerpt.
    http://www.juggling.org/papers/symbolism/#fn2

Qiu, Jane, "Inheriting Confucius," Seed Magazine, Aug. 13, 2008,
    accessed at http://seedmagazine.com/content/article/
    inheriting_confucius/

Spence, Jonathan. *God's Chinese Son: The Taiping Heavenly Kingdom
    of Hong Xiuquan.* New York: W.W. Norton, 1996, references.
    http://www.iun.edu/~hisdcl/g385_2001/Taiping%20religion.htm

Stevens, Nettie, "Studies in Spermatogenesis with Especial Reference to the Accessory Chromosome." Originally carried in a report of the *Carnegie Institute of Washington*, May 23, 1905, excerpts and context. http://incubator.rockefeller.edu/?p=432

Stewart, John. *An Account of Jamaica and its Inhabitants.* London: Longman, Hurst, Rees and Orme, 1808, excerpts. www.jamaicanfamilysearch.com

Stewart, J. *A View of the Past and Present State of the Island of Jamaica; with Remarks on the Moral and Physical Condition of The Slaves and on The Abolition of Slavery in The Colonies.* London: Oliver and Boyd, Tweeddale-House, and G. and W.B. Whittaker, 1823, excerpts. www.jamaicanfamilysearch.com

"Sugar Cane – history," *Plant Culture, Exploring plants and people*, a collaborative information resource between Britain and South Asia, organized by Royal Botanic Gardens at Kew, including, among others, Culture Online, an initiative of The National Archives and the British Library. http://www.kew.org/plant-cultures/plants/sugar_cane_history.html

The Free Enclyclopedia of the International Circus: http://www.circopedia.org/index.php/Category:History

"The History of the Sisters of St. Joseph of Tarbes in India," for information related to Christian missions in the Nilgiri mountains, and Father Jacques Dennis Peyramale of the Paris Foreign Missions Society in nineteenth-century Coonoor. http://sjtbangalore.org/SJT_Indian_History.pdf

Tortello, Dr. Rebecca, "The History of Falmouth: Boom Town of The 19th Century," posted online June 23, 2003 as part *The Jamaican Gleaner* series, "Pieces of the Past." http://jamaica-gleaner.com/pages/history/story0051.htm

INDEX

CAROLYN ABRAHAM is the author of *Possessing Genius: The Bizarre Odyssey of Einstein's Brain*, which was also a finalist for the Governor General's Literary Award for Non-fiction. The longtime senior medical-science writer for *The Globe and Mail*, she is a four-time winner of the Canadian Science Writers' Association's annual award for her medical reporting and winner of two National Newspaper Awards. She lives with her family in Toronto.